W9-DCW-736

Books in this Series

Gary & Anne Marie Ezzo

Growing Kids God's Way

Reaching the Heart of Your Child
with a God-Centered Purpose

Growing Kids God's Way
(Along the Virtuous Way)

© 2017 Gary and Anne Marie Ezzo

International Standard Book Number

ISBN-13 978-1-883035-03-7

Printed in the United States of America

ALL RIGHTS RESERVED
No part of this publication may be reproduced, stored in a retrieval system,
or transmitted, in any form or by any means–electronic, mechanical,
photocopying, recording, or otherwise–without prior written permission.

All Scripture quotations, except where otherwise indicated, are taken from the
New King James Version, Copyright © 1979, 1980, 1982 by Thomas Nelson Inc. Used by permission.
All rights reserved, and the Scofield Reference Bible,
Oxford University Press, © 1909, 1917, 1937, and 1945.

Growing Families International
Administrative Office
2160 Cheswick Lane
Mount Pleasant, SC 29466

Year: 11 13 15 17
Print Run: 96 97 98 99

Dedicated to our Grandchildren
with Unfailing Love

Ashley, Whitney, Katelynn, Kara,
Robert-Joseph, Bradon, Maddie,
Thomas, and Jessica

ACKNOWLEDGEMENTS

According to a host of on-line dictionaries, the purpose of an "acknowledgement" is to express a debt of gratitude and appreciation to someone who otherwise would not be recognized. This pages exist for that reason. While the cover of this book displays our names as "Authors", in truth there were many people from within our community of Faith who applied their time, energy and giftedness to help make this book a joint venture for the common good. Most readers will never personally meet these "behind the scene" individuals, but each reader will be the benefactor of their labor. Where do we begin the task of recognizing their contribution?

To our friends and associates, Joey and Carla Link, we extend our heartfelt thanks for their many hours of review, suggestions, editorial assistance and the years of helping us move the message forward. We wish to express our deep gratitude and appreciation to Nathan Babcock for providing the final editorial review of this book. The combination of his intellect and passion for clarity came at a critical intersection of this project and pushed us to another level of appreciation for the value of pithy details. There is also Joe and Nancy Barlow and the Prayer Team, whose spiritual encouragement and prayerful support have no bounds.

We also wish to acknowledge Pastor Don and Danna Delafield for their self-assessment exercise found at the end of Chapter Three, "Touchpoints of Love." We also wish to acknowledge Gary and Joy Hanson for designing the children's version of the Touchpoints of Love Assessment Test. We offer a special thanks to Pastors Robert Boerman and John Frame of Westminster Seminary for their theological suggestions and contributions to this edition. And to the people responsible for keeping us on track and moving forward, we wish to thank John Locklair and Paige Hunter, who serves this ministry behind the scenes in so many ways. There is of course, Lori Moore, our National Ministry Administrator, who is forever patiently "minding the store" freeing us to complete the project. Last, but not least, a special word of thanks to all those *Growing Kids God's Way* parents who, with the blessings of God, pioneered the moral revolution with us so many years ago. To all our contributors, we say "thank you."

Gary and Anne Marie Ezzo

Table of Contents

APPENDICES

Introduction to the Fifth Edition

In the title *Growing Kids God's Way*, we place our emphasis on God's Way—meaning the way of the Lord. We serve an ethical God. Moral rightness flows from His being. His ways are in accord with His unchangeable character. In short, God is absolutely perfect and His moral law is a reflection of His holy character (Psalm 19:7). More than that, He has shown man what is good and what is required of him (Micah 6:8).

The Bible provides with certainty the ethical standards necessary for successful living. With these standards comes a clear moral mandate for parents, "Be ye holy; for I am holy" (1 Peter 1:16). Practical holiness is not merely a state of mind but a lifestyle—a moral lifestyle established by God, and one in which parents are to instruct their children (Ephesians 6:4). Moral training in the Christian home should not only equate to training in biblical virtues and values which communicate the will and character of God but also His mercy and grace. We all must learn the way of the Lord and instruct our growing children in it. It is the authors' conviction that the duty, hope, and goal of every Christian parent is to raise a morally responsible child who comes to salvation in Jesus Christ, whose life is governed by the precepts of Christ, and whose life reflects the love of Christ.

The word "salvation" above is the all-inclusive word of the gospel. It brings together all the redemptive acts and processes—justification, redemption, grace, and forgiveness. The place where God claims lost people is at the Cross. The Cross is where Jesus died the death that we by all rights should die, and would die, apart from Him. Like adults, children may possess a clear knowledge of God but may not know Him personally. They need to be saved, God's way. Jesus Christ wants your child's heart, not just his head. It is eternally important that you make sure it is not just head knowledge and intellectual assent your son or daughter has given to the Lord. Christ commands a complete surrender of heart and life.

Growing Kids God's Way will not only speak about the good way of the Lord, but will also offer practical steps to implement His moral precepts into the life of children. After all, good theology, if it is not fleshed out into everyday, rubber-meets-the-road stuff, is just that—good theology and nothing more. At some point, biblical theology must express itself in practice. Without sound practice, we are prone to become hearers of the Word, not doers, and we only deceive ourselves (James 1:22).

Throughout this text we will stress the primary consideration of focusing on your child's heart and not simply modifying his or her outward behavior. There is something about the human heart that requires attention, and that needs to be the focus of child-training. We know that the heart is the center of all of life and behavior. Psalms 139:23 tells us that the heart is that portion of man that God looks upon and searches. In Matthew 12:34-35, Jesus said that all behavior and words have their origin in the heart. Proverbs 4:23 warns us that in the heart the impressions of a young life are molded, and that the issues of life flow from it. Proverbs 6:18 speaks of the heart's ability to devise wicked plans. Proverbs 22:15 tells us that foolishness is bound up in the heart of a child. Parents need to direct their attention to that which is in their child's heart.

The general goal of heart training, the part that parents can impact, is to help a child gain personal self-control. Self-control in turn helps the child control his tongue (Proverbs 13:3, 15:2), his actions (Proverbs 14:29), handle negative emotions (Proverbs 25:28), and make sound judgments (Proverbs 1:3). Training children in biblical virtues guides a child to a life that is honest life (Proverbs 10:9), is non-offensive (Proverbs 16:7), and is filled with righteous deeds (Proverbs 1:3). Most importantly, biblical training brings about the peaceable fruit of righteousness (Hebrews 12:11).

In early parenting, external pressure is necessary to bring about acceptable behavior even though a young child has no cognitive understanding of the reason for the behavior. The fact that a child has no moral understanding as to why food should not be intentionally dropped from his highchair does not mean we hold back instruction and restriction. There is a reason for that. With adults, beliefs precede actions; with children, the opposite is true—actions precede beliefs. Parents will insist on correct behavior long before the child is capable of understanding the associated moral concepts. But what does the Bible require?

It is our desire to show you through *Growing Kids God's Way* the practical side of biblical truth. Yet we offer this caution and point of understanding. Biblical principles are divine, most applications of biblical principle are of human origin. God gives the precepts and we will endeavor to provide the many sides of application. For example, Titus 3:2 instructs us to be courteous to all men. In the context of parenting and from a child's perspective, what does that look like every day? What are the various ways in which a child can demonstrate the biblical command to be courteous? There are God-given principles (that comprise the way of the Lord), and there are human applications. While application may vary from child to child and family to family (even culture to culture), God's moral precepts do not change because there is no variance in His character. As it is written, "Jesus Christ, the same yesterday, today, and forever" (Hebrews 13:8). Focus on what God has to say, and we will help you with the application.

It was the practical application of God's word that attracted our first *Growing Kids God's Way* class back in 1984. Six couples gathered together every Wednesday night for six months. We talked about right and wrong, good and evil, and what it looks like in everyday parenting. The six couples bore fruit and others began to inquire. We agreed to another class and much to our surprise, one hundred and sixty parents signed up to meet with us. The following year another four hundred came, followed by six hundred the next year. From community to community and state to state, the message has spread. Today, thousands of parents across the country and around the world attend *Growing Kids God's Way* classes each week. It has been this way for over twenty-five years.

One of the greatest blessings any author can hope to achieve is to read how his or her life's work impacted the hearts of the second generation. Just prior to press-time, we received a call from Amy Link (daughter of Joey and Carla Link, one of Growing Families International's National Ministry Overseer couples), asking if she and other teens might have opportunity to comment on various chapters and principles that were meaningful to them as children raised in homes that used the principles in *Growing Kids God's Way* for more than ten of their growing-up years. The idea sounded intriguing and we consented. What a blessing! Throughout this book you will notice comments in the sidebar columns by members of this first generation of Growing Families International (GFI) teens and young adults. We trust their words will encourage are readers.

What do their comments reflect? One thing! It showcases that the GFI ministry throughout the world has grown larger than Gary, Anne Marie Ezzo and their own children. That is, of course, the way it is should to be. Just as King David, in his last days, proclaimed a blessing on his son Solomon—that the generation to come will be greater in the Lord than the generation that was—so also did we hope for that outcome (c.f. I Kings 1:37, 47). And our hope was fulfilled! As a result, anyone looking for role models within the *Growing Kids God's Way* community can turn to the thousands of families whose children, teens and adult children beautifully and fully exemplify GFI's life-giving message, its vitality, and the wonderful relational outcomes that are evident in so many families. The second generation has exceeded the first!

This new print edition includes a number of structural and content changes. First, our long-time instructors will immediately notice that we removed the *"Foundations"* chapter. To relieve any concerns about this change, we assure leaders that we did not remove the content, but relocated much of it to various chapters and appendices. Some topics were transferred to our website for download access. Second, we revised some appendices, added new ones, and transferred others to our website: www. GrowingFamiliesUSA.com (the Internet home for the worldwide GFI community.) Two new appendices include "Let Them Play" (Appendix Two), which speaks to the important role of "play" in the life of a child and "The Growing Kids Topic Pool" (Appendix Four), where we consolidated a number of common topics in one location to better serve our readers. The appendices are there to read at your leisure or at the direction of your class leader.

Third, this edition includes sidebar columns with additional comments, Scripture quotations, quotes from recommended resources, including the *Mom's Notes* (written by Joey and Carla Link.) Carla Link's gracious assistance and sacrifice of time to help compile many of the references, resources, and quotes in the sidebar columns is greatly appreciated and deserves a special acknowledgement. Throughout the text you will find reference to the "Mom's Notes Bookstore" (www.Momsnotes.com). The store assists parents with quality print material for parents and children. Each book was reviewed by them for biblical content, relevancy, and its similarity to GFI's parenting philosophy. While we may not endorse every statement made in every book, we can endorse the author's overall parenting philosophy as consistent with that of the GFI curriculum. Additional resources, including our comprehensive video library, can be found on the GrowingFamiliesUSA.com website.

As was the case with the previous edition, this curriculum is not intended to give all the answers or provide you with all you will ever need to know about the process of raising a child. Therefore, parents guided by the Holy Spirit and their own convictions have the ultimate responsibility and duty to research parenting philosophies available today, and then make an informed decision as to what is best for their family. The tools of this endeavor included prayer, observation, experience, personal study, wisdom, and most importantly the Holy Spirit. We are a husband and wife, a father and mother, co-laborers in ministry, and two observers of human nature. It is our desire that the truth presented on the pages to follow fall somewhere between correction and challenge, enlightenment and confirmation. Thank you for joining us.

Gary and Anne Marie Ezzo
Charleston, South Carolina

From the first wave of *Growing Kids God's Way* teens and young adults come words of encouragement and welcome. When asked what they would say to parents attending a *Growing Kids* class for the first time, they were happy to share. Here are a few of their responses:

"Parents attending a *Growing Kids God's Way* class should always seek to understand the moral and biblical reasons behind every concept they implement. Not only will this provide the motivation and encouragement to faithfully continue down this path of training, it will also give parents the tools to help their children understand the moral reason why. When children can understand the moral reason why, they will begin to make the principle their own." - *Sarah, age 22*

"If a couple were taking a *Growing Kids God's Way* class for the first time, I would encourage them to work on the fundamentals first. These would include couch time (when the marriage is going well the children will feel the effect and there is more harmony in the family), first-time obedience (which is a necessity throughout life in regards to a walk with God), and time together as a family. Play games together and have family devotions. Don't give up and don't give in. To have a family who looks to each other for their support and strength is worth it." - *Briana, age 21*

"This is what I would share with those parents just starting their journey with *Growing Kids God's Way* principles: Eat meals together as often as possible. Make sure Mom and Dad show their kids that they love each other. Teach your kids to study the Word of God. I believe the family is the basic social unit as planned by God, so that unit should be as unified as possible. Some of my best (and most formative) memories in my family involve times when I was worshipping with my family, or simply enjoying their company at the table, knowing that my parents have a secure relationship. That is truly wonderful." - *Christopher, age 20*

"Please be faithful and consistent. Persevere looking beyond the hardships of parenting to a high standard, to a future in Christ. Consider how by holding your ground on Biblical principle you are ultimately training your children to know who God is and live in wisdom. You, by living your part within the perfect structure God has set up, are giving your children an opportunity to behold a glorious glimpse into the magnificent Character of God." - *Mollie, age 18*

"My advice to families taking the *Growing Kids God's Way* class is to teach your children to have self-control. This is absolutely critical. Whether someone has an issue with controlling anger, melt-downs, tone of voice, or even talking, eating, or sleeping, self-control and balance for all family members are absolute keys to family life." - *Kristen, age 17*

"Two important things that I would share with parents just starting with *GKGW* that will improve the quality of family life is to put a premium on teaching their children respect for authority and how to become others' centered." - *Laura, age 16*

"My advice to parents just starting out in *Growing Kids*, is to stay strong. Work hard on building Family Identity. Have meals together so you can talk with each other. Have the entire family go to the activities everyone is in so you can be each other's biggest cheerleaders. Get First-time Obedience and keep it. It is very important for both parents to be involved in training their children. Kids need to know that Dad and Mom work from the same standard. Be consistent! "'Train up a child in the way he should go and he will not depart from it when he is old'" (Proverbs 22:6). - *Amy, age 19*

"I would tell parents who are taking the parenting class for the first time that family life will be good if parents get their children to respect and obey them." - *Timmy, age 13*

"I would encourage parents who want to improve the quality of their family's life to be very consistent with the training of their children and to help develop good strong relationships within the family." - *Stephen, age 14*

"What would I tell parents who are taking the *Growing Kids God's Way* class for the first time? Teach your children to be best friends. I can't imagine not being able to talk with each other and trust each other as my sisters and I do." - *Jara, age 17*

"As a Mom of two little girls, *Preparation for Parenting* and *Growing Kids God's Way* has become a way of life for our family. The principles are timeless passing from one generation to another. I know this because before there were DVD's, videos or audio recordings, there was a small group of parents, hungry for biblical parenting, meeting weekly with Mr. and Mrs. Ezzo. My mom and dad were part those first classes. The gift of understanding Mom and Dad received was passed on to us, and now my husband and I are passing it on to our children. *Growing Kids God's Way* is touching the third generation." - *Sheri, age 26*

Session One Outline
and Chapter One

How to Raise a Moral Child

I. Introduction
    A. We believe that one of the greatest areas of concern that you should have for your children is a concern over their _____ health.

    Growing Kids God's Way is all about helping parents in their duty of raising _____ responsible and biblically responsive children.

    B. One of the goals in this series is to help you help your child internalize biblical values. That means as moms and dads you must give attention to not only _____ is imparted, but _____ it is imparted.

    C. Looking Back Historically
        1. Authoritarian Parenting
            a. A child was told, "You will do it or _____."
            b. Parents were more preoccupied with _____ waywardness than elevating good.

        2. Permissive Parenting
            a. Permissive parenting is neither concerned with suppressing evil in a child nor elevating good. The method of parenting is elevated above the results.
            b. Conflict avoidance is elevated above conflict _____.

    D. Four Foundational Questions
        1. If we are going to raise a morally responsible and biblically responsive child, then what is the standard? From where do our values come?
        2. What roles do temperament and personality play in moral training?
        3. With whom does moral training begin?
        4. How do you raise a morally responsible child?

II. Question One
     If we are going to raise a morally responsible and biblically responsive child, then what is the standard? From where do our values come?

     A. Of all of the ethical systems in the world, there is no higher standard, nor more pure motive for right behavior than the standard that comes from the _____.

Justification: Only the system of biblical ethics is other-oriented, not as a way to salvation but as a _____ of our salvation.

B. My behavior towards you is based on how precious you are to ____.

C. What is the ethical moral mandate of Scripture?

It is looking for and responding to the preciousness of those outside of _____.

III. Question Two
What roles do temperament and personality differences play in moral training?

A. All parents should be working toward the same _____ of moral excellence regardless of the child's personality or temperament.

B. Regardless of personality distinctions found in your families, the persistence of moral training should not vary from child to child because God's moral _____ do not vary from child to child.

IV. Question Three
With whom does moral training begin?

A. Text

Deut. 6:4–6 "Hear, O Israel! The Lord is our God, the Lord is one. And you shall love the Lord your God with all your heart and with all your soul and with all your might. And these words which I am commanding you this day, shall be in your _____."

B. Training Children Diligently

Some of the greatest periods of moral training take place in periods of non-_____.

V. Question Four
How do you raise a morally responsible child?

A. The reason we are not producing morally responsible children in our churches is because parental instruction too often lacks moral reason.

We tell our children _____ to do, but do not tell them _____ they should do it.

B. Knowing how to do right and knowing why to do right are definitely two different things. The first one represents moral _____; the second represents moral _____.

C. By the time a child hits three years of age, parental instruction should become more characterized by including the moral reason _____ when giving moral instruction.

D. Ryan's Story
In the mind of the child, today's "no" without moral principle is only for _____.

E. Understanding Context and Legalism
1. Context prevents a parent from becoming a _____.

2. Legalism removes the principle from the heart and the _____ of the child.

Key Principle: Without moral principle placed within the heart, the heart will not be stirred.

1

How to Raise a Moral Child

Today,. morality comes in all shapes and sizes. "If it feels right, do it" says one bumper sticker. Even in Christian homes values may differ. There's a tendency to end up with a potluck of morality—some from our folks, some from Bible teachers and book writers, and some from society's subtle influence. What's so wrong with taking a potluck approach? Why do parents need to measure their values against the standard of God's Word? First and foremost it is all about virtue.[a] Christian virtues reflect the person of Christ. When taught to our children, such virtues trigger a child's consciousness of God and eternity. The natural world is seen, heard, felt, smelled, and tasted, but the supernatural world is revealed through quiet and unseen things like the Holy Spirit revelation, faith, and the virtues that reflect both.

The belief in a personal God is necessary if one intends to establish ethical laws that are absolute and universal. Without God, there is no basis for objective ethics, and individual and societal behavior is governed by subjective, personal preference. All values become relative. Biblical morality serves to reveal God's call to holiness, establish a standard of acceptable behavior, and reveal sin. As Henry Blackaby writes: "Christianity is an intimate, growing relationship with the person of Jesus Christ. It is not a set of doctrines to believe, habits to practice, or sins to avoid. Every activity God commands is to enhance His love relationship with His people. Religious activity apart from fellowship with God is empty ritual."[b]

THE MOTIVE FOR DOING RIGHT

Of all the ethical systems in the world, there is no higher standard or virtuous motive directing moral behavior than that which comes from the Bible. The justification for that statement is basic: only the system of biblical ethics is other-oriented, not as a way to salvation but as a result of salvation. That last distinction is basic to all that we believe regarding the application of biblical principle.

There are many wonderful religious and ethical teachings in the world, but the motive for doing deeds of kindness is the pursuit of salvation—that is, man seeking favor with God. For many, individual acts of goodness are but steps to heaven. Not so for the Christian. We do right because positionally we have already come to the city of God, the heavenly Jerusalem (Hebrews 12:22-23). We are to set our affections on the things above (Colossians 3:1-2). Our goodness, then, is a love response to God, rooted in our relationship with Christ. "We are to love one another, for love is of God" (1 John 4:7a). Therefore, we who are targets of God's love ought to be targets of one another's love. This is the summation of the Ten Commandments and the duty of man as stated by

References / Notes

" My mom and dad taught me not just to serve other people but to find the joy in serving others. There is a satisfaction derived from knowing that I did something for someone else that I didn't need to do, (even my sister's household chores when she had exams or was working and couldn't get to them). Learning to appreciate service to others is a gift from my parents that will follow me the rest of my life." - Titus, age 16

a. There is an unfortunate confusion with the two terms, "values" and "virtues." In Christendom, we interchange the words as if they mean the same thing. They do not. Values are general beliefs concerning what is good or bad that are shared by individuals or cultures. It is good to say "please"when you are asking for something. This belief is shared by society in general, so there is value in doing so.

Where values originate with man, virtues originate with God. Virtues do not change because of the source of virtues is God, not man. As Jesus Christ is the same yesterday, today, and tomorrow (Hebrews 13:8), so are the virtues that reflect His character. Virtue is what God looks like on the outside and that is what He has asked us to look like. Paul says that we are to "Put on Christ" (Romans 13:14). In Greek dramas, "To put on a person" is to assume his character and peculiarities, as an actor does on the stage. So we are to imitate Christ, as actors imitate those whom they represent. What we are "putting on" are the virtues of Christ. Thus, biblical morality serves to reveal God's call to holiness, establish a standard of acceptable behavior, and reveal sin.

b. From "Experiencing God Day-by-Day" by Henry and Richard Blackaby, pg. 85.

References / Notes

c. In her book, "The Shaping of a Christian Family," Elisabeth Elliot writes: "Nothing trains and teaches so powerfully as love. Love attracts; it does not coerce. If the aim of the parents is to teach their children to love God, they must show their love for Him by loving each other and loving their children. God is love. Whoever lives in love lives in God, and God in him." (pg 148, 1 John 4:16b)

d. Philippians 2:6-8: Who, being in very nature God, did not consider equality with God something to be grasped, but made himself nothing, taking the very nature of a servant, being made in human likeness. And being found in appearance as a man, he humbled himself and became obedient to death — even death on a cross!

e. John 3:16: For God so loved the world that He gave His only begotten son, that whoever believes on him shall not perish but have everlasting life.

f. Matthew 25:35-40: "For I was hungry and you gave me something to eat, I was thirsty and you gave me something to drink, I was a stranger and you invited me in, I needed clothes and you clothed me, I was sick and you looked after me, I was in prison and you came to visit me.' Then the righteous will answer him, 'Lord, when did we see you hungry and feed you, or thirsty and give you something to drink? When did we see you a stranger and invite you in, or needing clothes and clothe you? When did we see you sick or in prison and go to visit you?' The King will reply, 'I tell you the truth, whatever you did for one of the least of these brothers of mine, you did for me."

g. The "one-anothers" in Scripture are found in Romans 13:8, 14:13, 15:7, 15:14; Ephesians 4:2, 32; Colossians 3:16; Hebrews 3:13, 10:24; 1 Peter 1:22; and 1 John 3:11, 4:7, 4:11.

h. From "Character Matters" by John and Susan Alexander Yates (pg. 88).

Jesus—love God and love your neighbor (Mark 12:29-31).[c]

The following illustration exemplifies the point. One Christmas, our daughter Jennifer received a Holly Hobbie doll that she cherished for many years. There was an occasion when she asked if I would hold her doll while she made up Holly's bed. "Be very careful how you hold her, Daddy," was a common instruction. Her mother and I would look at that patched doll with its stained clothing and missing hair and focus on its material value. We often thought that pile of cloth must cost more to maintain than what it was worth. To us, that doll was valueless, but not to its owner. To Jennifer, that doll was *precious*. And the more tattered it became, the more care and love she gave it. Jennifer's words, "Be very careful how you hold her," governed our care. We held that doll, not based on our perception of its value, but on the value assigned to it by its owner.

We humans are like that Holly Hobbie doll; we have an owner, Jesus Christ. To Him we are absolutely precious. We are so precious that He left the splendor of heaven to come to earth to die for us (Philippians 2:6-8).[d] It was because "God so loved the world. . ." (John 3:16a)[e] that set a value on mankind. Therefore, we do not direct our conduct toward others based on how valuable they are to us but on how beloved they are to God. Our kindness is a gesture we make on His behalf.[f] Our children need to grasp that reality.

SCRIPTURE'S MORAL MANDATE

What is the moral mandate of Scripture? It requires looking for and responding to the preciousness of those outside of self. That response is not at the expense of self but in harmony with self (Proverbs 3:3-4); it is living out a manner of life that reflects Christ in us (John 13:34-35; Philippians 2:3-5). Jesus was other-oriented and set the ethical standard for the "one-anothers" of Scriptures.[g] We are to follow His example by ordering our behavior in accordance with the preciousness of others. We must consider those who come behind us, who stand at our sides, and who go in front of us. That is what biblical ethics is all about. It is a rational preoccupation with the concerns of those around us—a "love God, love our neighbor" sensitivity (Mark 12:28-31; 1 John 4:19-21).

Christ points us to *others* who are our neighbors. At the heart of how we teach our children to view life is this very principle which stands in contrast to the current thinking of our society. It is as John and Susan Alexander Yates write: "Today's rule, 'Use others to get what you want,' is becoming a standard, replacing the Golden Rule, 'Do unto others as you would have them do unto you.' Our challenge is to halt the trend and recapture Christ's call to love others as He has loved us—sacrificially—as a servant. A servant's heart is not natural. It must be cultivated, and this begins in the family."[h]

MORAL TRAINING AND PERSONALITY DIFFERENCES

The training of children should be characterized by a consistent standard of moral excellence regardless of their personality, temperament, or gender. We do not lower the standards for the child but bring the child to the standard. Many parents are guilty of dismissing the need for virtuous training based on their child's individuality. They will say to us, "Oh, but my child is different." This is not a legitimate exception clause in the ethical scheme of the Bible.

We recognize that all children are different. Brothers and sisters can be as different from each other as from the child next door. Every child has a unique temperament and personality combination that distinguishes him or her from all others.[i] However, personality development and moral training are not the same thing.

Personality is like the various sizes and styles of homes offered by a single contractor. Moral training is the consistent standard of craftsmanship found in each home regardless of style. Regardless of the personality distinctions found in your children, persistent moral training should not vary from child to child because Scripture's requirements for moral craftsmanship do not vary.

Children represent different personality types. But which does the Bible exempt from demonstrating kindness, patience, self-control, gentleness, humility, endurance, obedience, respect, honesty, integrity, and other virtues? None of the personality types, of course. We strongly encourage parents to recognize and appreciate the uniqueness of each child, but to understand that uniqueness does not change the standard of ethical training. Temperaments, personalities, and even gender ("He's all boy") cannot be used to excuse wrong.[j] The virtues of life are the same for all and apply to all at all ages regardless of gender or temperament. The duty of parents is to continually bring their children to a consistency of virtue that is pleasing to God, but never lower the standard to suit the child.[k]

IT BEGINS WITH MOM AND DAD

When it comes to developing a moral common ground, Moses had an overwhelming task. Hundreds of thousands of Israelites left Egypt with values turned and twisted by four hundred years of idols and false gods. In Deuteronomy 6:4-7, Moses told the parents of Israel, "Hear, O Israel! The Lord is our God, the Lord is one! You shall love the Lord your God with all your heart, with all your soul, and with all your strength. And these words which I command you today shall be in your heart. You shall teach them diligently to your children, and shall talk of them when you sit in your house, when you walk by the way, when you lie down, and when you rise up."[l]

From these four verses we glean three principles of moral instruction. First, unlike the Egyptians, there is only one God to please vYahweh. He is an absolute God, and His commandments are consistent with His character. God is morally perfect and all biblical values are an extension of His character. Potluck morality is out!

Second, the starting point of moral training is with the parents. Before you diligently teach your children, Moses said, "These words shall be in your hearts." If the principles of moral conduct are not resident in your own heart, you cannot pass them on to your children. It is a mistake to think moral training is the duty of the teacher at Sunday school, day school, or Christian school. It is not! Whether by intent or neglect, parents are the greatest moral influence on their children. Not only do parents teach principles of moral conduct, they validate them in the context of daily living. Thus the words of Moses speak to the heart

---

References / Notes

i. We use the term temperament in accordance with its twentieth century meaning, which speaks to broad categories of behavioral predispositions. We believe that temperament is inborn and God-given. It refers to the individuality and uniqueness of a person. As a child's temperament begins to interact with the influences of life, his personality forms. And while our child's personality may change, his temperament will not.

j. Each temperament blend has both strengths and weaknesses that must either be fostered or discouraged. Parents often wonder why they continually see their child demonstrate a behavior they have consistently dealt with. It is likely because the root of the behavior is linked to a weakness in the child's temperament. Training children to learn to have self-control regarding temperament issues is a process that takes years. Do not be discouraged by this because in their adult years, they will be strong in their character in ways that will bless all they come into contact with. The Mom's Notes presentations, "Working with a Child's Besetting Sin," Parts 1,2,3 provide information on understanding the 'besetting sins' of each temperament and describe ways to work with your children regarding them.

k. A good resource for understanding human temperaments is presented by Pastor Tim LaHaye in his book, 'The Spirit-Controlled Temperament.'

l. Moral training is progressive. That is, all virtues placed in the heart of a child develop from the general to the specific. For example, when learning the virtue of honesty, a three-year-old child will first learn, "Thou shall not steal." At five, the understanding of the virtue broadens. "Thou shalt not steal" includes, "Thou shall not manipulate a situation to gain an advantage over another child's toy." By age seven, different specific meanings include "Thou shall not extort from another." At twelve, the meaning expands further, continuing the progress until the child comes to the fullness of that virtue. With proper parental guidance at every stage, the child will mature morally, and the meaning of the virtue will expand.

References / Notes

m. When children are young they follow their parents. Paul wrote, "Follow me as I follow Christ." (I Corinthians 11:1) Your children will imitate you at the beginning of the process that leads to imitation of Christ. All along the way, you must set the example of relating to Christ. This underscores the tremendous responsibility of parenthood concerning your own personal life. (Heaven Help the Home Today, by Howard Hendricks, pg. 80)

" My parents instilled within my heart the principle of putting others first. This is a" hands-on" way that teaches that life isn't all about me. Putting myself first can lead to grief; but putting others first is the essence of servanthood, which has It is own joy-filled rewards. It is, in a way, the heart of Christ and a means by which I draw closer to the Lord." - Christopher, age 20

n. Compounding the problem is the value parents place on training during the time of conflict. Think about it for a moment. Parents tend to teach a moral lesson in periods of conflict, telling their children what not to do, rather than in moments of non-conflict, directing their children in what they should do. Negative moral training leaves a void that may cause serious moral compromise in the future. When a greater emphasis is placed on teaching children what not to do, and too little on what to do, the path to virtuous deeds is left highly undefined for the child. As a result, children understand what is not the right thing to do, but they never completely grasp what is the right thing to do.

of the matter—the parents' heart.[m]

Third, moral training is to take place during the normal activities of the day. "You... shall talk of them when you sit in your house, when you walk by the way, when you lie down, and when you rise up." By implication, moral truth is best communicated in periods of non-conflict. That Does not mean we will not teach at times of correction, but it does mean healthy doses of moral enlightenment should take place throughout the day and in moments of non-conflict when the child is not in a position to have to defend his or her actions.

The charge to parents from this passage is to know the God of moral truth, to live His moral truth, and from that experience, to teach their children that truth.

WHAT NOT TO DO

Do's and Do nots are both a part of moral training, but too often Christian families concentrate on the Do nots. While studying child-rearing patterns in Christian families, we discovered that many parents are more preoccupied with suppressing the wrong of a child's behavior than with elevating good behavior. That is, when teaching moral principles, parents will tell their children what is wrong and what not to do, rather than what is right and what they should do. Certainly, suppressing the waywardness of a child's behavior is important, but when this is done in the absence of elevating good, ultimately you end up redefining what good really means.[n]

Restraining waywardness must be accompanied by instruction in righteousness and by encouragement in virtuous living (Proverbs 1:1-7, 8:33, 9:9; Micah 6:8). Both must be taught by parents if a child is to have a healthy perspective of right and wrong, and good and evil. For example, a child taught the skill of empathy—being sensitive to how other people feel in situations—has a stronger basis for future positive behavior than one merely taught to control his anger. Teaching our kids to do deeds of kindness is greater than teaching them not to be unkind. Restraining evil has to be balanced by elevating good. Moral restraint and moral assertiveness are two sides of the same coin. Both are needed in the training process.

Parents are in a position of great influence when it comes to helping their children internalize godly virtues. But how is that goal best achieved? Here are three considerations.

THE HOW'S AND WHY'S

It is not enough to teach your children how to act morally; parents must also teach them how to think morally. To accomplish that goal, you need to precede them in thinking in accordance with biblical virtues. Moral thought is a prerequisite to the process of raising a morally responsible child.

One major reason children do not internalize virtues or complimentary values is because parental instruction too often lacks moral reason. By that we mean mothers and fathers often tell their children what to do, but Do not tell them why they should do it. That distinction must be emphasized, because knowing how to do right and knowing why to do right are definitely two different things. The first speaks to moral action, the second to moral principle.

Many children know how to apply moral directive, but not as many know the "why" behind it. When they go to church, children are told how to act; when they go to school, they are told to obey; when they go to Grandma's house, they are told how to behave. Thus, a greater emphasis is placed on the "how-to's" than the "why-for's." As a result, some children reach adulthood appearing to be moral on the outside but lacking a moral sense on the inside. They know how to respond in different circumstances only because they have been trained to the circumstance, not because they understand the governing moral principle.[o]

Here is a word of caution. When we say parents should provide a "why" in their instructions, we Do not mean parents are obligated to provide an explanation for every decision or instruction on demand. There will be times when the explanation, "Because Mommy said so," is enough. This is especially true in the toddler years. But from three years of age and up, parental instruction should become increasingly characterized by the inclusion of the moral and practical reasons why they should do what we tell them.[p]

TEACHING THE MORAL WHY

After morning services, some of the third grade boys began running on the church patio in between church-goers. When Ryan handed his Bible off to his dad to join his friends, his father stopped him and asked about his intentions. "I'm going to run around the church with the guys," Ryan told him. His dad responded with, "Ryan, I'm going to ask you not to do that." Then he did what is characteristic of proper biblical training; he gave his son the moral reason why. Ryan's father explained that running on the church patio was not appropriate because of the presence of others. He pointed out mothers with their babies, senior citizens coming and going (some with canes), folks in wheelchairs, and the people chatting with hot coffee in their hands. He helped Ryan see the potential danger and explained why running around in such circumstances was not morally acceptable. This time, Dad governed Ryan's behavior; next time, Ryan can do so on his own, because the principle has been placed in his heart.

To further illustrate the importance of giving our kids the moral reason behind our instructions and restrictions, we can extend this hypothetical situation. Let's assume that Ryan's father denied him the opportunity to run with his friends but never gave the moral reason why. We have found that when "no" is given without explanation, kids view the rule as applying only for today. Next week, when Ryan's friends once again invite him to run around on the patio, Ryan will have no good reason not to do it, because no moral reason was placed in his heart. If there is no principle to stir the heart, the heart will not be stirred.

Providing the Practical Why

Not every explanation offered by a parent is necessarily associated with moral training.[q] Some explanations serve only a practical purpose. As a general rule, parents should offer a moral reason when a situation concerns people and a practical reason when a situation relates to things. For example, Nathan's dad was

o. *Providing moral and practical reasons why is the duty of every parent. Yet children will initiate their own questions which can be classified into three general categories: (1) The why of curiosity (non-moral); "Why do birds build their nests in trees?" "Why are the men working on the road?" "Why is the grass green?" (2) The why of comprehension (moral); "Why did you help the man in the wheelchair?" "Why should we always tell the truth?" "Why should we obey the park rules?" (3) The why of challenge (moral); "Why do I have to?" "Why can't I?" "Why should I?" Of the three categories, parents should respond positively to the first two, the why of curiosity and comprehension. The third category requires some form of correction.*

p. *The Auntie Anne series by Gary and Anne Marie Ezzo features more insights into the importance of moral training. Please see "Let's Ask Auntie Anne How to Raise a Moral Child."*

q. *Knowing the virtuous motivation for behavior prevents robotic behavior. Children who do all the right things without knowing why they are right are moral robots. They often respond to situations and circumstances correctly but not from any guiding principles of the heart. In contrast, children who govern their behavior by moral principle are anything but robots. They are morally free, governing their behavior by intrinsic principle, not extrinsic circumstances. Getting the heart involved in life choices will be an invaluable asset in adolescence. It is a prerequisite to leading your teens by your influence, a concept that we will develop in later lessons.*

References / Notes

"When my parents explained to me the moral reason why, it helped me to realize how what I am doing can affect other people and myself and helped me to make wise decisions."
- Benjamin, age 13

r. *Yet the time must come and will come when your child will learn to own his own convictions. As Howard Hendricks states, "Parents teach their children the biblical convictions the parents have. At some point these convictions must be made the personal property of each individual child so that he or she can successfully navigate the moral dilemmas of the present and future." (Heaven Help the Home Today, pg. 71)*

s. *Children of legalistic parents are often frustrated with their parents' decisions, and do not feel that there is fairness or justice in the relationship. They are more worried about complying with their parents' standards than with God's standard. (Mom's Notes presentation, "Legalism vs. Permissiveness, Where's the Balance?")*

working on a weed problem near the fruit tree. His busyness attracted Nathan's curiosity. Instead of his dad commanding, "Nathan, move away from that tree," he warned, "Nathan, move away from the tree because Dad just sprayed poison around the trunk. It is not safe." In this situation, the restraint of behavior is for a practical reason (health and safety) not a moral one. Since Nathan received information about what was going on at the tree, his curiosity was not further challenged. This minimized the tension between Nathan's need for obedience and his natural curiosity. His dad satisfied his childlike need to investigate.

Providing the Moral and Practical Why

While walking through the grocery store, Sean became fascinated with the black and white plastic price labels staring him in the face. He found it amusing to slide each bold number back and forth in its track. His mother said, "Sean, do not touch the price tags." She followed that request with the reason why. "Sean, if you move the price tags, the people coming behind us will not know how much to pay for the items they need." His mother's explanation was both moral and practical—concern for others coming behind as well as to prevent pricing mistakes.

The most significant point about this illustration is that the moral explanation meant something to four-year-old Sean. His mom and dad ordered their private world according to biblical ethics. They managed their lives, home, and children from these values. Because the family was other-oriented, Mom's reason fit naturally into Sean's developing world view. Not moving the numbers made perfect sense to this little guy. He even communicated that principle to his little three-year-old sister, encouraging her not to touch the numbers. Sean took personal ownership of his parents' values.[r]

That ownership comes as a result of several factors working in harmony to achieve the goal. Certainly, ownership starts by instilling biblical values into the heart of the child. The process includes parental example, trusting relationships, parental honesty, security of the husband and wife relationship, the expression of family loyalty, and many more relational components. All of these factors encourage children to integrate Mom and Dad's value system into their lives.

AVOIDING LEGALISM IN PARENTING

In developing common moral ground, one thing to guard against is crossing into legalism. A legalistic approach to parenting is very dangerous, especially in the teen years. It leaves in its wake a frustrated child, for the form of truth is elevated above the substance of truth. Legalism creates prohibitions by elevating the rule over the principle from which the rule was derived.[s] The legalist sees all decisions in life as either black or white, immoral or moral. He or she acknowledges no heart or motive areas. No room is made for individual strengths and weaknesses. The legalist tends to demand that the consciences of every believer be identical.

We have all heard the exhortation, "Let's keep things in context." The most notable aspect of a legalist is that he rejects context. Responding to the con-

References / Notes

text of a situation does not mean we must suspend biblical truth or principle, but that we apply it in the most appropriate way. One of the greatest skills to acquire in parenting is learning how to recognize and discern the moral appropriateness of any situation.[t] They do this when they look into the context of the behavior. This will help guard against legalism in parenting and the abuse of parental authority.

The following example illustrates this point. When Ryan's father said, "Stay in bed and leave the light off," he was expecting total compliance. When his little brother Nathan fell out of bed in the middle of the night, Ryan got up, turned on a light and help his brother. The legalist might see that as a charitable gesture, but also a clear act of disobedience. But was his behavior actually a violation of his father's intentions? In this illustration, it was never the father's original intent to keep Ryan in bed under all circumstances. Often the immediate (or moral context) requires a different response than the original instructions called for.[u] Our fear is the number of children who would lay in bed fearing to get out to help, because they were trained to the letter of the law and not the principle of the law. Failing to teach the moral reason why (that being the moral principle), deprives children of moral sensibility.

SUMMARY

The Bible represents ultimate authority and moral sufficiency. In its pages are the moral virtues that reflect God's righteousness and wisdom. There are no moral variations in its precepts. The values that govern conduct and define good and evil are the same for all people and for all time. As a parent, you need to realize that it is not enough to teach your child how to act morally; you must also teach your child how to think morally. To accomplish that goal, you must think in accordance with biblical values. That thinking is crucial to the process that you have begun—the process of raising a morally responsible child.[v]

Questions for Review

1. What is the moral mandate of Scripture?

2. Explain the relationship between temperament, personality, and moral training.

3. With whom does moral training begin? Why?

t. The more fully parents understand the vital role that 'context' plays in their parenting, the better equip they are to teach their children. Children need to learn how to discern and distinguish between obeying the intention behind Mom and Dad's instruction and doing the right thing in light of those instructions.

u. Life is full of conflicting moments such as when two equal values come into conflict simultaneously with each other. That is why there are times when circumstances in life force moral dilemmas. For example, under normal circumstances and within appropriate context, disobedience is considered wrong. The Hebrew midwives were faced with a moral dilemma when they had to choose between obeying Pharaoh or killing the Hebrew babies (Exodus 1:15-19). They chose life as the greater virtue and considered disobedience a lesser evil. Rahab likewise lied to save the lives of the Jewish spies in Jericho (Joshua 2).

v. Take the principles of Growing Kids God's Way home to your children through the "Growing Kids Coloring Book." It is a fun learning experience and a great way to help instill the values and virtues that Mom and Dad are learning through the curriculum. You will find this resource at www.GrowingFamiliesUSA.com.

4. What is the difference between knowing how to do right and knowing why it should be done?

5. Based on the illustration of Ryan running on the patio, explain what happens when parents fail to give a child the moral reason why.

6. What is one of the greatest skills to acquire in parenting? Explain your answer.

This Week at Home

1. Be prepared to share with the class how providing the moral or practical why of instruction helped your child with a right response.

2. If your child is characterized by asking why, note whether giving the moral reason helps curb that behavior. Determine into which of the three categories your child's "why" questions fall. Remember to support your moral reasons with Scripture according to the child's level of understanding.

Session Two Outline
and Chapter Two

Right Beginnings

I. Introduction
    A. The two related evils that threaten successful parenting and lead to the demise of the family are:
        1. Not understanding the _____ of the husband-wife relationship in the parenting process.

        2. Child-centered _____.

    B. The Premise
        The greatest overall influence that you're going to have in parenting will not come while you are in your roles as a mother and father, but rather while you are in your roles as a _____ and _____.

II. The Biblical Foundations of the Family
    A. Two central questions:
        1. Why did God create the woman?
        2. Why did God establish marriage?

    B. "It is not good for man to be alone; I will make him a helper suitable" (Genesis 2:18).
        1. Alone
            "Not good to be alone," refers to the absence of another like Adam with a view toward completing the total person. God is talking about the concept of _____.

        2. Helper

    C. Naming the Animals
        "And out of the ground the Lord God formed every beast of the field and every bird of the sky, and brought them to the man to see what he would call them; and whatever the man called a living creature, that was its name. And the man gave names to all the cattle, and to the birds of the sky, and to every beast of the field, but for Adam there was not found a helper suitable for him" (Genesis 2:19-20).

D. Creation of the Woman

"So the Lord God caused a deep sleep to fall upon the man, and he slept; then He took one of his ribs, and closed up the flesh at that place. And the Lord God fashioned into a woman the rib which He had taken from the man, and brought her to the man" (Genesis 2:21-22).

Creation Summary

1. Please note that God did not create nor did He recreate a _____ being, but rather He took from Adam's side a portion of his being and fashioned that portion into a woman.

2. The act of bringing the woman to Adam was more than just the creation of another species; it was the establishment of a social relationship called _____.
   a. This was affirmed by God in _____.
   b. This was declared by Moses in _____.
   c. This was reconfirmed by Jesus in _____.
   d. The apostle Paul followed up on this in _____.

3. Why did God create the woman?
   Because man was alone and needed someone to _____ him.

4. Why did God establish marriage?
   Because through marriage, partners may serve one another, and through their lives, serve _____.

E. There are no children included in the garden.
   The woman completes the man and the man completes the woman. Children do not make the family; children _____ the family.

III. Principles to Live By
   A. Principle One: By God's design, the husband-wife relationship is the first _____ relationship established in Scripture.

   B. Principle Two: By God's design, the husband-wife relationship is the first in a system of _____ relationships.

   C. Principle Three: The husband-wife relationship must be viewed as the _____ relationship in the family.

   D. Principle Four: Since it is the priority relationship, all other relationships function _____ to that of the husband and wife.

IV. Child-Centered Parenting
   A. Child-centered parenting too often produces a _____-ism attitude.
       Healthy families produce children with a _____-ism attitude.

   B. Child-centered parenting and insecurity
       The three basic emotional needs of early childhood are:
       1. A child has a need to know _____ he is loved by Mom and
           Dad.

       2. Every child has a need to know _____ he fits in Mom and
           Dad's world.

       3. A child has a need to know that Mom and Dad _____
           each other.

Key Principle: One of the greatest gifts parents can give their children is the
confidence that Mom and Dad love each other.

2

Right Beginnings

The family is the primary social unit of every society—one worth protecting and keeping. As professionals providing health and educational services to parents and children, we know the tragedy that can befall a family when basic principles of parenting are violated. We have counseled mothers and fathers who, with the best of intentions, started their parenting with love and nurturing only to see their dreams of a beautiful family reduced to a nightmare of survival. The problem was not wrong motives but wrong methods.

From our perspective and experience, there are two related evils that threaten successful parenting and lead to the demise of the family. The first is downplaying the significance of the husband-wife relationship in the parenting process, and the second is falling into the trap of child-centered parenting. To avoid these threats, parents must learn early on that God pre-programmed all factors for success into His divine plan. As with all matters discussed in Scripture, if you violate the principles, you forfeit the blessings. When you embrace His commandments, the blessings of joy and fulfillment will be yours.

THE HUSBAND-WIFE RELATIONSHIP

The greatest overall influence you will have on your children will not come in your role as a dad or mom but as a husband or wife.[a] Our society has forgotten and even rejected this basic biblical truth. The result is a society consumed with child-centeredness which is the precursor to self-centeredness.

Many times parents lose sight of the fact that, when children enter their family, they enter an already established social structure. Many parents act as if the marriage union was only a preliminary relationship to nest-building, rather than perceiving it as the ongoing priority relationship throughout the child-rearing years. That attitude is a dangerous start to parenthood, because it violates the divine pattern within the family structure.

The opening chapters of the Bible establish the biblical foundations of the family. In the second chapter of Genesis, God amplifies the details from the sixth day of creation for our understanding. The Lord wants us to know exactly what He was thinking when He made man and formed the family.

Genesis 2:7-17 records the setting of the stage when the Lord planted a garden east of Eden (in Mesopotamia) and created a single man to till and keep it. Adam, standing alone in the garden, framed the backdrop for the next major events—the fashioning of the woman and the establishment of marriage. The passage addresses two central questions: Why did God create the woman? What was His purpose for marriage?

References / Notes

"There is something wonderful about growing up in a home where your parents are truly in love with each other. They laugh together, play together, pray together and parent together. As siblings, we have a 'best friend' relationship with each other. We learned that from watching Mom and Dad." – Aimee, age 14

a. *The companionship and completeness that God intended for marriage grow out of communication as two people share each day and the meaning of their lives. Satisfying companionship and a sense of completeness develop as husband and wife learn to communicate with openness and understanding…The glory in Christian marriage is in accepting the life-long task of making a continual adjustment within the disorder of human existence, ever working to improve communication skills necessary to this task, and seeking God's enabling power in it all. (Communication, Key to Your Marriage by Dr. H. Norman Wright, pgs. 8-9, 186)*

References / Notes

b. Some great resources on the topic of marriage include:

1.

"Love and Respect" and "Love and Respect Workbook" by Emmerson Eggerich - Integrity Publishers

2. "Communication, Key to Your Marriage" by Dr. H. Norman Wright - Regal Books

3. "His Needs, Her Needs" by Willard F. Harley, Jr. - Baker Publishing

4. "What Makes a Man Feel Loved" by Bob Barnes - Harvest House Publishers

5. "What Makes a Woman Feel Loved" by Emilie Barnes - Harvest House Publishers

(These titles can be found at the Mom's Notes Bookstore - www.Momsnotes.com.)

c. Intimacy speaks of emotional closeness between two people and refers to the portion of a relationship that is most private and personal. Intimacy involves the blending of two persons into oneness and sameness.

d. When a husband and wife are not one with each other in regard to emotional, physical, social, and companion oneness, they are alone in that part of their life that is missing. When that happens, they fail to achieve total harmony and total intimacy. The act of two complete persons coming together as one is reduced to the act of fractured parts coming together only to make up a fractured whole. A couple cannot separate physical intimacy from the rest of their marriage.

Man Alone

In Genesis 2:18, God clearly states man's condition by saying, "It is not good for man to be alone; I will make him a helper suitable for him." In that one verse, God declares His intent for the creation of woman; man was alone, and that was not good. When we look into the context of this verse, we find that man in the truest sense was not alone. That fact qualifies God's statement. Not only was Adam surrounded by all of creation, but more substantially, he had a perfect relationship with God! Yet, in spite of those realities, God states that it was not good for man to be alone. Obviously, the implied meaning of "alone" is not in reference to Adam's ascending vertical relationship with God nor Adam's descending vertical relationship with creation.[b]

A second point to consider is the total implication of God's pronouncement. The statement "It is not good for man to be alone" implies a total person and not just a single aspect of man's being. Consequently, the verse implies that it is not good for man to be alone spiritually, it is not good to be alone socially, it is not good to be alone emotionally, or physically. God's pronouncement includes all of those dimensions. "Not good to be alone" refers to the absence of another being like Adam with a view toward completing his total person. In the truest sense, there was a void of relational intimacy in Adam's life.[c] It was the type of intimacy that blends two persons into oneness and sameness. Adam was alone, lacking an intimate relationship with one of his own kind.

God made man to be a social creature, both in the broader context of the community in which he lives his public life and in the narrower context of the intimacy of his private life. God made man with the capacity for relationships, not only with Himself, but also with someone with whom he can intimately share life.[d]

Adam's Helper

Genesis 2:18 begins with God announcing His dissatisfaction with man's lonely condition and ends with His solution: "I will make a suitable helper for him." The phrase "suitable helper" must be taken back to the Hebrew perspective. It refers to more than just a physical helper, such as one needed while tending the garden. The implication was that Adam's needs were special and more specific than anything God had created up to this point.

The context of verses 19 and 20 makes that truth obvious. "Suitable helper" does not mean that Adam needed a warm, physical body to set in motion all of humanity. Rather, it speaks of one who could complete and complement Adam in every way and one with whom he could be intimate. Eve was suitable for Adam but different from him. The two together represented the fullness of God's character.

Continuing with verses 19 and 20, God uses the naming of all the animals as an illustrative teaching device to arouse in Adam a deeper understanding of the need for one like himself. As Adam named all the animals, he realized that nothing yet created could satisfy the condition God called "alone."

Here Comes the Bride!

Genesis 2:21-24 says, "The Lord God caused a deep sleep to fall upon the man, and he slept; then He took one of his ribs and closed up the flesh in its place. The rib which the Lord God had taken from man He made into a woman, and He brought her to the man. And Adam said, 'This is now bone of my bones, and flesh of my flesh; she shall be called "Woman" because she was taken out of Man.' For this cause a man shall leave his father and mother and shall be joined to his wife; and they shall become one flesh."

The crown of creation was the holy union of the man and the woman. It was more than the creation of another after the "kind of man." The Scriptures state that God brought the woman to the man. He did not leave her in the garden to scamper around with the animals until they found each other, but He united the two Himself.

Adam immediately responded by naming his new companion "woman." What kind of relationship was this? Verse 24 states, "For this cause a man shall leave his father and his mother and be joined to his wife; and they shall become one flesh." The phrase "for this cause," also translated "therefore," guides us to the answers to our previous questions concerning why God created the woman and what His purpose was for marriage. The woman was created because it was not good for man to be alone. God provided a companion who was suitable to meet his intimate needs, one with whom he could share his life. For this cause, not only was the woman created, but the institution of marriage was designed. Marriage is the holy reality of two becoming one. God instituted it first and foremost for the sake of partnership, and it is described throughout Scripture as a one-flesh union.[e]

e. God is the author of the one-flesh relationship. Marital intimacy is rooted in the security of belonging, being complete, and feeling needed as a completer. God has so designed the inner person that we cannot be truly satisfied with just the physical side of the marriage relationship.

THE SIGNIFICANCE OF THE ONE-FLESH UNION

The phrase "and the two shall become one flesh" carries both a primary and a secondary meaning. The primary meaning speaks of a union of the man and woman. As stated earlier, the Hebrew perspective appraises man far beyond the physical dimension. "One flesh" speaks not only to oneness in body, but also to oneness in emotions, reasoning, and spiritual life as well.

More practical in application is the secondary meaning. It illustrates that a husband and wife become one in relation to the community. Through marriage, a new social unit emerges. When a man and woman separate themselves from their parents, they form a new nucleus and identity as one unit.

The New Testament clearly reconfirms this one-flesh concept.[f] The writers of the gospel record, and the epistles strongly emphasize the value of marriage and marital intimacy. For example, Ephesians 5:25-33 gives us a magnificent picture of the marriage relationship. Marriage involves two persons coming together for the purpose of mutual love.

Why then did God create woman? Because man was alone and needed someone who could complete him—one whom he would neither worship like God, nor rule over like an animal. Why did God establish marriage? Because through their marriage, partners may serve one another, and through their lives they may serve others. Thus, the crowning achievement of creation was the holy

f. The Bible exalts marriage to the highest level, symbolizing the Lord Himself as a bridegroom and the believer as His bride. Love is the centerpiece of the relationship. In Matthew 19:4-6 and Mark 10:7-8, Jesus cites the creation account. In both cases He quotes the second chapter of Genesis and reaffirms the institution of marriage as well as the significance of the one-flesh doctrine.

g. Genesis 1:27: "God created them, male and female did He create them." Men and women have a trail of masculine and feminine adjectives descriptive of their natures. Why is it important to understand the two natures, male and female? Every element of the man's nature perfectly complements every element of the woman's nature, and the reverse is equally true. Neither Adam nor Eve could represent God's character alone. It is the cleaving together, both spiritually and physically, that represents the totality of God. In your role as Mom and Dad, God's character is best represented by the two of you. Motherhood is not an entity unto itself, and neither is fatherhood.

union of man and woman. Once the woman had been fashioned, God declared that "it was *very good*" (Genesis 1:27-31) and rested from His work.

Notice a very important exclusion; children were not present with Adam and Eve when God rested from His work of creation. After He had formed the woman, God authoritatively declared that His creation was very good.[g] We believe that statement to be significant. If children were necessary to complete man and woman, God would have created them before making such a declaration. Therefore, the marriage relationship lacks nothing. Woman alone completes man, and man alone completes woman. Thus, the husband and wife form the nucleus of the family unit. Children do not complete the family; they expand it.

PRINCIPLES TO GUIDE YOUR FAMILY

From the verses above, we suggest four principles to govern all family relationships.

Principle One: *By God's design, the husband-wife relationship is the first social relationship established in Scripture.*

God made man to act, react, and interact with other human beings. He divinely orchestrated the principles of social interaction. In His wisdom, God began all human relationships with that of a husband and a wife. Other relationships, such as father and son, mother and daughter, and brother and sister came later.

Principle Two: *By God's design, the husband-wife relationship is primary in the network of dependent relationships.*

The concept of dependency was inherent in all creation. What God created on the second day depended upon that which was created on the first day. Likewise, what He created on the third day depended on what was created the first two days. The same idea is vital to God's design for human relationships, especially those relationships found in the family.

Moreover, the quality of the parent-child relationship depends on the quality of the relationship between husband and wife. That truth will never change. Much of a child's basic security depends on what he observes between his mother and father. When he sees them demonstrate love and affection for each other, he feels more secure.

Principle Three: *The husband-wife relationship must be viewed as the priority relationship in the family.*

Priority refers to the prevailing attitude that must be present for successful parenting. If you love your children, you must make the husband-wife relationship a priority. Letting your children know that Dad loves Mom and that Mom loves Dad is more important than anything you can buy or do for them.

Together as unified husband and wife, you are the head and heart of the family.

Principle Four: *Since marriage is the priority relationship, all other relationships must be subject to it.*

This principle speaks of the authority structure within the family. Parental authority is God-given and is necessary to enforce God's moral law in the life of every child. Structure and order are important elements in a child's development. Democratic parenting, the idea that reduces parents to an equal status with their children, was never God's intention. If there is to be harmony and love in the family, parents must assume their God-given roles by leading the family. If you remove parental authority, you simultaneously dismantle the notion of law and order in the home and society.[h]

CHILD-CENTERED PARENTING

Often parents leave their first love, each other, and focus extensively on their children. Although this may be done in the name of good parenting, it is the first step to the break-up of family relationships. This leads to the second threat to successful parenting: the belief that children are the center of the family universe, rather than welcome members of it. Parents who center their entire world around the nurture of their children at the expense of the husband-wife relationship are child-centered. Instead of integrating the child into the family where he learns the basic give and takes of life, they elevate the child above the family.[i]

The Problems of Child-Centered Parenting

Child-centered parenting threatens successful family life. Listed below are five dangers associated with this style of family government.

1. Child-centered parenting attacks the husband-wife relationship by reducing its biblical significance. In marriage, neither man nor woman can lose themselves. Marriage forces revelation. We are revealed for what we are. Child-centered parenting wrongly authorizes one or the other to pull away, ignoring that Jesus said, "What God has joined together let no man separate" (Mark 10:9). We are less revealed in parenting, thus less honest about who we are. Attempting to avoid the truth about ourselves, we conveniently find, in the name of fatherhood and motherhood, a more pleasing image, so some think. Whenever we pull away from marriage, no matter how noble the goal, we withdraw from our responsibilities.

2. Child-centered parenting reverses the natural process of moral development by prematurely creating within a child a false sense of self-reliance. The child becomes, in his thinking, self-sufficient prior to the establishment of needed self-control. That happens because the philosophy grants freedoms beyond the child's ability to manage those freedoms. Self-reliance apart from self-discipline is a destructive influence on young children.

h. God designed the husband to be the head of the home (Ephesians 5:23). The husband and wife are partners, but for a partnership to work well, one has to be the leader. Spiritually, husband and wife are equal in God's sight. But being equal does not mean they have the same roles. In order for the marriage and the home to run smoothly, God designed a functional distinction between husband and wife. To distort those functions is to devastate the relationship. The husband being described as the head of the home gives him authority. When the children become the center of the home, they become the head of the home, and mom and dad's authority becomes powerless. (Heaven Help the Home Today by Howard Hendricks, pgs. 27-28)

i. There are certain aspects of the husband-wife relationship that children need to witness routinely. They need to see an ongoing love relationship that includes Mom and Dad enjoying each other as "friends", not just parents. They also need to see their parents talking, laughing and working together and resolving conflict with a mutual respect for each other.

References / Notes

j. It is easy to fall into the trap of continually putting our children before our marriage. This is bad for them, and it is bad for us. They need to know that Mom and Dad are first in each other's lives. This gives them security in a world of broken relationships. ("And Then I Had Kids" by Susan Alexander Yates, pg. 94)

"When my parents had couch time consistently, my siblings and I were more obedient and there was harmony in the family. It does not seem like a big deal, sitting on the couch talking to each other every night, but it makes a big difference in the home." - Justin, age 17

k. Children of all ages think they can make their own decisions and run their own lives. The problem however is multiplied ten-fold when that child comes from a home that is child-centered. The absence of reasonable boundaries in child-centered homes creates a void. Without boundaries there is no need for control on the parents part or self-control on the child's part.

3. Child-centered parenting fosters family independence, not family interdependence. Children who perceive themselves to be the center of the family universe too often grow into selfish independence. Family independence rather than family interdependence becomes a way of life, a lonely one. Independence robs a child of the opportunity to invest. Where there is no relationship investment, there is no reason for family loyalty. Other people (parents, siblings, and peers) matter only to the extent that advantages are gained by maintaining relationships. What the child can get out of relationships, rather than what he can give, forms the basis of his loyalty. Child-centered parenting fosters that conclusion.[j]

4. Child-centered parenting magnifies the natural conflict between the natural way of the child and his need for moral conformity. With child-centered parenting, the standard is perceived to be the problem rather than the faulty philosophy.

5. Child-centered parenting, for some, comes perilously close to idolatry. When a child's happiness is a greater goal than his holiness, when his psychological health is elevated above moral health, and when the child, not God, becomes the center of the family universe, a subtle form of idolatry is created. Children become little gods who have parents worshiping their creation and not their Creator.

Stevie's parents are child-centered. They do not realize that all their good intentions are fostering a sinful disability called *me-ism* or self-centeredness. Stevie's perception of his place in life depends significantly on feedback and stimulation from those persons outside of himself. If that stimulation leads him to perceive himself as the center of the family, he will develop a self-centered perception that he will carry into each relationship as his world around him expands.

God created us with the capacity to both give and take. Stevie's parents are training him to take but not to give. They wrongly believe that if they demonstrate giving all the time, he will naturally become a giver. He will not; he will only become more intense in his desire to take. If he wants the swing, he will just push another child off because he has not learned patience. He responds to selfish impulses because his parents never trained him in self-control, which means denying oneself at the appropriate times.

Other people simply will not matter to Stevie. He will have difficulty with siblings and peers. He will grow up ill-prepared for real life, in which the ability to give and take is a prerequisite for healthy and enduring relationships. He will suffer in school and at work because other people will not cater to him as quickly as Mom and Dad. As a result of the choices of his parents, life for Stevie will become terribly frustrating.[k]

In contrast, Ryan's mom and dad are integrating his life into the existing family structure. They are creating within their son a propensity for close and loving relationships. When a child perceives himself as a welcome member of

References / Notes

the family, as opposed to the center of it, he will learn to move in and out of new and expanding social relationships with flexibility and emotional comfort. Being a welcome member of a family produces *we-ism*, which represents an attitude that accepts one's role in the family as a team member, giving to others as much as receiving. This relationship is the prerequisite to living a balanced life.

A Safe and Secure World

As professionals, we cannot overstate how necessary a healthy husband-wife relationship is to the emotional well-being of a child. Like his brother and sister, the most basic of all of Ryan's emotional needs is his need to know that his world is safe and secure. Child-centered parenting robs children of that confidence. In contrast, strong marriages create a sense of certainty; a trustworthy love that is predictable. What takes place between parents establishes that sense of confidence. When Ryan observes their special friendship and emotional togetherness in the normal course of a day, he is more secure because he does not have to question the legitimacy of their commitment to each other.

How amazing it is to realize that children who are only two and three years old have a radar device that hones in on parental conflict! When a child perceives more weakness than strength, a low-level anxiety is produced that ultimately affects every other learning discipline. Children know intuitively, just as you and I knew when we were growing up, that if something happens to Mom and Dad, their whole world will collapse. If the parents' relationship is always in question in the mind of a child, then that child tends to live his life on the brink of emotional collapse.

In contrast, when a child has confidence in his parents' relationship, he is emotionally free to get on with his life. This freedom is a truth that Ryan realizes but cannot articulate. When there is harmony in the husband-wife relationship, there is an infused stability within the family. A strong marriage provides a haven of security for children as they grow.

ACHIEVING A BALANCE AND MEETING NEEDS

It is very easy to become child-centered parents. Children are greatly dependent on parents for everything. That fact heightens the gratification of the parenting experience. There are ways you can meet all your child's needs and not be child-centered. Here are a few suggestions that can help you achieve the balance.

1. Life does not stop when you have children. It may slow down, but it does not stop. When you became a mother, you did not stop being a daughter, a sister, a friend, or a wife.[l] Those relationships were important to you before the children were born, so be sure to maintain them afterward.

2. If you had a date night once a week before the children came along, get back to it as soon as possible.[m] If you did not have one, start now. You do not have to do anything in particular, nor stay out any great length of time, but it will be good for you to get back into the habit of dating your mate

" When my sister Emily and I were young we loved it when Mom and Dad had couch time. I could not have explained why back then. There was just something right about it, comforting and secure. We contrived all sorts of things to make them comfortable like getting them tea when they sat down. Now we realize that 'Couch time' was for us as much as it was for them." Aubrey - age 16

l. Elizabeth George has written two books that will help Mom give priority to the relationships in her life and find balance in getting everything done. They are: 'A Woman After God's Own Heart' and 'Life Management for Busy Women.'

m. If we say that our spouses are important, then time alone with them will show up on our calendars. Before we were married, wise friends counseled us to take one night a week for a date night to go out alone as a couple to cultivate the friendship between us. This is one of the most valuable pieces of advice we have ever gotten. ('And Then I Had Kids' by Susan Alexander Yates, pg. 94)

References / Notes

"Out of all the wonderful things my parents implemented into our family life, couch-time is the one I most want to have in my own family when I get married. Growing up, I felt more secure knowing that my parents were taking the time to communicate and verify that they were a united team. This is how I know that my parents love our family and they loved each other" – Sarah, age 22

n. *Here are some helpful hints to get couch time going in your home.*

• *Schedule a time daily, Monday – Friday. Pick a time you can be consistent with.*

• *Treat that time as a non-negotiable appointment.*

• *Do not answer the phone.*

• *If Dad is traveling have him call home when the children are not yet in bed. Dad speaks to each child on the phone and then asks for Mom, letting the children know this is their couch time.*

• *Have a special box of toys set aside for play during couch time only.*

• *If you have preschoolers, start with 3-5 minutes. When they are not interrupting you and play nicely during this time, increase it to 10 minutes. (Taken from Mom's Notes presentation, "Finding the Balance in Biblical Parenting", Part 1 – 'Fundamentals')*

and letting friends or relatives watch your children. Children do not go through separation anxiety when Mom is with Dad.

3. Couples often did special things for each other before children came into the family. If there was a special meal you enjoyed preparing, plan that into your weekly meal schedule. Men, when you bring home a gift for your children, bring one home to your wife. Continue to do those things that were markers of your special relationship before the children came.

4. Invite friends over for a meal or for an evening of fellowship. Being hospitable forces you to focus on your home for the sake of ministering to others. This healthy distraction obligates you to plan your child's day around serving other people and is a good way for your children to participate.

5. Practice "couch time." When the workday is over, take ten or fifteen minutes to sit on the couch as a couple. Couch time is to take place when the children are awake, not after they go to bed. Couch time provides children with a visual sense of your togetherness. It is one tangible way your child can measure Mom and Dad's love relationship and have that inner need satisfied. In addition, couch time provides a forum for Mom and Dad's personal and relational needs to be met.[n]

SUMMARY

It is our desire that your family life be filled with joy, abounding in sweet memories and untainted by regret. This is not a statement of idealism, but one of direction and encouragement. Priority relationships are not arbitrary; they are not dictated by circumstances or social fads. Relationships within the family function best when they are orchestrated by the common goals of family love and unity.

If you desire to achieve excellence in parenting, you must protect your marriage. A strong marriage acts as the stabilizing factor against the shocks of life. As you maintain your priority relationship as a couple, you are simultaneously hedging against child-centered parenting. From the very beginning, children are to be welcome members of your family, but not the center of it. The relationship you have with your child in the earlier years will be that of a parent, teacher, and governor, but not of a peer.

Questions for Review

1. What is marital intimacy? What does it involve?

2. For what reason did God create woman and establish marriage?

3. Write out four principles that govern family relationships, underlining the key words in each principle.

Principle One:

Principle Two:

Principle Three:

Principle Four:

" My parents have shown me how very important having dates and couch time on a regular basis is for a good marriage relationship. When they spend time with each other, it shows us that they love each other." – Rebecca, age 14

4. Define child-centered parenting and give some reasons why it is wrong.

5. Compare and contrast *me-ism* with *we-ism*.

6. What is meant by the statement, "All children seem to be born with a radar device that hones in on parental conflict"?

This Week at Home

1. Are your children welcome members of your family, or are they the center of your family? List some activities that would move parents away from child-centeredness and share them with the class next week.

2. Dad, when you come home from work this week, take the first fifteen minutes and spend it with your wife, then take time with your children. When the class meets next week, share the responses from your children.

Session Three Outline

and Chapter Three

Touchpoints of Love

I. Introduction
    Questions to Consider

II. Learning to do the Words of Love
    A. God put within man the capacity to _____love, and equally impor-
        tant, the capacity to _____ love.

    B. God is _____ and He commands us to love.
        "Beloved let us love one another, for love is of God and everyone who
        loves is born of God and knows God. He who does not love does not
        know God, for God is love" (1 John 4:7-8).

        Love is so important to God that He made it the distinctive identifying
        _____ of his people (John 13:34-35).

    C. Love has two sides.
        1. We love in _____ (the giving side of love).

        2. We love in _____ (the receiving side of love).

    D. The problem
        Husbands, wives, and children all have different primary_____
        points of love.

III. The Five Touchpoints of Love
    A. What does love look like?
        1. Encouraging _____

        2. Acts of _____

        3. Gift-_____

        4. Quality _____

        5. Physical _____ and closeness

B. Examples of missed love
   1. Matt and Sue: Physical Love vs. Words of Encouragement

   2. Acts of Service vs. Quality Time

C. Understanding your children's love languages

D. Summary points
   1. Love languages are not biblical injunctions. _____ is the biblical injunction.

   2. Your primary love language is evidenced in two ways.

      You tend to _____ it more often than the others, and you _____ most loved when it is spoken to you.

   3. These touchpoints in children begin to emerge with some order by the age of _____.

   4. Feeling love is not the basis of right _____, no more than not feeling love is the justification for wrong behavior.

   5. We believe the _____ of a person's love language is God-given.

   6. Every day we choose to love, and every day we choose _____ to love.

IV. Recognizing Your Touchpoint of Love
   Do you know each family member's love language? Here is an exercise that we want you and your kids to try. Within each group, rate the sentence 1 to 5 according to what would make you feel most appreciated and loved by your spouse (or children). The number 5 represents what you most appreciate; number 1, in contrast, is what you least appreciate in each group. (No individual grouping can have a number repeated twice.) Please note that some questions distinguish between male and female. Answer those appropriately, according to your gender and position in the family.

   Group One

   A____ Your spouse/child says, "You really did a great job on that. I appreciate it."

B___ Your spouse/child unexpectedly does something in or around the house or your room that you appreciate.

C___ Your spouse/child brings you home a surprise treat from the store.

D___ Your spouse/child invites you to go on a leisurely walk just to chat.

E___ Your spouse/child makes a point to embrace and kiss you before leaving the house.

Group Two

A___ Your spouse/child tells you how much he or she appreciates you.

B___ Your spouse/child (male) volunteers to do the dishes and encourages you to relax. Your spouse/child (female) volunteers to wash your car and encourages you to relax.

C___ Your spouse/child (male) brings you flowers, just because he cares. Your spouse/child (female) brings you home a special food treat from the local bakery.

D___ Your spouse/child invites you to sit down and talk about your day.

E___ Your spouse/child enjoys receiving a hug even when you're just passing by room to room.

Group Three

A___ Your spouse/child during a party shares about a recent success you had.

B___ Your spouse/child cleans out your car.

C___ Your spouse/child surprises you with an unexpected gift.

D___ Your spouse/child surprises you with a special afternoon trip.

E___ Your spouse holds your hand as you walk through the mall or your child/parent stands by your side with an arm around your shoulder at a public event.

Notes

Group Four

A___ Your spouse/child praises you about one of your special qualities.

B___ Your spouse/child brings you breakfast in bed.

C___ Your spouse/child surprises you with a membership to something you always wanted.

D___ Your spouse/child plans a special night out for the two of you.

E___ Your spouse/child sits next to you on the couch to watch your favorite television show, even though they do not care for it.

Group Five

A___ Your spouse/child tells you how much his or her friends appreciate you.

B___ Your spouse/child takes the time to fill out the long complicated applications that you had hoped to get to this evening.

C___ Your spouse/child sends you something special through the mail.

D___ Your spouse/child kidnaps you for lunch and takes you to your favorite restaurant.

E___ Your spouse/child gives you a back rub.

Go to score sheet on next page.

Score Sheet

(Transfer your scores from your test questions to this scoring profile.)

	Encouraging Words	Acts of Service	Gift-Giving	Quality Time	Touch
Group 1	A____	B____	C____	D____	E____
Group 2	A____	B____	C____	D____	E____
Group 3	A____	B____	C____	D____	E____
Group 4	A____	B____	C____	D____	E____
Group 5	A____	B____	C____	D____	E____
Totals	A____	B____	C____	D____	E____

Key Principle: Every day we choose to love, and every day we choose not to love.

3

Touchpoints of Love

In the last chapter, we emphasized the role that stable marriages play in healthy families. We believe children who are assured of their parents' love for each other will have greater confidence in their parents' love for them. From that confidence comes the emotional energy to give love to others. This does not imply that children must experience a particular feeling before achieving right behavior. Rather, the confidence a continued feeling of love brings to a child advances strong relationships and righteous training; it does not hinder them.

In this chapter, we will explore the means of communicating love. Practically speaking, what are the various ways we can communicate love?[a] What does loving another person look like? How does a mother or father know whether their efforts to communicate love are actually having an impact on the one we direct our love toward?

THE CAPACITY TO LOVE

God put within man the capacity to feel love and, equally important, the capacity to communicate love to others. These capacities make sense since man is made in the image of God (Genesis 1:26-27). We know that God is love. "Beloved, let us love one another for love is of God and everyone who loves is born of God and knows God. He who does not love does not know God, for God is love" (1 John 4:7-8). Love is so important to God that He made it the distinctive identifying mark of his people. In John 13:35 Jesus said, "By this all will know that you are My disciples, if you have love for one another." The verse has a basic application. Loving one another is evidence that we are Christians. Love is the badge that identifies us as disciples of Jesus Christ. God wants us to love each other so the world will know that we belong to Him.

From the few verses above, we derive two basic truths. First, love is a command, and second, it serves a kingdom purpose as an identifying mark of all who belong to God. Knowing how to love correctly is vital to our Christian witness, and the place to learn about love is the Christian home.

Two Sides of Love

The two sides of love are giving and receiving. Giving love is the action side; receiving is the feeling side. Giving love can often be frustrating because we are not always sure that our actions are interpreted as love. That is because husbands, wives, and children all have different primary touchpoints of love. These touchpoints are like different languages—love languages. Have you ever attempted to communicate with someone who did not speak English, and you

References / Notes

" I do not know what my relationship with my parents would have been like without my having been raised with the principles in Growing Kids God's Way. But I have seen families that did not have these principles, values, and love in their home and they are broken and hurting. I am so grateful for this tool God gave my parents and how He has used it in our lives." – Emily, age 19

a. In his book, 'How to Say I Love You' (Downer's Grove, IL: Inter-Varsity Press, 1972), Judson Swihart puts forth the core of the concepts that are found in this chapter. He is the ground-breaker for these concepts but does not receive enough credit for his insights and contributions to the Christian community. Sadly, his book is out of print. In addition, we offer many thanks to our friend Dr. Gary Chapman for his additional insights and expansion of the practical applications. We highly recommend his book, 'The Five Love Languages' (Northfield Press: Chicago, 1992), for a more complete discussion on this topic.

References / Notes

"When my love language need is filled, it makes me feel understood and appreciated." – Russell, age 16

b. Wear your parenting badge with pride. If you look, you will indeed find something to compliment, thank, or encourage your son or daughter about every day. You can provide affirmation not only with positive remarks, but also by attending games, science fairs, concerts, and other activities in which your child is involved and offering genuine praise for his or her effort. In this way you are telling your children you are honored to be identified with them. Affirmation builds trust ('Heaven Help the Home Today' by Howard Hendricks, pg. 90)

c. Children with the Sanguine temperament tend to have a high need for the love language of 'encouraging words.' If you have a child with this temperament, please be sure you find something about this child to encourage him/her every day.

did not speak their native language? You may connect some ideas, but you do not fully connect all your thoughts and intents.

The following story can help explain this concept. On a trip to the former Soviet Union, I had opportunity to visit the Kremlin and its historical Red Square. Walking through the square, I noticed a crowd gathered in the center. As I walked toward them, I found them standing in front of Lenin's tomb waiting for a single event—the famous changing of the guards. Those around me spoke Russian, but I do not. Their words were meaningless to me. As the replacement guards started their march toward the tomb, I heard off to my left side, "Hey, Larry. Come on over here. You can get a great shot with your camera." Instantly, I turned to the sound of English. I connected with it. Amazingly, no one else connected with it. It was not their primary language.

We lived in Southern California long enough to become familiar with Spanish. If Spanish was spoken that day in Red Square, I would have identified it, not as quickly as English, but I would have identified it as my second strongest language. Since French is my third most familiar language, I would have picked it out as well, although I would not have tuned into French as quickly as Spanish and certainly not as fast as English. The languages we are most familiar with are the ones we commonly hear.

While the crowd stretched to see the event, I accidentally bumped into someone and immediately said, "Excuse me." Although I said it naturally, I realized the person I said it to had no idea what I was saying. English was a foreign language to him.

The events of that afternoon provide a great analogy. What happens with foreign languages occurs with emotional languages. We may speak our primary emotional language, but it often comes across to other people as an unknown tongue. We say "I love you" in one language, while emotionally they say and receive it in another. As a result, our efforts to demonstrate love are frustrated, and we are tempted to emotionally walk away from our children and our mates thinking no one cares about our efforts to love. To avoid that frustration, we must first learn the basic languages of love and then learn the primary love languages of each family member.

There are five ways of expressing love to our mate and children that correspond with the five touchpoints of love. Let's discuss these in detail.

Communicating Love through Words of Encouragement

The apostle Paul identified the power of love when he told the Corinthians that love edifies or builds up (1 Corinthians 8:1). One way of expressing love is to build up others through verbal encouragement.[b] Here are some examples: "You are such a compassionate person. I need to learn from you," "The flower garden looks beautiful. You must have worked on it all day," or, "That dress really complements you."

Taking the time to verbally pat someone on the back is a way of saying, "I love you." For some, there is no greater way to express love than by words of legitimate praise and recognition.[c]

References / Notes

Communicating Love through Acts of Service

The apostle John encouraged Christians to love with action and in truth (1 John 3:18). That is another way of communicating love—through sincere acts of service.[d] This means doing something special for another person that you know he or she is going to appreciate. It is doing something outside the norm of everyday life. Maybe for a husband it means putting gas in his wife's car on Sunday night so she does not have to think about it all week. Maybe it is shown by fixing the leaky faucet or by getting around to making those shelves she wants for the closet.

When a husband comes home from work knowing the patio needs sweeping and finds it already done by his wife, there is a heightened appreciation for that act of love. Because he did not expect it, the act means more, knowing that she did it because she knew how much he would appreciate it. Whenever you do something for another person beyond the normal course of events, you are saying "I love you" in action.

Communicating Love through Gift-Giving

The greatest gift of love the world has ever known is Jesus Christ, who gave Himself for His church (Ephesians 5:25). Gift-giving is a third way of saying "I love you." Although often a simple gesture, it packs great meaning because of what it represents. Impromptu gift-giving (unlike giving gifts on occasions such as birthdays or holidays) sends the message, "When we were apart, you were on my mind. This gift is a token reflecting my thoughts for you." A modest gift is a meaningful token that can say to a needy heart, "I love you." Think of "gifts" as giving this child something that has value to him or her, not necessarily something that has value to you. The gifts do not have to be big; a pack of gum for some children would suffice to get your love message across. Collect several gifts for him and put them away. Put one on his pillow one day, then one in his coat pocket on another day, and so forth, once a week until they are gone. Just put a sticky note on each gift saying "Because you are special! Love, Mom and Dad". We cannot tell you how much this will mean to this child.[e]

Communicating Love through Quality Time

The gospel record provides insights into the quality time Jesus had with His heavenly Father and with the men He discipled. Although His goal was to train His disciples for ministry service, He recognized that they needed to spend personal time with Him. That time with the Master brought conformity to their thinking. We can best define quality time by stating what it is not. It is not sitting on the couch reading the newspaper or watching television together. It involves more than just communicating impersonal facts like the five o'clock news.

Quality time requires that you invest yourself in the other person by giving him your undivided attention.[f] It involves two people who are actively participating in the conversation and going beyond the fact level of communication. The time may only be for ten minutes, but for the child whose love language is quality time, those ten minutes are precious.

d. Do not abuse the love language of 'acts of service' by asking your children to help you because you know they will. If you want to show this child you love him/her, you need to do 'acts of service' for him. Surprise him by making his bed for him one morning while he is in the bathroom, leaving a note on the pillow saying, "Have a great day today! Love you, Mom". Write in your day planner/calendar one such 'act of service' you are going to do for him every day, or several times a week. (Mom's Notes presentation, "Working with Your Child's Besetting Sin," Part 3 – 'The Melancholy')

* It is good to know the love languages of the members of my family, because I know exactly how to love and encourage them when they are having a bad day." – Garrison, age 14

e. Find more practical helps in Mom's Notes, "Finding the Balance in Biblical Parenting," Part 1 – 'Fundamentals')

f. Does your child have the love language of 'quality time'? This can appear to be difficult for a busy parent given the demand on their time and attention. And who has extra chunks of time to spend with just one child? It will not always be the 'quantity' of time you spend the counts but the 'quality' of time that can make a difference.

g. No amount of discipline will be effective if a child's emotional needs (especially for love) are not being met. The following are some ways to discern your child's love language needs. Keep in mind, they tend to demonstrate what they themselves are known for.

• Is she always telling you that she loves you, how nice you look, how good dinner was? Consider 'words of encouragement.'

• Does he tend to give you gifts such as a picture he colored or a bright stone he found in the yard? Consider 'giving gifts.'

• Does she follow you around trying to help as mom cleans the house or dad works in the garage? 'Consider acts of service.'

• Can he not walk by you without grabbing your leg or climbing in your lap? Do you find him sitting in your chair when you get ready to watch television? Consider 'physical touch and closeness.'

• Is she always asking you to read a story or play dolls with just her? Consider 'quality time.'

(Mom's Notes presentation, "Finding the Balance in Biblical Parenting," Part 1 - 'Fundamentals')

Communicating Love through Physical Touch and Closeness

Think of what it would have been like to have been one of the children described in Mark 10:13-16 whom Jesus held and used as an example. Physical touch and closeness is a special way of saying, "I love you." Holding hands, putting your arm around your spouse's or your child's shoulder, or just standing close to each other sends a special love message.

A husband may be working in his garden, and his wife may choose to sit down outside with a book in hand and begin to read. The fact that she could have read the book anywhere in the house but decided to be close to him sends a message of love. Some couples enjoy being near each other even when silence prevails. Just knowing the other person is right there is enough to confirm a partner's affection and care.

IDENTIFYING YOUR PRIMARY TOUCHPOINTS

Out of those five ways of communicating love above, one is your primary language. One of those modes of expression connects with you personally more than the other four. Your primary love language reflects your primary touchpoint of love. It is the one you most enjoy receiving and the one you tend to communicate to other people.[g] Learning how to appropriately say, "I love you," means learning and choosing to speak all five languages. Here are some scenarios to help demonstrate why.

Scenario One

Bill and Sally had a good marriage but sometimes felt frustrated in the way they communicated their love to each other. Bill's primary love language was physical touch and closeness. He spoke this language and felt loved when it was spoken to him. The language that meant the least to him was words of encouragement. In contrast, "words" was Sally's primary language, and the last on her list was physical touch and closeness.

In this example, the couple loved each other but did not know how to communicate it in a familiar language. Bill would say, "How about a hug?" Sally would say, "Write me a letter." She wanted words of encouragement, while he wanted physical touch and closeness. She would do many special things in the front yard, hoping that when he walked through the door he would say, "The rose garden looks beautiful. Thank you for your efforts." Often he would walk by the garden and appreciate her work but would rarely communicate his pleasure in her primary language, words of encouragement.

Bill and Sally learned that every day you choose either to communicate love or not to do so. When they understood this basic truth, each of them chose to love the other in their spouse's primary language. Bill now says, "I love you," with words of encouragement. He leaves notes around the house or calls his wife during the day; he chooses to communicate love verbally. Sally now speaks his language of physical touch and closeness. She initiates holding hands, giving hugs, and standing close during social gatherings. As a result of both of them choosing to love in accordance with each other's primary language, the fullness of love has returned to their marriage.

Scenario Two

For twenty-five years, Betty complained when her husband Mike brought her home a gift. "It's frivolous," she thought, "and something I do not need." When Betty understood the dynamics of communicating love, she wept. She realized for the first time that she was rejecting her husband's expressions of love to her. What compounded her sorrow was learning that gift-giving was on the bottom of her list of love languages and realizing that she rarely spoke that language to him, except at holidays. How discouraging it is to say, "I love you," only to have it rejected time and time again!

We must not only learn to speak the primary love language of our partner but also to receive graciously all the expressions of love that come our way from those around us.[h]

"I think it is important to know your sibling's love language so you can show them the kinds of love they value. I think doing something for them that meets their need in this area overflows from them back to you." – Titus, age 16

Scenario Three

In this illustration, gift-giving was last on the list for both a mother and a father but first for their oldest son. They noticed on each trip to the store, he consistently asked for money to buy something. For years they interpreted his requests as abnormal materialism. They worked extra hard to break him of that trait.

Once they realized their son's primary love language was gift-giving, they were better able to work with him. They started to bring home little gifts like a pack of gum, some pencils, or a fancy eraser—nothing expensive, just a little something to say, "I love you." That practice virtually eliminated his asking in the store. Mom and dad learned to say "I love you" in a language he could readily understand. When parents strive to understand their children at such a level, they pave the way for understanding and communication in the teen years.

h. You can find a children's love language test at www.*GrowingFamiliesUSA.org* The test has questions specifically designed for younger children through preteens.

LEARNING YOUR CHILDREN'S LOVE LANGUAGES

It is needful for parents to learn each of their children's primary love language. Gift-giving is the primary love language of our younger daughter. Many times, we entered our home to hear Jennifer say, "I made you a surprise." Whether she baked a cake, pie, or cookies, she was saying "I love you" through gift-giving. In this case, she did not give us something she had purchased, but a gift she had made as an act of love. We would do the same for her. It wouldn't be a big gift. We could buy a ribbon for her hair resulting in her face lighting up because that little gesture confirmed our love in her heart.

Quality time is our older daughter's primary language. When we realized that, one of the two of us would take Amy out for a leisurely lunch. By our actions, she knew we were saying "I love you" in a language she could easily understand—quality time. Moments of quality time came throughout the week, but when we sat down at lunch and gave her undivided attention, love was confirmed in her heart. In contrast, Jennifer found lunch time a fun time, but it did not have the same emotional impact as it did for her sister.

Bad Attitude or a Wrong Language?

Parents often misdiagnose a child's behavior and misjudge motives, result-

References / Notes

i. *It is sometimes hard to discern if a child's love language is "acts of service" or "encouraging words". Children whose emotional love tanks are low will do acts of service to get the words of encouragement. If your child is one who needs encouragement, purchase or make up several note cards and write something you are thankful for about him on each one. Dad and Mom can each do a couple of cards together and some individually. Each week place one in his backpack, on his pillow, or in a coat pocket where he will unexpectedly find it. Do this every so often as a great way to fill his emotional love tank. (Mom's Notes presentation, "Working with Your Child's Besetting Sin," Part 2 – 'The Sanguine')*

" Everyone in the family should know what each other's love language is. Parents can then encourage all family members to look for ways to bless one another by doing simple things that will build long-lasting relationships." – Kristin, age 18

ing in frustrated parents and confused children. Coming home from a weekend trip, we would bring a little something for our children. One such time it was teddy bears. When we gave one to Jennifer, she said with exuberance, "Mom, Dad, thank you. This is wonderful. I love this teddy bear." As she smooched and hugged us, we responded, "That girl has such a thankful and grateful heart."

Then we gave Amy her gift. She replied, "This is nice. Can I talk to you?" "Come on Amy," we pled. "Play with your new teddy bear?" After attempting to convince her how wonderful the gift was, Anne Marie and I turned to one another and concluded that Amy was not as thankful as Jennifer.

That was the wrong diagnosis! Amy was as thankful as Jennifer; we just misinterpreted her actions. They meant something different than what we thought. Not understanding the dynamics of communicating love can be costly to a relationship.[i] It is easy to misdiagnose a child's motives based on how we interpret his or her actions. That is why knowing a child's language of love is critical to the developmental process.

SOME PRINCIPLES TO CONSIDER

1. Your primary love language is evident in two ways: You speak it more often than the other languages, and you feel most loved when it is spoken to you.

2. You have the ability to speak all five languages, and you should try speaking all of them regularly.

3. Love languages in children begin to emerge before seven years of age but become more identifiable by age seven. Before that age, it is difficult to distinguish a language and assign a priority ranking. Of course, all children under seven like presents, hugs, and quality time. By age seven, however, we believe a child's primary love language has developed sufficiently enough to be recognizable.

4. We believe that the arrangement of your love languages is God-given and not learned. Although the ranking will probably never change, your expression of them may be positively or negatively influenced by your upbringing.

5. Most importantly, every day we choose to love or not to love. Choosing to love your mate in his or her love language is a greater act of love than exercising your own primary language. Jesus loved us when we were least lovely; that is how we should love one another–"Even as I have loved you" (John 13:34b).

SUMMARY

We want you to learn how to love each other and your children with a biblical love. Biblical love not only fills a child with confidence in your love, but it also fosters a love for others. Biblical love looks outward, not inward, yet at the same time, it satisfies all the inner needs. In order for your children to acknowledge the preciousness of others, they need to have a sense of love from you.[j] Having a confirmed sense of love is not the basis for right behavior, but it does clear the way for a more comprehensive love of others.

When biblical love is in the life of a child, he or she will not be held back by the shackles of self-love, self-interest, and self-protection. The same is true for you, the parent. In one sense, we all remain children in having a childlike need to feel loved. That is why the family is so important. It should be a haven and the center from which love flows. The ongoing demonstration of love between Mom and Dad should spill over to the children. When we express love rightly in the context of the family, it makes it easier for each member to say "I love you" to those outside the family. When we love with a biblical love, we rightly represent God to the world.

This Week at Home

Do you know each family member's love language? Here is an exercise that we want you and your kids to try. Within each group, rate the sentence 1 to 5 according to what would make you feel most appreciated and loved by your spouse (or children). The number 5 represents what you most appreciate; number 1, in contrast, is what you least appreciate in each group. (No individual grouping can have a number repeated twice.) Please note that some questions distinguish between male and female. Answer those appropriately, according to your gender and position in the family.

Group One

A ____   Your spouse/child says, "You really did a great job on that. I appreciate it."

B ____   Your spouse/child unexpectedly does something in or around the house or your room that you appreciate.

C ____   Your spouse/child brings you home a surprise treat from the store.

D ____   Your spouse/child invites you to go on a leisurely walk just to chat.

E ____   Your spouse/child makes a point to embrace and kiss you before leaving the house.

Group Two

A ____   Your spouse/child tells you how much he or she appreciates you.

B ____   Your spouse/child (male) volunteers to do the dishes and encourages you to relax. Your spouse/child (female) volunteers to wash your car and encourages you to relax.

References / Notes

j. It may take years of investing your life into your children, showing them that you are genuinely interested in their welfare before you begin to realize the dividends. Children know if you sincerely want to be with them or if you are "going through the motions." Put the newspaper down, turn off the television, hang up the phone, put the golf club down, exit your computer program, and give your children some undivided attention. It does not have to be long; even ten minutes of genuine interest in their day can fill their empty tanks. If you do not, they will grow to resent the things that you love and value the most – even if what you value the most is God. ('Light Their Fire for God' by Anne and David Harper, pg. 28)

" My dad communicates love with encouraging words. He not only encourages me in what I have done but with my dreams and goals for life." – Kara, age 14

C ___ Your spouse/child (male) brings you flowers, just because he cares. Your spouse/child (female) brings home a food treat from the local bakery.

D ___ Your spouse/child invites you to sit down and talk about your day.

E ___ Your spouse/child gives you a hug even when you are just passing by room to room.

Group Three

A ___ Your spouse/child during a party shares about a recent success you had.

B ___ Your spouse/child cleans out your car.

C ___ Your spouse/child surprises you with an unexpected gift.

D ___ Your spouse/child surprises you with a special afternoon trip.

E ___ Your spouse holds your hand as you walk through the mall or your child/parent stands by your side with an arm around your shoulder at a public event.

Group Four

A ___ Your spouse/child praises you about one of your special qualities.

B ___ Your spouse/child brings you breakfast in bed.

C ___ Your spouse/child surprises you with a membership to something you always wanted.

D ___ Your spouse/child plans a special night out for the two of you.

E ___ Your spouse/child sits next to you on the couch to watch your favorite television show, even though they do not care for it.

Group Five

A ___ Your spouse/child tells you how much his or her friends appreciate you.

B ___ Your spouse/child takes the time to fill out the long complicated applications that you had hoped to get to this evening.

C ___ Your spouse/child sends you something special through the mail.

D ___ Your spouse/child kidnaps you for lunch and takes you to your favorite restaurant.

E ___ Your spouse/child gives you a back rub.

(Transfer your scores from your test questions to the scoring profile below.)

TOUCHPOINTS ASSESSMENT FOR CHILDREN

We have put together a children's touchpoints of love assessment and score sheet. The questions were adapted for elementary age children. You will be thrilled with the results and your children enthused with taking the assessment. Visit www.GrowingFamiliesUSA.com. Under "Parent Support" you will find a PDF copy of this specially adapted test.

Score Sheet

	Encouraging Words	Acts of Service	Gift-Giving	Quality Time	Touch
Group 1	A____	B____	C____	D____	E____
Group 2	A____	B____	C____	D____	E____
Group 3	A____	B____	C____	D____	E____
Group 4	A____	B____	C____	D____	E____
Group 5	A____	B____	C____	D____	E____
Totals	A____	B____	C____	D____	E____

Compare your scores with those of your spouse/child/parent. Write down from the primary to the least of the love languages of each family member.

1._____

2._____

3._____

4._____

5._____

Be prepared to share with the class how today's lesson affected relationships at home, church, and work.

Session Four Outline

and Chapter Four

The Father's Mandate

I. Introduction
    A. Quality vs. Quantity Time
        The practice of quality and quantity time as it relates to the development of human relationships, especially a father's relationship with his children, is a _____ concept, not a biblical one.

    B. Spending quality and quantity of time with our children is not the goal; it is only the _____ to take us to our goal.

    C. The quality and quantity of trust our children have in us is the only legitimate _____ measuring our relationship with them.

II. Learning to Build Trust
    The eight mandates of a father
    1. Fathers must cultivate a sense of family _____.

        a. Verbally _____ your children.

        b. Know where you're _____ with your family identity.

    2. A father must provide an ongoing demonstration of _____ for his wife.

    3. A father needs to understand and respect his child's private _____.

        Three worlds.

        a.

        b.

        c.

4. A father must give his children the _____ to fail.

5. Fathers need to be the _____ of the family.

6. As a father, you must guard your tongue and your tone and learn to measure your response against the _____ on their faces.

7. Fathers need to _____ their children.

8. If you are going to build a trusting relationship with your children, it must be built on _____ truth and not on man's wisdom.

Key Principle: The quantity and quality of trust our children have in us, as fathers, is the only legitimate benchmark of our relationship with them.

4

The Father's Mandate

"There are two important roles that my dad fills that make me feel loved. The first is when he is my hero, whether that is killing spiders or fixing my broken jewelry. The second is when he is my leader, both by walking with God and breathing life into my dreams and goals." – Sarah, age 22

Our daughter Jennifer stopped by the house one day with two of our grandchildren. It was to be a quick visit to consult nurse Anne Marie about some running noses and feverish cheeks. While Jennifer and daughter Katelynn found their way to Grandma's office, eighteen-month-old Kara came into my study. In need of hugs and kisses, she wobbled over to my chair, put out her hands, and uttered one word: "Up."

I raised her first to my lap. Then, seeing she needed even more comforting, I brought Kara to rest on my chest and patted her as if she were a newborn. She snuggled into a comfortable position. I began to stroke her hair. Soon, she fell asleep, at peace with the world.

At that moment I thought, "How long has it been? Has it really been over twenty-five years since I held my own little girls like this?" Kara had come to me expectantly; her heart was filled with innocent, unconditional trust. In her little mind, there was no question about my love. There was no hesitancy, no doubt that I would bring her soothing comfort. At this age, Kara innocently believes that to receive love, all she has to do is open her arms and embrace it.

One day Kara will trade her boundless, innocent trust for a more knowledgeable trust in human love and unconditional acceptance.[a] She will learn through disappointment that the problem with trusting people is they are not always trustworthy. The degree to which her trust is violated in the future will determine whether she ultimately views relationships through a cloud of suspicion and doubt or with confidence and clarity.

Your child, too, will face countless disappointments in the future. Friendships, work relationships, and romantic entanglements all provide opportunities for doubt. Your child's life will be filled with uncertainties, but you do not have to be one of them. Make sure your child has no reason to doubt you. Are you worthy of your child's trust? Does he or she know that no matter how fearful life becomes, Dad will be there to love, accept, help, and guide?[b]

a. All children are born with an inherent sense of trust in Mom and Dad. In the primary years, they believe everything Mom and Dad tell them, whether it is true or not. By our correct words and deeds, we help them interpret life. Equally potent are our corrupt words and deeds. These, too, will shape their personal world. As surely as there is ink on this page, the innocent trust of early childhood will become metered and measured. As children grow, they trade their unquestioned trust in Mom and Dad for a more experienced opinion about the trustworthiness of both. There is no point at which it is acceptable for us to grow lax and assume that our believability does not matter; it will always matter.

b. Our children need to sense that our relationship with them is our highest priority in the human realm. Many times, because we are more interested in their outward behavior, what we communicate to our children is that we only care about what they do, not who they are. ('Parenting the Heart of Your Child' by Diane Moore, pg. 34)

DEFINING TRUST

Trust is not a human emotion but a feeling of sustained confidence in a person, place, or thing. We step into an elevator because we believe the machinery to be capable of sustaining a lift. Every time we drive over a bridge, we demonstrate our trust in the security of the city's building codes. We go into surgery only after being assured of the skill and wisdom of the doctor holding the scalpel.

In much the same way, children trust their parents in many ways and for many things. They trust us for both the mundane and important details of life.

References / Notes

c. All children have basic needs. They need to know that they are loved, that they belong, and that they are accepted for who they are. For a child, trust is the bridge that links his need to know that he is loved with an understanding of being loved, his need to know that he belongs with a sense of belonging, and his need to be accepted with the knowledge that he truly is accepted. This is where we fathers come in. Dads are bridge-builders. Without the bridge of trust, children have no point of relational connection back to the family.

d. A significant amount of research finds that adolescents who feel connected to their parents and siblings are less likely than their peers to suffer from emotional distress, experience suicidal thoughts and behaviors, exhibit violent behavior, smoke cigarettes, drink alcohol, or use drugs. They perform better in school, enjoy deeper relationships, and are well-adjusted.

e. It is amazing how many homes do not have "Family Night." Perhaps it is because they do not know what to do. Spending time as a family means more than renting a DVD and popping popcorn once a week. Here are some practical suggestions to make Family Night a true time of connecting. First, think about assigning your children a week each month to plan a Family Night activity. This helps each member of the family take ownership in the process. Second, there two good resources filled with ideas for Family Night activities. They are "Simply Fun for Families" by Gwen Ellis and "Homespun Memories from the Heart" by Karen Ehman, Kelly Hovermale and Trish Smith (both from Baker Publishing).

Because we continually provide them food, clothing, and shelter, they learn to trust us for their physical well-being. They learn to trust our judgment on matters common to life. "The stove is hot. Stay away." "The wind is too strong. You'll lose your kite." They trust us to give them basic facts about life. "Milk spoils when it isn't refrigerated." "Water freezes at thirty-two degrees Fahrenheit." They learn to trust our wisdom. "Bad company corrupts good morals." "A soft answer turns away wrath." "Black ice is dangerous to walk on."

Perhaps the greatest role trust plays in parenthood is connecting our souls to those of our children. I speak now of the trust that binds together human relationships, especially family relationships. Think carefully about this next statement, for it qualifies everything that is to follow. *The quantity and quality of trust our children have in us, as fathers, is the only legitimate benchmark of our relationship with them.* Intimacy, the soul of human relationships, cannot be present if trust is absent or in doubt. Think back to the questions at the end of this session's introduction. Do your children trust you to provide them simply with sustenance, facts, and judgments, or do they trust you as a person? Do they connect with you?[c]

How important is connectedness? Extremely important. That is because the family provides a place for learning about meaningful relationships. This is where a child can be vulnerable without fear and where he can test his strengths, weaknesses, and limits. Through his or her family, a child begins to develop an understanding about the world; the meaning of life comes into perspective. Connected children have a greater sense of servanthood, self-respect and relate better with siblings and peers.[d] This sense of connectedness occurs when each member of the family understands and accepts that he is part of something bigger than himself—his family. But before this can happen, there must be trust between family members. Children and teens who do not trust their parents cannot be connected to Mom and Dad.

As you think about your fathering, consider the role trust plays in your relationship with your kids. The bottom line is this: if your children cannot trust you, then childhood peers will shape their future more than you will. How can you build a trusting relationship with your son or daughter? It will not just happen, but there are some practical things you can do to aid the process. Here are eight relationship-building ideas to help you develop trusting relationships with your children.

MANDATE ONE: CULTIVATE A SENSE OF FAMILY IDENTITY

If you want to build a trusting relationship with your children, start by cultivating attitudes that lead to a strong sense of family identity. Family identity is the mutual acceptance of who we are as a family. Family identity is based on trust, acceptance, and a growing loyalty between members. It is a significant factor in the life of every child, including your preteen. Even negative peer pressure is minimized when a solid family identity is established.[e]

A Christ-centered family identity is one in which family members are devoted to one another as Christ is devoted to His church. This devotion results in relationships that are based on trust and acceptance of each family member as an individual, as well as loyalty to the family as a unit. These virtues of trust and loyalty are seen, not just in family members' feelings and attitudes, but also in their actions.

When our children were young, family ties were never optional. Our children knew without question that God put us together for the purpose of representing Him to the world. Consistent loyalty to our family values sealed our identity as a unit. That attitude made us mutually accountable. Each person knew the team was counting on every family member to stay committed to the code of ethics that represented who we were as a family.

Fathers need to verbalize their commitment to the family whenever appropriate.[f] To speed up the process of bringing cohesiveness a Dad must be assertive in leading his family in words of encouragement. He cannot afford to be a spectator, observing his wife's efforts to hold the family together; rather he must be equally as active in the process of verbal encouragement. Why is this important? Because when Dad is excited and encouraged about the family, children feel the same way. When he is silent about the family, the question lingers in their minds—"Does he really care about us?" A father's silence communicates a great deal to children—disinterest, or worse, fatherly disapproval or rejection. This is why we urge fathers to verbalize their pleasure and excitement with their family. When fathers cultivate family identity, they aid in the process of trust-building. The two go hand-in-hand. To nurture a strong family identity, fathers must weave trust into the fabric of each relationship.

MANDATE TWO: DEMONSTRATE AN ONGOING LOVE FOR YOUR WIFE

The marriage relationship is the stage upon which the performance of trust is acted out before your child's watchful eyes. Make no mistake; your son or daughter is observing you closely. What he or she sees can have a tremendous impact, for the love and nurture you give your wife will help elevate your child's level of trust in you. Children thrive on the demonstration of love between parents. They need to feel confident that Dad is tremendously in love with Mom. A father can be wonderfully involved with his children—hiking, fishing, skating, taking walks, and helping with homework—but still nullify the results of his efforts if he does not continually cultivate a love relationship with his wife. Loving your wife is a prerequisite to building trust with your children.

From a child's perspective, how much trust can he have in a dad that cannot take time to be with his mom? How much trust can he have in a dad that speaks harshly to his mom, or is not patient with her? One of the greatest emotional needs a child has is the need to know that Dad and Mom love each other. Fathers, the best thing you can give your children is a loving demonstration before their little eyes of how much you love their mom. It is the most fundamental point of security and takes us right back to the basic question, "How much trust can I have in a dad who is not continually loving my mom?" Not very much.[g]

MANDATE THREE: UNDERSTAND YOUR CHILD'S PRIVATE WORLD

If you want to find out what is going on with your child, you need access to his or her inner private world. Every person lives in three worlds—public, personal,

f. While driving in the car or sitting around the dinner table, encourage your family by making statements such as, "This is really a terrific family." "I am so thankful the Lord put us all together." "You kids have such a great mom." As you talk about the family, you gain credibility in your role as the head of the home. Your child's confidence in you grows as he or she sees that Dad is on board.

g. So how is your "couch time" going? Are you staying committed to this simple demonstration of your ongoing love relationship as a husband and wife?

References / Notes

" My Dad invests in me in the things that I enjoy doing. That makes me feel loved because it gives me a sense that he cares about the things that I like, or like to do." - Bryan, age 16

h. *Open windows are moments in time when your children will invite you into their private worlds. These moments may happen when you're going on a walk, putting one to bed, or sipping hot chocolate in front of a fire. Unexpectedly, the child opens up the window of his or her heart to invite you in.*

i. *Resist the urge to lecture when your child fails or makes a mistake. They will only turn "deaf ears" to you. Take them out for ice cream or a soft drink to create a time of non-conflict for the two of you. Listen to your child share what happened, and ask questions to guide him to the lesson that needs to be learned from this experience. (Mom's Notes presentation, "Training Elementary School Age Children")*

and private. The public world includes much of the time we spend away from home (e.g., work and social activities) and allows us to keep relationships at a safe distance. Our personal world includes time spent with friends and relatives. In such settings, we are more relaxed and vulnerable.

But it is within our private world that we can be bold one moment and fearful the next. We can feel overwhelmingly discouraged or gleefully sing songs from the heart. We can be anxious or at peace with life. It is a place of personal thoughts, big wishes, and hopeful dreams. Our private world is the most secret of all places. No one can visit our private world without an invitation, for our private world takes place on the inside. Children have a private world that is constantly changing and developing. Fathers need to be particularly sensitive to this world.

There is an interesting phenomenon with children we call the "open window" that is often missed by parents who are too busy.[h] One evening while tucking daughter Amy in bed we had a few minutes to talk. I inquired how her day had gone at school. A short moment of silence preceded her response. She was contemplating. And then suddenly she asked: "Daddy, do you think I'm pretty? Do you think anyone else thinks I'm pretty?" At that moment, she was taking a risk with her dad. She was trusting me with the treasures of her heart.

When your child is willing to share the issues of his or her heart, you must seize the opportunity. When your child invites you into his or her private world, you must listen with your heart as well as your head. Although there are no guarantees in parenting, this statement comes close to being a certainty: if you can prove your trustworthiness during the vulnerable moments in the early years, your son or daughter will come to you when he or she is older and faces life's challenges in the teen years. Your child will not forget you in times of need.

A father can establish a trusting relationship in the secret places of his child's heart, but he can destroy it there as well. That is why it is critical that you respect your child's private world.

MANDATE FOUR: GIVE YOUR CHILD THE FREEDOM TO FAIL

Giving your child the freedom to fail almost sounds un-American. In our country, we love winning. At times, I wonder if this love has caused us to abandon our perspective and appreciation for what we can learn from losing. It is a crippling thing for a young creative mind not to have the freedom to fail in front of Dad. Reassure him or her that failure is acceptable, as long as he or she makes an honest effort.[i] Your child needs to know that you view his or her failures as the first steps to success. As it is with so many experiences in life, it is better to try and fail than not to try at all.

A father's wrong attitude toward failure can prevent his children from stretching themselves to their full potential. Imagine a child who is afraid to fail in front of his father because he senses Dad is not going to be pleased with him or fears that his father will not love him as much if he does not succeed. This child makes the status quo his standard. He will not develop the full range of talents and abilities given by the Lord. He would rather hold back, achieving only enough to get by, than face Dad's lukewarm reaction or angry dissatisfaction if he fails. Each time such an interaction occurs, the relationship slips back another notch.

Your children want you to be pleased and proud of them. If you continually respond to their failure with negative, sarcastic, or hurtful statements rather than turning the situation into an opportunity for encouragement, you will do nothing to build trust.[j] Use the Scriptures to encourage and teach your children in the midst of trials and failure. Romans 8:28, Romans 5:3-4, and James 1:2-3 are passages we read and explained to our kids in such times. You, too, can use times of failure to instill biblical wisdom. Teach your child about the trials of the Old Testament character Joseph (Genesis 37:1-50:26) and how his right response to each trial allowed God to exalt him.[k]

Your children need to know that you too have failed and can share in their feelings of hurt and disappointment. Your kids need to be assured that your parent-child relationship is based on neither failure nor success. Please note that it is not the fear of failure itself that holds a child back but the fear of failing someone. Often that someone is Dad. You must give your child reason to trust in a father who will remain loving and accepting when he or she fails.

MANDATE FIVE: ENCOURAGE YOUR CHILD

There is a big difference between an encouraging remark and an encouraging father. Real encouragement flows out of a relationship. It is more than a word now and then; it is your smile, expression, and very presence that communicate encouragement. Fathers need to be a source of encouragement because encouragement builds trust. Here are some practical activities for encouraging fathers.

Dad's Little Notes

I often wonder how many young fathers wish their dads had written them just one note—something simple and encouraging. Something that ended in the three little words, "I love you." It doesn't take much effort to occasionally put a little note in your child's lunch box. How much time does it take to write something like that? How much meaning can it have to your child? During the course of working with parents, we received the following short letter which demonstrates the potential such notes have to impact kids.

Dear Gary and Anne Marie,

I am writing to thank you and testify to the truth you imparted to us during last month's conference. I brought my husband to the seminar in the hope that he would be more willing to take a positive role in fathering if he heard things straight from you.

A few days after we returned home, we were talking about fathers leaving notes for the child instead of Mom, something I had been doing for a few months. My husband agreed to put a note in the lunch box of our eldest boy, who is now seven years old. The next morning the note was written with instructions to place it in the box, which I did. It was just a simple note saying, "Hope you have a nice day at school. See you when I get home. Love, Dad."

Upon our son's arrival home, he handed me his lunch box as usual. When I opened it, the note was there. He obviously hadn't seen it so I said, "You

j. *Children with the Melancholy temperament tend to be perfectionists. As a result, they are terrified of failure. Because of this, they will not try things they do not think they can do perfectly on their first attempt at it. This includes joining sports activities all the other children they know their age are participating in. Dad needs to work with this child to join anyway, and find ways to encourage him despite the inevitable mistakes that the child will make. (Mom's Notes presentation, "Working with Your Child's Besetting Sin," Part 3 - The Melancholy)*

k. *Fathers must look at failure with an eye to the future, realizing that vulnerable moments of learning often accompany times of failure. In the Ezzo household, when our children failed, either in an achievement or a relationship, Anne Marie and I attempted to help them find the secret blessing. We often said, "Do you realize the number of adults who have not learned the lesson the Lord allowed you to learn today? Do you realize how many people live foolishly because they lack the wisdom you now possess?" Those were not words of condemnation or correction but of encouragement. They were not meant to dismiss the pain of failure, but to help our kids see that out of defeat can come a victory they never expected. We knew they would be tested again in a similar fashion, and when that day came they would be ready to face it with wisdom. They would then turn failure into victory, and when that victory came, Dad (and Mom) would be there with praise.*

" I love it when my Dad writes me a note or letter of encouragement. This shows me that he loves and cares for me and that he is thinking of me and that I'm special to him. It warms me inside."
- Kassidy, age 13

References / Notes

" Ever since I can remember my Dad has written the notes in our birthday cards. I have always treasured those notes as the highlight of my birthday." - Aubrey, age 17

l. *"Throughout history the written word has recorded emotions that otherwise would be lost forever. How many times has a father missed a little opportunity to capture with words a moment. Words go where Dad cannot always be. Little notes help build trust with children. Not just hearing them but seeing them on paper. This is a way a father can multiply his influence."* (Let's Ask Auntie Anne How to Raise a Trusting Child)

m. *There may be times when parents cannot think of anything their child is doing well enough to encourage or praise him for. Make a list of the things he/she does well. Does he make his bed every morning without having to be reminded? Did she help with the baby until Mom could feed him without being asked? Jot things down and on those days when things are not going well, share one thing on the list with him. Nothing makes a child feel more loved than to get a word of encouragement from his parents on those days when he knows he has been out-of-control. If you cannot find it in yourself to speak the words, write them down and put the notes in a place where the child will find it before bedtime.* (Mom's Notes presentation, "Finding the Balance in Biblical Parenting," Part 1 - Fundamentals)

missed something in your lunch box today." He took the note and read it, and then, before me, my son broke down and wept. I hugged him and waited a few moments, then asked why he was crying. He replied, "I didn't realize Dad loved me that much." How can I ever thank you enough for such a priceless moment in the life of our child?

The time invested by this father was probably thirty seconds, but the impact of his thoughtfulness cannot be measured. The older the child, the more he or she needs to hear from Dad in writing. Take time to write your children a letter at least once a year. Sign it, seal it, and mail it. Your child will quietly realize the letter he or she holds is from a man unlike any other in the world—Dad. Letters from their friends may eventually get thrown out, but Dad's letters get safely put away. And in the future, during those discouraging moments or perhaps on lonely days, those notes come out again and again, bringing the reader an assurance of at least one certainty—Dad's love.[1]

We also recommend that fathers sign family Christmas and birthday cards. There is something very special about knowing Dad took the time to endorse the warm thoughts enclosed in the envelope. Children do not usually question Mom's commitment to the family, but such gestures confirm Dad's devotion. Wonderful memories result when Dad takes the time to compose special notes and sign cards.

Take your child's need for encouragement seriously. What may not be a big issue to you may be a major issue to your child. In the process of growing up, you have certainly experienced many of life's disappointments. You know from hindsight that you made it through and everything turned out fine, but your child doesn't know that. Many times a father underestimates a child's sense of urgency. What may seem trivial to you may be insurmountable to your son or daughter. Listen for the cues; realize there will be some matters of major importance packaged in an insignificant statement. Seize the opportunity to encourage your child through his or her difficulties by imparting your experience and wisdom.[m]

MANDATE SIX: GUARD YOUR TONGUE AND YOUR TONE

One day, twelve-year-old Barry came home from school with great news; the teacher had selected him to be first-chair trombone in his seventh-grade band class. That evening when his dad came home from work, Barry ran into the kitchen and shouted, "Guess what, Dad! I made first chair!" Overcome with enthusiasm, he let his imagination soar and cried out, "I'm going to be a musician when I grow up!"

The feelings this announcement evoked in his father ranged from shock to sincere concern regarding his child's future. "Not if you want to make any money, you're not," he said sharply. Barry's face fell. He hung his head and turned away. As his father watched him retreat from the living room, he realized he had made a grave error. His son had tried to share with him something that was of great importance to him. In his rush to protect his child, Dad had stolen the joy from his son's heart. In that moment, Barry did not need an analytical assessment about his career aspirations; he needed to share his accomplishment. He wanted Dad to enter into his sense of excitement.

Consider these two guiding principles when responding to your child: 1) guard your tongue and your tone, and 2) learn to measure your response against the excitement on your child's face. I wish someone had shared this principle with me when I was a young father. I remember the morning Jennifer came running into the house with an enormous pine cone. In her desire to share this discovery she set the item in question on the kitchen table and exclaimed, "Dad, look at it!" Her entire face was glowing. The only thing she wanted was to share her feeling with Dad.[n]

In that moment, I failed her and myself. What Jennifer saw was a beautiful treasure. What I saw was a mess. Disturbed, I turned and abruptly shouted, "Jennifer, get that thing off the table. It is full of ants and sand and goo." My words floated in the air before landing on the innocent child. They were words that destroyed a special moment in the life of a little girl.[o] As I watched the joy and excitement drain from her face, I realized that I could never pull those words back. I asked myself why? Why that tone? Why those words?

Since that time I have learned this vital lesson that I now share with young fathers. When your child comes to you with excitement and joy written on his or her face, make sure you guard your tongue and tone. Read your child's face, the glow of the eyes, and the width of her smile. If we fail our kids in their moments of discovery, we potentially lose more than the moment; we lose our children's sense of security and trust in knowing they can share life with Dad and Mom.

MANDATE SEVEN: ROUTINELY EMBRACE YOUR CHILD

Within the family, a gentle hand, a tender hug, a pat on the back, and a good-night kiss all communicate intimacy in a relationship. To hold and be held communicates vulnerability and closeness that is reserved for trusting members of a family. In the Ezzo household Anne Marie was the primary hugger. She came from a non-hugging family and vowed that our family would be different. It was. As a family, when we greeted in the morning, we hugged. Before going out the door, we hugged. Just before bed, we hugged. We were devoted huggers, though we did not realize at first the emotional benefits of physical touch.

There is something very special about Dad's arms. Mom's arms are comforting, but Dad's arms are secure. Neither time, age, nor gender should limit a father's touch. Our children are never too old to be kissed, hugged, or held—never! Even as a full-grown man, I would give anything to be held one more time by my own dad, who passed away in 1972. I fear for the vast number of families whose fathers still have the opportunity to hold their children but do not.

Holding your child does more than provide security. It meets special emotional needs that one day will be met by your child's mate. For boys, a father's routine hug and embrace confirms a son's sense of masculine identity. Grandfathers and uncles also aid the process. For daughters, especially those beginning to blossom into womanhood (eleven to thirteen years of age), a father's embrace is even more critical.[p] In the course of our travels, we visit

n. The pathway of responsibility and independence is very difficult for the child who lives with criticism. He learns to condemn himself and to find fault with others. He learns to doubt his own judgment, to disparage his own ability, and to distrust the intentions of others. Above all, he learns to live with the continual expectation of impending doom. ('Heaven Help the Home Today' by Howard Hendricks, pg 37)

o. Ephesians 4:29 "Let no corrupt communication proceed out of your mouth but that which is good for the use of edifying that it may minister grace unto the hearers." This is one verse all fathers should pay attention to. Contained in these words is a profound message of life, a message that reaches all the way back to the Garden of Eden and the Tree of Life. Fathers need to learn how to speak to their children and wife with words of life, not death.

References / Notes

"There is no safer feeling than being in my father's arms. Whether scared, confused, delighted, or just in need of a hug, his arms are always open and I know that he is willing to listen to my concerns and praises, disappointments and triumphs." – Kristen, age 17

p. Warning: Many dads unconsciously begin to back away physically when their daughters reach this stage in life. This is most painful for the girl who not only has to cope with her changing body, but also the devastating loss of Dad's physical affection. Dads, there is still a little girl yearning for the security of Dad's arms around that maturing little body. Your daughter is still your little girl. She still needs hugs and kisses. If you fail to communicate your love through your touch, you will leave behind a yearning heart that can be taken captive by anyone willing to give it attention. Do not leave your child open to the affections of the wrong person.

q. What is a hug? Author Paul Planet says it best. "Hugging is very healthy. It helps the body's immune system. It keeps you healthier. It cures depression and reduces stress. It induces sleep. It is invigorating. It is rejuvenating. It has no unpleasant side affects. Hugging is nothing less than a miracle drug. Hugging is all natural. It is organic and naturally sweet. It contains no pesticides, preservatives, or artificial ingredients, and it is 100% wholesome. Hugging is practically perfect. There are no movable parts, no batteries to wear out, no periodic checkups, no monthly payments, no insurance requirements. It offers no energy consumption and returns a high-energy yield while being inflation-proof, nonfattening, theft-proof, nontaxable, nonpolluting, and fully returnable." (Let's Hug [Bayside, NY] Once Upon a Planet, 1981)

many families. In some homes, we find children starved for physical affection. It is not that the parents are purposely neglectful, but the tyranny of the urgent dominates their lives, and their children's need for touch goes unmet. Sometimes we are not in a home more than five minutes before we have a child on our laps seeking to be cuddled. Silently, they are telling us, "Would you hold me? My dad is too busy." Many little boys and girls who have all the material things of life lack what they really need—a routine hug from Dad.[q]

MANDATE EIGHT: BUILD TRUST ON GOD'S WORD

The need for trust in any relationship is basic. Trust starts and ends with God. Between those two points is the family. When a father takes the time to teach his children the discipline of trust, he creates within them a disposition for establishing lasting relationships as they grow older. At the same time, he is helping them recognize and enjoy the blessings of God.

Trust cannot be separated from truth. Jesus said, "Thy word is truth" (John 17:17). All the practical helps listed above are useless if a father is like the foolish man who builds his house upon the sand (Matthew 7:24-27). For when the storms of life sweep in and pound on your relationship, will anything be left after they pass? Without biblical truth, the family has no ultimate meaning or direction.

Parenting is a discipling relationship in which truth passes from one generation to another. Without the truth of God's Word, there is the potential that a child can be spiritually lost. What is the father's mandate? To rightly reflect the truth of God, to develop a relationship of trust with his children based on that truth, and to communicate with his sons and daughters the biblical message of salvation through Jesus Christ.

A father's mandate is to be concerned first about the quantity and quality of trust his children have in him. We must not think in terms of time but of relationships. How can you guide your children if they do not trust your leadership? Think relationship—a trusting relationship. Fathers need to take spiritual leadership in the home. Read and teach the Word of God to your children. Act as an Old Testament intercessory priest—bring to the Lord a sacrifice of prayer with and for your family. How can you love and lead your family in the "way of the Lord" without relying on prayer?

Questions for Review

1. Is trust a human emotion? Explain.

2. What is a legitimate benchmark of a father's relationship with his children? Explain your answer.

3. What is family identity and upon what is it based?

4. Why is it critical that you respect your child's private world?

5. What do the authors mean by the following: "Measure your response against the excitement on their faces"?

6. What happens to boys and girls when fathers fail to communicate love through touch?

This Week at Home

As a couple, sit down and list the eight non-negotiable duties covered in this lesson. Select three duties to specifically work on. Report to the class next week what they were and how your children responded.

Session Five Outline
and Chapter Five

Your Child's Conscience

I. Introduction
    Some facts about the conscience
    A. Used over 860 times in O.T.

    B. Used over 30 times in N.T.

    C. Often translated: The _____
       e.g. 1 Samuel 24:5
       e.g. Acts 23:1

II. How Does the Conscience Work?
    A. The conscience can be divided into two functions, or two components.
       1. _____ conscience

       2. _____ conscience
       (Lower/higher conscience or trained/untrained conscience.)

    B. The fundamental difference between the two is:
       1. The primary conscience is _____ in human personality.

       2. The moral conscience is _____ into human personality.

    C. Primary Conscience
       1. "For when Gentiles who do not have the law do naturally the things of the law, these not having the law are a law to themselves, in that they show the works of the law written in the hearts, their conscience bearing witness, and their thoughts alternately accusing or else defending them" (Romans 2:14-15).

       2. The apostle Paul was appealing to that reality in Romans 2:14-15. His point was that even without the Law, man still has a basic _____ of right and wrong.

Notes

D. Moral Conscience

1. The moral conscience is suited to receive _____ instruction.

2. The _____ of right and wrong is written on the moral conscience while the sense of right and wrong is inborn in the lower or the primary conscience.

3. The natural sense of right and wrong without the aid of biblical revelation will produce _____ inadequacy.

III. Establishing the Moral Warehouse

A. Psalm 119:11–"Thy word have I hid in my heart that I might not sin against Thee."

1. The action: David hid something
2. The object: The Word of God
3. The place: His heart
4. The reason: To maintain a right relationship with God

B. Psalm 119:11 speaks to the capacity of the heart.

1. The heart _____ instructions.

2. The heart _____ instructions.

3. The heart _____ instructions.

IV. The Four Activities of the Conscience

A. Negative

1. Your conscience will _____ you when you are about to do wrong.

2. When you do wrong, your conscience will _____ you through the mechanism of guilt.

B. Positive

1. The conscience _____ us to do right.

2. When we do right, it _____ us.

V. The Moral Search Mechanism

VI. Positive and Prohibitive Training

A. The human conscience is developed both positively and prohibitively.

1. Prohibitive training is used predominately in the _____ years.

2. Positive training is used predominately after _____ years of age.

B. Warning! You must make the transition.

C. Signs of a healthy and unhealthy conscience
The healthy conscience says, "I ought to because it's _____," or, "I should not because it's _____."

D. The prohibitive conscience
1. The prohibitive conscience says, "I have to or _____."

2. The prohibitive conscience is not a guilty conscience, but a conscience that functions in an ongoing state of _____ guilt.

How do parents create it?
a. Manipulating their children by creating fear of losing Mom or Dad's _____, or approval.
b. Manipulating the conscience by making the child feel _____.
c. Failing to provide the _____ reason why.

VII. Prohibitive Conscience Test
Scale   1 = Never true of me
        3 = Sometimes true of me
        5 = Half yes/half no
        7 = Usually true of me
       10 = Always true of me

(If a question does not apply, think of how you might respond.)

1.____ When someone says, "I need to talk with you right away," I get nervous and begin to wonder what I did wrong.

2.____ Even as an adult, somehow I am made to feel guilty by my mother or father if I do not do what she or he asks or demands.

3.____ Somehow my mother-in-law/father-in-law makes me feel guilty if I do not do what she or he asks or demands.

Notes

4.____ If fifty people told me I did a good job, but one person did not like what I did and was critical, the discouragement from the one person would be greater than the encouragement of the fifty.

5.____ Sometimes I go to church even when I do not want to just out of the fear that someone might say something about me if I were not there.

6.____ My tendency, when I am in a disagreement with another person, is to give in and say to myself, "It really doesn't matter anyway."

7.____ I constantly seek affirmation from those who are closest to me.

8.____ When I'm asked to help a friend or relative, and I need to say no for legitimate reasons, I still feel guilty.

9.____ I am the one who usually says, "I'm sorry."

10.____ I fear losing my child's love when I discipline him or her.

(To score, see end of Chapter Five)

Key Principle: A deficient moral warehouse forces the child to make moral decisions based on the fear of reproof or hope of praise, rather than the merits of the situation. Because there is no moral principle to stir the heart, fear of reproof and not the love of virtue drives the child to action. The properly trained conscience knows wrong even when there is no signpost saying it's wrong.

5

Your Child's Conscience

C aleb, I found these two Matchbox cars near the couch," I said, handing our three-year-old guest the sleek, shiny, new red and white cars. "You must have missed them when you cleaned up the track you brought over." The little blond-headed boy turned over the cars placed in his hands. Widened eyes belied his intuitive comprehension of what it would mean to add these beauties to his collection. Yet he paused midway through that thought. Something seemingly stopped him cold; then he lifted his head, shaking it slowly back and forth. "No, these are not my cars. They belong here. Mrs. Ezzo keeps them for children who visit." Caleb reached out and placed them carefully back in my hand.

Let's look at the facts present in this scenario. Fact one: the cars did not belong to Caleb. Fact two: he knew it. Fact three: Caleb was the only one present who had all the facts. He could have easily taken the cars home. After all, Mr. Ezzo offered them to him. Incredibly, he did not. Here, moral sanctions were at work in a three-year-old heart. Sooner or later every child makes decisions based on what he believes to be right. Indeed, all children from age three years and up begin to acquire a functioning conscience, controlled by a developing system of beliefs, ideas, values, and virtues that internally decree what is right, wrong, good, or evil. This is what determines how one should respond to situations. In the case above, the forming of Caleb's conscience had begun.[a]

What occurred inside Caleb's heart can take place inside the heart of your preschooler. This special "something" acts as the silent voice stirring within the heart, monitoring conduct for moral accountability. Yes, even starting at three years of age. As Mom will not always be with her children at all times, this "something" will be everywhere your preschooler goes—whether it be to visit Grandma, or the play-group, or to attend a family reunion, where all the kids merge into one noisy herd sighted in hourly intervals around the cooler full of drinks. This special "something" is known as the conscience.

While the study of the human conscience is less popular than the study of neural wiring or the complex workings of the brain, it is a more important subject to ponder. The destiny of a child's life is shaped by his conscience. To be quite honest, as parent educators we are surprised by the absence of public teaching on this subject, especially when it comes to child training. We suppose conversation about the conscience could be politically incorrect. It is possible that guilt and shame, two components associated with the conscience, are now socially considered vices of the soul rather than reflectors of moral misconduct. If that is the case, guilt and shame are getting a bad rap.

There are some hard facts about the developing human conscience that every parent needs to understand and act on. It starts with the single fact that

References / Notes

" I'm not sure if this is the good side of something negative or the negative side of something good, but there were some aspects of Growing Kids God's Way that were frustrating during my early teens. For example, coming of age to realize that many of my friends had no convictions, no sense of right and wrong or family identity or how to respect their parents. The absence of these basic Growing Kids principles made best-friend relationships very difficult." Rebecca, age 17

a. When we speak of the conscience, we are not referring to a state of consciousness or unconsciousness but to a God-given, moral faculty of man. The Greek word, 'syneidesis' (translated conscience) appears 30 times in the New Testament and 19 times in Paul's writings. The Old Testament, essential equivalent, 'leb' (translated heart) is used more than 860 times, often in reference to the work of the conscience. Leb is used in 1 Samuel 24:5, where "David's heart (conscience) had troubled him because he had cut Saul's robe." That is, he felt guilty about what he had done. In 2 Samuel 24:10, his heart condemned him after he had numbered the people, which was something God told him not to do. Obviously, there was a sense of guilt. Job lost all of his earthly possessions but said, "My righteousness I hold fast, and will not let it go; my heart shall not reproach as long as I live" (Job 27:6). The pagan king Abimelech spoke to God about the integrity of his heart (Genesis 20:5). David walked "in the uprightness of his heart" (1 Kings 3:6). So too, the apostle Paul lived before God in all good conscience (Acts 23:1). 1 Timothy 4:2 tells us that it is possible to sear the human conscience. That is, it can be made hard, calloused, and unresponsive to God. The conscience, then, is the seat of moral testimony. It is that portion of our humanness that receives and reflects values that represent what the mind perceives as morally right and wrong, good and evil.

References / Notes

parents are the primary architects of the consciences of the family and of each child within the family. In the beginning, a child has no functioning conscience, no preset scale of values. Before he can behave morally, he must learn general concepts of right and wrong and then advance to specific concepts of right and wrong. The home environment is the primary classroom, and parents should be the first teachers.

How one learns to get along with other human beings shapes his future as much as a good education or any acquired skill. The essence of community is bound by the reality of our collective conscience. A good conscience prevents calamities, afflictions, and miseries. What good health is to the body, a good conscience is to the soul. There is inward satisfaction of conscience when a good action is done, when virtue is practiced. The most natural beauty in the world is honesty and moral truth.

THE CONSCIENCE: WHAT IS IT AND HOW DOES IT WORK?

"Something's stinky here!" blared Erin, stepping off the elevator onto the full-time care floor at the nursing home. Heads turned, and since the messenger was barely more than two feet tall, smiles erupted. This time anyway. Yet between that moment and the next several inches, a moral truth regarding kind words needs to be planted in this preschooler's conscience.

The conscience is a moral faculty, a guiding voice from within, the faculty or principle by which we distinguish right from wrong. It's the voice that helps us control our thoughts and actions and monitor our words. In everyday life, one can find illustrations of a properly working conscience—from determining whether a Matchbox car belongs with your collection to returning the extra money that a clerk mistakenly gave you when making change for your purchase. And every day one can find illustrations of a not so well-trained conscience—lying about cheating or keeping money that is not theirs.[b]

b. The Bible does not offer a detailed explanation of the activities of the conscience, but it does hint at them indirectly. What we do know, we have pieced together from various passages. The terms that we have chosen to describe those truths are attempts to accurately represent scriptural intent. In Romans 2, the apostle Paul speaks of the working of the conscience. Speaking of the Gentiles who did not know the Law of Moses, yet they "show the works of the Law written in their hearts, their conscience also bearing witness, and between themselves their thoughts accusing or else excusing them" (Romans 2:14-15).

To act against the conscience is to act against moral reason. The conscience raises its voice in protest whenever anything is thought of or done contrary to the values of the heart. As a mentor and a friend, it warns that danger could be ahead while you are still thinking about how you are going to act. When you have done something you know is wrong, it punishes you as a judge. Conscience is the voice of *Self*, which says "yes" or "no" when you are involved in a moral struggle. It is a call from within to act rightly or avoid wrong. And it flashes the warning to keep quiet when something's stinky.

The conscience, then, is the seat of moral testimony. It is that portion of our humanness that receives and reflects values that represent what the mind perceives as morally right and wrong, good and evil. Most importantly the conscience is not something you stir up in a child, but rather something you shape in the child—carefully and with purpose.[c]

c. Our teaching of children should enable them to intuitively know right from wrong, to trust their own carefully honed judgment, and to go directly to the Lord and His Word for guidance. ('Heaven Help the Home Today' by Howard Hendricks, pg. 81)

When referring to moral training, we are specifically addressing how parents influence the habits of the heart and train their children both in virtues of life and the governing values of the family and society. The activity of moral training has a specific destination within the child. The final stop is a fully shaped, faithfully functioning conscience. Prior to three years of age, moral training centers on controlling outward behavior and pointing the child in the right direction morally speaking. That approach takes priority because prior to three years of age, a child's intellect has not reached sufficient maturity, nor is it advanced enough to understand how the virtue of "otherness" (putting others first) works. Nor is there sufficient moral self-control to consistently apply virtue. The *Me, Myself, and I* phase is still operative and continues to be so up through the age of three years.

However, around three years of age, a child's intellect is sufficiently developed to the extent that he is ready to receive the "why" of moral training. The *Me, Myself, and I* phase begins a metamorphosis from the dominate "me-ism" moving to a practical "we-ism." Emphatic feelings for others start to emerge and virtues begin to make sense. At three years of age, your child is ready to receive basic moral precepts upon which he will build a lifetime of values.[d]

A WALK IN THE PARK

This is where it starts. It's springtime and two-year-old Becky is strolling with Mom through the formal gardens at the park. Beautifully arranged tulips in full bloom appear along the pathway ahead. Becky wanders over and reaches out for a tulip. Instantly envisioning the scenario of falling petals and a flowerless stem, Mom calls out, "No, Becky, do not touch the flowers." Becky pulls back her hand, restrained by Mom's instruction. Becky has already learned that disobeying Mom brings a consequence. That part is not new. She mimics right moral actions (she didn't pick the tulip) only because Mom made it happen and not for any altruistic reason on Becky's part. At two years of age, Becky has neither the moral or intellectual capacity to understand that if every child walking in the park picked the pretty flowers, there would soon be no flowers left for others to enjoy.

But things change around the age of three. Becky's world of understanding grows rapidly. She reaches a milestone in her cognitive development. She has a new awareness and growing understanding of life outside of herself. Until a child satisfactorily reaches this stage, parents can only manage outward behavior. You might be managing behavior with moral implications in mind, thus sowing good seeds of right behavior, but your efforts of helping the child internalize moral precepts will not take place until the conscience awakens and joins itself to moral understanding.

When this milestone is crossed, parents embark on a new pathway of training that continues for the next twelve to fifteen years. You begin transitioning from controlling outward behavior only to pro-actively shaping inner attitudes and heart responses. You are now actively shaping the conscience that will rule your child the rest of his life.[e]

Here's the transition—the following springtime, Becky and Mom are strolling through the park and come upon the same border of tulips. Attracted by the colors, Becky moves closer to touch one and then contemplates picking one. Now she hears her guardian's voice (conscience) say, "No, Becky. We do not pick flowers in the public garden," followed by this moral explanation: "Becky, those flowers are here for everyone to enjoy and to be shared by all. If each person

d. We need to be careful not to overwhelm our children with too much moral knowledge at one time. It is not possible to teach children to be kind, be patient, be truthful, be polite and so forth in the same period of time. Choose one character quality (virtue) you want to work on with each of your children. They may be the same or they may be different, depending on what a particular child needs to work on. Designate one hour weekly per child to "train their conscience". Make lesson plans as any teacher would. Pick a different Bible story each week for a month for this virtue. Choose two stories that show the positive side of the virtue and two that show the negative side. A good concordance will help with this. There are many resources that will assist parents in finding activities that go along with teaching children virtues. Each week, have your child grade (A, B, etc.) himself on how he is doing with this virtue. At the end of the month, take him out for ice cream if he earned A's or B's. Choose another quality to work on the next month. Working on one quality a month gives the child time to work on it in his daily life so it becomes a habit, which is the goal of all training. (Mom's Notes presentation, "Using the Bible in the Instruction and Training of Your Children")

e. The Bible puts forth a high standard of conduct that is pure and right. A child's heart is like a garden; it needs careful attention to keep back the weeds so that the planted good seed can mature and eventually flourish. The good seeds are God's principles for conduct, and parents are the ones who plant them. Weeds from the sin nature will always be a problem, but in a healthy garden the gardener prevents them from dominating the soil. ("Christian Parenting in the Information Age" by Dennis and Dawn Wilson, pg. 81)

References / Notes

f. "For Instruction in Righteousness," "Proverbs for Parenting," and "Parenting with Scripture" are books that will assist you in teaching biblical virtues to your children. Did you know that most of the books referenced in this manual can be found at www.momsnotes.com? The Mom's Notes Bookstore was established to assist parents by providing books for all ages of children. The books have all been researched, are consistent with GFI teaching, and are based on biblical principles. It is a place parents can go to and know they can find quality books for themselves and their children.

g. Other titles attributed to the higher conscience include: the heart of a child, heart of man, the moral conscience, and the trainable conscience.

" When I see the decisions my friends make and I am able to see the long-term consequences of their choices I am so thankful my parents gave me the tools to discern right from wrong, wisdom from foolishness, and why it is so."
- Stephen, age 18

picked a flower, there would be none for others to enjoy."

Please note this transition carefully. Mom's guiding restraint came first to two-year-old Becky: "No, Becky, do not pick the flowers . . ." (This controls outward behavior). That is followed by offering the moral reason, "Flowers are here to be shared by everyone." (This is introduces and reinforces an "otherness" value). The knowledge of why flowers should not be picked from public gardens serves to guide three-year-old Becky's future responses. Thus, the transition from external to internal authority takes place. Please note—this is a process that takes place over time as more deposits are made into Becky's moral account.

Similar scenarios will be repeated a number of different times and ways throughout Becky's early years. Becky is now learning many moral truths and "otherness" virtues. The emphasis is not only on what Becky should not do, but also on what she should do. Like a single bank account, all deposits end up in one place. That place is called the conscience.[f]

HOW DOES THE CONSCIENCE WORK?

The human conscience actually functions at two levels of existence—a lower and higher conscience. The lower conscience contains an innate sense of right and wrong, which all humanity shares. The higher conscience is subject to training and receives the specific standards of right and wrong formed by beliefs and values.

While this chapter deals specifically with the higher conscience, there is a fascinating account about the lower conscience contained in the early writings of the Hebrew Bible. In Genesis chapter four God pronounced a curse on Cain for the murder of his brother Abel. He was to become a vagrant and a wanderer of the earth. Cain responded, "Whoever finds me will kill me." Here we see an example of the lower conscience operating. How did Cain know others would require his life as a result of killing his brother? No law at that time had been established. Even God acknowledges the probability of that action by marking him as "one not to be touched." Cain was operating off his innate sense of right and wrong. Here is a story over five thousand years old reflecting an anthropological description of mankind then and now.

Much more central to parenting is the function of the higher conscience.[g] Aristotle acknowledged and pointed out the trainable side of the human conscience. It is here that the knowledge and standards of right and wrong are written on the heart. It is the place where values, virtues, prohibitions, and moral initiatives are located. In the illustration above, Becky's mom made a deposit in Becky's conscience by giving her the moral reason for not picking flowers in public places. The specific elements of right and wrong were deposited into Becky's higher conscience, connecting with a group of otherness virtues.

All parents have a social obligation to train their children in community values. With their moral pen they write a prescription of right and wrong, what to do and what not to do, and all the moral reasons why or why not. Since parents offer instruction both by precept and example, attention must be paid not only to what moral truth is imparted to a child, but how it is imparted. This point will be demonstrated later in a very tangible way. The balance of this chapter is devoted to explaining how the conscience actually works. What are the parts? How do they work together? What role do parents play in shaping the conscience? Our discussion centers on four areas:

- Establishing the Moral Warehouse
- The Four Activities of the Conscience
- The Moral Search Mechanism
- Signs of a Healthy and Unhealthy Conscience

ESTABLISHING THE MORAL WAREHOUSE

The ability to receive and store moral principles speaks to the capacity of the conscience.[h] Every person of normal birth possesses this capacity. It is the place where parents make deposits of moral knowledge. You are constantly teaching your child in many different ways, in a number of differing contexts throughout the day. You instruct your child to share, be kind, tell the truth, be patient, ask nicely, be polite, show respect, act courteously, and say please and thank you. This is a process that takes place day in and day out, week by week, and year by year. Believe it or not, those moral impressions are going somewhere. They are stored in the child's moral warehouse—the conscience.

We have all seen them—those large metal warehouses. Imagine an industrial warehouse in your neighborhood. You step inside the door onto a glistening, clean cement floor. In front of you is a neatly divided warehouse made up of aisles and metal shelving used for storage. Some shelves are bursting full of various virtues while others are spilling over with admirable character qualities. You recognize each of these items because you and your spouse have placed them there. On one shelf rests your teaching of kindness. On another, the virtue calling for honesty, and down the aisle there is a group of virtues that demonstrate respect for elders, parents, teachers, and authority. Not far from there are the virtues of sharing, kind speech, and self-control. Each is marked with a dangling red identification tag making these virtues easy to find and retrieve. This is a picture of your child's moral warehouse. Some shelves are packed with virtues and others empty, waiting for future instruction.

When training children, the management rights to that warehouse belong to parents. You are the managers of your child's conscience. You have the marking pen. You write the values on their hearts. Some parents do this with fervency and intent while others take a nonchalant approach. Fervency is highly preferred. As the shelves begin to fill, the four activities of the conscience can start their work.

THE FOUR ACTIVITIES OF THE CONSCIENCE

Remember Becky from our previous story? Now eight years old, she hopped out of bed early—eager to finish her painting-by-numbers started the night before. It only came to a halt because Mom insisted that it was time for Becky to go to bed. Mom also instructed Becky to complete her morning routine before she reopened her paints. But Mom is still sleeping and ... Becky's rational thoughts faded to silence as another voice, that "special something" voice began to speak.

References / Notes

h. In the book of Psalms, David writes, "Thy word have I hid in my heart that I might not sin against Thee" (Psalm 119:11). Note what is taking place here:

- The action: David hid something

- The object: The Word of God

- The place: David's heart

- The reason: To maintain a right relationship with God and man.

According to this verse, we place and store the principles of moral conduct in our heart. Psalm 119:11 speaks to the capacity of the heart. It receives instruction, stores instruction, and governs instruction. The heart then, is a type of moral warehouse in which one deposits moral knowledge to be used at a later time.

* * *

"I am thankful that my parents worked diligently to fill my moral warehouse with the 'moral reason why' because instead of just doing a particular thing according to a code of rules, I am able to think on my feet and decide what is right for every situation." – Aubrey, age 17

References / Notes

i. *Little sins that are never made right will affect us the rest of our lives. If there are little sins that are not taken care of, we will have guilt which will be a hindrance in our relationship with God and others. Guilt does to relationships what injuries, handicaps, diseases, or poison does to the body. They hinder the way it functions. ('Making Brothers and Sisters Best Friends' by Sarah, Stephen, and Grace Mally, pg. 111)*

" *If my parents had not shown me the ways of right and wrong, I'm sure I would have been influenced by such things as peers and media. These would have led me to a misguided understanding of right, wrong and even what 'truth' is.*"
- *Titus, age 16*

Guidelines for morning activities were clearly established in Becky's home. Knowing her bed must be made, hair brushed, and other responsibilities performed before she was free to do what she wanted to do. Becky swiftly worked through these tasks in hopes of getting to her project before breakfast. This eight-year-old's conscience monitored her activity and redirected her energy to accomplish what was required first. This process began years ago, when she was a preschooler taking a walk in a garden of tulips. Be a wise steward with the time you have with your children.

The conscience has the ability to assess behavior in any moment and render judicial opinions, either by accusing or defending one's actions. Accusing speaks to the negative side of the conscience, while defending speaks to the positive side. When we say our conscience accuses us, we are referring to its ability to make a judgment on a potential moral violation based on what is in the warehouse. The conscience (that inward voice) warns man when he is about to do wrong. If he does not heed that warning, his conscience will accuse him. This is done through the mechanism of guilt.[i]

Guilt, shame, and empathy are moral emotions common to the human experience. Any attempt to get rid of guilt is an attempt to get rid of the conscience. Guilt is not a condition of the healthy or the sick, but of right versus wrong. When we cross the boundary of our own conscience, guilt is activated. We did something we knew we should not have done. Guilt is there to remind us to take care of our misdeeds. If a person never experiences guilt, either his conscience has been hardened, or he has an empty warehouse desperately in need of filling.

The good news is found in the positive function of the human conscience. The conscience will also prompt us to do right and confirms us when we do. For example, you see a crumpled piece of paper lying in the hallway. You sense a prompting from within—"Pick up the paper even though you didn't drop it." You do so and suddenly that feeling of "rightness" comes over you. That sense that you complied with the integrity of your heart is your conscience saying, "You did the right thing."

So the conscience will prompt us to do right and then confirms us when we do. It also warns us of potential wrong and then accuses us if we cross the line. For example, a gum wrapper casually slips from your hand. Even as your feet move forward, a thousand impulses begin to prompt you to stop. "Guilty! " your conscience screams, until you glance around to see if anyone else can hear it. The next question is—How is this possible? Why is my conscience bothered by my behavior? Here is how it works.

THE MORAL SEARCH MECHANISM

The four activities of the conscience—prompting, confirming, warning, and accusing—operate in harmony with the values stored in the warehouse. The conscience also has the ability to monitor the moral horizon and alert one to potential ethical situations possibly in need of a response. Once alerted to a need, the prompting or warning mechanism moves us to action.

Every day we participate in numerous potential ethical situations. Whether you are shopping, at work, doing laundry, driving home, watching television, sitting in the grandstands of your child's soccer match, or chewing gum—you are constantly confronted with ethical circumstances challenging the values in your warehouse. The moral search mechanism, like a continuous scanning radar beam, looks over the horizon, taking in data, evaluating it for moral liability, and then responds by going to the moral warehouse in search of a value or virtue to act on.[j]

At a private memorial service, an elderly pastor stepped into the room, joining the men and women already gathered in the prayer chamber. All the seats were taken, and one could not help but notice that this senior saint needed a place to rest. In the back of the room, at least one young man's search mechanism, found in his conscience, was on the move. The situation for him presented a moral dilemma—elderly pastor; chair needed. This information was sent through the warehouse carried by the search engine robot. Scanning the aisle looking for related values, the robot pinpointed two red tagged virtues needing consideration. One was labeled "Respect and honor age." The second file carried the heading "Preferring others over oneself."

Lifting these values off the shelf, the robot, lights flashing, rushes back to the conscience waving the files, announcing, "These values need attention!" The prompting mechanism says, "Honor this man by offering your seat." The warning mechanism replies, "You are dishonoring age by ignoring this man's need for a seat." Both mechanisms call for a moral solution. In response, the younger man rises, greets the elderly pastor, and offers his seat. The gentleman accepts. This action satisfied the moral standard written on the young man's heart, prompting the right response. That is how it works.

You have a search mechanism operating in your warehouse. You know the sensation of the prompting to do what is right, and you are familiar with the sensation of warning when you are about to do something you know is wrong. Both sets of feelings operate in conjunction with your moral warehouse and the values and virtues placed there. But what happens when a person grows up without sufficient moral guidance?

Let me add a little twist to the true-life experience illustrated above. What if, as a child, that young man's parents never emphasized the value of respecting age or preferring others? The search mechanism begins its scan of the aisle. Not finding a corresponding value tagged "Respect Age," it returns empty-handed. There is no prompting or warning because nothing is found.[k]

What does that mean for parents today? If there is no principle to stir the child's heart, the child stays morally immature, either becoming the victim or the bully because of his lack of social discernment. There is truth to the old proverb that says, "For as a man thinks in his heart, so is he." Our life is the product of what is in our heart. What is in the heart of a child is the product of parents putting their moral convictions into their child's moral warehouse.

The only difference between you and your child's conscience is the amount and complexity of the life values resident there. Children start with a simple sense of right and wrong that grows into a complex moral scheme reflective of the home and society at large.

References / Notes

j. Think of the search mechanism as a busy, bright red R2D2 robot that at a moral prompting begins moving up and down the aisles, searching each shelf. It is looking to see if there is a corresponding value in need of satisfying. If it finds many or just one, it pulls it off the shelf and immediately demands, "You need to do something about this!" If nothing is found on the warehouse shelves, the search ends and nothing happens.

k. Help your child to build a mental catalog of what to do in all kinds of crises and situations. Through prayer, private talks, and by imparting a growing trust of God's Word, you can build a reservoir of strength, peace, and wisdom in your child. ('Heaven Help the Home Today' by Howard Hendricks, pg. 35)

References / Notes

l. "A person without clear convictions will learn to give in to the greatest source of pressure rather than courageously do what is right." ('Character Matters' by John and Susan Alexander Yates, pg. 115) In other words, there is not enough biblical virtue in his moral warehouse to steer his conscience away from wrong-doing. It takes courage to stand up for what is right when no one else thinks you should. "Who's going to know what we are doing?" is the mindset of most. Sadly, many Christians would say this too. A child of any age without clear convictions will always 'follow the crowd,' no matter where the crowd decides to go.

m. Modeling is different from teaching and training children. To teach our children is to instruct them in a way of thinking. We are models for our children every time we are around them. Our children are learning and observing what we put before them in how we live our daily lives. To train our children in Godly character, we must start with opening up our hearts before God and asking Him to help us work on our own character. (Mom's Notes presentation, "Understanding Character Training," Part 1)

SIGNS OF A HEALTHY AND UNHEALTHY CONSCIENCE

Positive and prohibitive are terms describing conditions of the heart as a result of right or wrong training. The healthy, positive conscience says, "I ought to do this because it is right," or, "I ought not do this because it is wrong." The prohibitive conscience says, "I must do this or else I'll be punished." With the latter, the motivation to do right is not because of the love of virtue but rather because the individual fears reproof or punishment.

Positive development takes place when parents build into their child's conscience the reason why "right is right" and "wrong is wrong."[l] A child will develop a healthy conscience when his parents are good models[m] of the qualities they desire to see in their child and when they encourage the child to do right as opposed to only discouraging him from doing wrong. Such a child sees obedience as attractive, not as a distasteful action done merely to avoid punitive retaliation for failure to comply.

In contrast, the prohibitive conscience is not a guilty conscience, but an on-going state of potential guilt. Adults who live this way have not necessarily done anything wrong, but live their lives as if they were on the verge of doing wrong or constantly worrying what others will think. This type of response happens, when as a child, a greater emphasis was placed on not doing wrong, without the child ever being told why wrong is wrong, or right is right. As a result, the child carries into adulthood the burden of right and wrong, but without the *why* of right and wrong. That is what creates the sense of prohibitive thought, which often leads to a person who over compensates. This will be the person who says "Thank you," five times because they are not sure the first four times were sufficient. The unhealthy development of a prohibitive conscience occurs when:

• A child grows up believing Mom or Dad's love is conditional and based on performance. Approval and love comes when parents are please, but disapproval brings scorn and shame. What is carried into adulthood is a gnawing doubt of acceptance.

• In childhood minor, unintentional mistakes are treated with the same weight of punishment as major intentional wrongs. The "guilt" that is normally associated with malicious conduct becomes a false guilt associated with an honest mistake. For this child, avoiding guilt becomes the motivator for right behavior.

• Parents fail to provide the moral reasons for behavior. As a result, the constant fear of punishment, reproof, and rejection—not the love of virtue—becomes the motivation for right behavior.

The effects of a prohibitive conscience can be lifelong. Do you have a conscience like that? Take this subjective test, and then score yourself. Many parents find this self-evaluation helpful in understanding what makes them tick from a moral standpoint. This test serves only as a guide to gain understanding of your own heart with the hope that you will better appreciate what must be put into your child's heart.

PROHIBITIVE CONSCIENCE TEST

Scale: 1 = Never true of me
   3 = Sometimes true of me
   5 = True 50% of the time/Not true 50% of the time
   7 = Usually true of me
   10 = Always true of me

(If a question does not apply, think of how you might respond.)

1. _5_ When someone says, "I need to talk to you right away," I get nervous and begin to wonder what I did wrong.

2. _5_ Even as an adult, somehow I am made to feel guilty by my mother or father if I do not do what she or he asks or demands.

3. _7_ Somehow my mother-in-law/father-in-law makes me feel guilty if I do not do what she or he asks or demands.

4. _10_ If fifty people told me I did a good job, but one person did not like what I did and was critical, the discouragement from the one person would be greater than the encouragement of the fifty.

5. _1_ Sometimes I go to church even when I do not want to, just out of the fear that someone might say something about me if I were not there.

6. _1_ My tendency, when I am in a disagreement with another person, is to give in and say to myself, "It really doesn't matter anyway."

7. _3_ I constantly seek affirmation from those who are closest to me.

8. _5_ When I'm asked to help a friend or relative and I need to say no for legitimate reasons, I still feel guilty.

9. _5_ I am the one who usually says, "I'm sorry."

10. _5_ I fear losing my child's love when I discipline him or her.

(To score, see the end of the chapter.)

WHAT CAN I DO ABOUT MY PROHIBITIVE CONSCIENCE?

If you struggle at all with a prohibitive or fearful conscience, the first step of correction is to acknowledge it, even if it is only to yourself. To use a computer analogy, you have "corrupt data" in need of purging. Here are three workable solutions.

• First, pursue moral excellence for yourself. Many people are not sure what

References / Notes

" It was so important that my parents filled my moral warehouse and clearly taught me what was right and wrong. There was no confusion in my mind and no loopholes I could try to get through. It enabled me to judge my own actions and see how what I had done or was thinking of doing was either right or wrong."
– Rebecca, age 17

References / Notes

" Because I have an understanding of right and wrong, I am able to make good choices with more confidence."
- Stephen, age 14

n. *The person who lives with a prohibitive conscience has not necessarily done anything wrong but lives his life as if he were always on the verge of doing wrong or constantly worried that others will think he has done something wrong. That is a terrible weight to carry in life and a burden that you do not want to pass on to your children. Because children learn by imitation and absorb subtle attitudes as quickly as a dry sponge does water, getting your own heart right is a prerequisite to helping your child get his heart right. You can do it, and for the sake of your children, you must do it!*

the right response is in certain situations and, thus, tend toward a prohibitive conscience. Without understanding the moral "why" driving their decisions, they default to second-guessing every decisions. The more we understand about God's character of love and how to communicate it through our everyday conduct, the calmer the troubled waters of our moral experience will become. Some of the most fearful people in the world are those who do all the right things but do not know why they are right. As a result, they second-guess every decision they make.[n]

• Second, accept at face value God's promise that nothing can separate you from His Love (Romans 8:38-39). The Lord knows everything about us, including our strengths and weaknesses. His love is not dependent on our performance. Ultimately, He is the only audience we play to, and the only one we desire to please; and when we do, we usually end up being a blessing to all.

• Third, if a prohibitive conscience controls your behavior, then resolve to retrain your heart's understanding as it relates to all matters of civility. The one who possesses civility will always be in control of the moment. The civility we speak of is not the generic "civility" tossed back and forth by political pundits on Sunday talk shows, rather, it is a civility deeply informed by the nature of God's goodness. Christians do not act kindly with the hope that people will be kind in return, but rather, we do so because God is kind. We do not act virtuously to get people to respond to us in like manner. We live virtuously, because God is virtuous. The reflected expressions of God's love impact all social relationships, from how we greet people, respect their property, and honor the aged ones in our midst, to how we share a meal with each other. Everything is connected to a purpose greater than ourselves, and that is precisely what separates the civility derived from God's nature and love and the counterfeit civility birthed from moral relativism. Civility is an antidote for a prohibitive conscience. If you know civility, you will never have try and be something your not.

Finally the book of Proverbs is a good place to learn correct, biblical responses. Here are a few examples from Proverbs.

10:12   "Hatred stirs up strife, but love covers all sins."

15:1   "A gentle answer turns away wrath, but a harsh word stirs up anger."

20:22   "Do not say, 'I will repay evil.' Wait for the Lord, and He will save you."

21:23   "He who guards his mouth and tongue, keeps his soul from troubles."

26:4   "Do not answer a fool according to his folly, lest you also be like him."

29:11   "A fool vents all his feelings. But a wise man holds them back."

Questions for Review

1. The lower conscience provides the sense of right and wrong and the higher conscience provides the standards. Explain the difference.

2. Explain the relationship between the moral warehouse and the search mechanism of the conscience.

3. Explain the importance of the transition process in moral training.

4. Is a prohibitive conscience a guilty conscience? Explain your answer.

5. What must happen before you have a morally responsible child?

6. List three negative parenting practices that lead to a prohibitive conscience.

    a.

    b.

    c.

7. Summarize three responses that will help someone with a prohibitive conscience.

    a.

    b.

    c.

8. Scoring if all ten questions were answered.

76 – 100 pts.   Excessively high prohibitive conscience
61 – 75 pts.   Seriously high prohibitive conscience
46 – 60 pts.   High prohibitive conscience
35 – 45 pts.   Low prohibitive conscience (You can work it out.)
25 – 34 pts.   Healthy conscience
10 – 24 pts.   Moving toward a hardened conscience*

* A "hardened" conscience does not mean a person is indifferent to right and wrong, but may not be aware of the rightness or wrongness of any given moment. It can also mean the person has adopted from childhood an "I don't care what other's think" attitude. Unfortunately, that is not healthy either, for such and attitude closes the door on the type of admonishment that can be used to make a person a more productive or morally sensitive individual.

This Week at Home

1. Be prepared to share with the class a few examples of negative and positive training that took place this week at home. Follow the example given in this chapter. What difference did you see in your child's behavior?

2. Review the prohibitive conscience test with your mate or a friend. Honestly share how each can help the other with his prohibitive conscience.

Session Six Outline
and Chapter Six

Respect for Authority and Parents

I. Introduction
A. What is character?
1. Character is not your temperament, nor is it your personality, but the governing _____ and values of both.

2. Human temperament is _____. Personality is the combination of your temperament and upbringing.

3. Character is the _____ quality of your personality. It is the outward reflection of the inner man.

B. Character training and morality

Moral training and character development are the same thing. Our morality _____ our character, and our character reflects our morality and what is in our hearts.

1. What is the basis of our morality?

The basis of our morality is God's _____ law.

Definition: God's moral law is a prescription for moral living that reflects the _____ and character of God.

2. God's moral law is derived from both the Old and New Testaments.

C. The ultimate purpose of character training
1. In the Christian community, our collective character is to be a unified reflection of God's _____ law.

2. God desires to be made known to the world, so this is what He has done.
a. He has _____ a people on the Earth to represent Him.

"But you are a chosen people, a royal priesthood, a Holy Nation–a people belonging to God" (1 Peter 2:9a).

b. What was His purpose?
"That you may declare the praise of Him who called you out of darkness into His wonderful light" (1 Peter 2:9b). This means He wants our behavior to be a reflection of His character, which is in fact the means by which we declare His praises, and in so doing, His presence.

c. What is this called?
This is called Holiness. Holiness implies _____ and _____.

d. What is the purpose for Holiness?
The purpose of a holy lifestyle is to communicate God's presence to the world. That is why character training in the Christian community is so important. That is also why, "Whether you eat or drink, do all to the glory of God" (1 Cor. 10:31).

   1) Defining glory
   Glory means to make _____.

   2) How do we glorify God?
   Jesus said, "Let your light so shine before men, that they may see your good works and glorify your Father in heaven" (Matthew 5:16).

e. The ultimate purpose of character training
Biblical values that represent the person of God, lived out in the families of the Christian community, are to serve two purposes.
Our behavior, which is
   • governed by our morality
   • derived from God's moral law
   • a reflection of God's moral character and His will
Allows us to serve these purposes:

   1) Define God to the _____.

   2) Help the _____ find God.

II. Character Development
The six natural relationships which provide context for character development

We all have a natural relationship with:
1. Authority
2. Parents
3. Age
4. Siblings/Peers
5. Property of others
6. Nature

III. Respect for Authority
   A. Examples of authority

   B. Scripture and authority
      1. "Obey your leaders and submit to them" (Hebrews 13:17).
      2. "Let every person be subject to the governing authorities, for there is no authority except from God, and those which exist are established by God" (Romans 13:1).
      3. "Submit yourself for the Lord's sake to every human institution, whether to a king as one in authority or governors sent by him" (1 Peter 2:13-14).
      4. "Honor all men. Love the brotherhood. Fear God, and honor the King" (1 Peter 2:17).

   C. Defining authority
      1. Authority is not the _____ but the power to _____ the law.

      2. Authority does not mean making everyone _____ but treating everyone equitably.

      3. Authority must be understood as _____ - _____.

   D. The supreme importance of authority
      Authority is the genesis of freedom. To dethrone the notion of authority is to dismantle the concept of _____ and _____, for law and order are inseparably linked to the concept of authority. The two are dependent on authority.

Notes

IV. Respect for Parents

A. The fifth commandment, "Honor your father and mother, that your days may be prolonged in the land which the Lord your God gives you" (Exodus 20:12), is linked with the first four commandments. The first five deal with man's relationship to God; the last five deal with man's relationship with man.

B. The Warning

1. "The eye that mocks a father and scorns a mother, the ravens of the valley will pick it out and young eagles will eat it" (Proverbs 30:17).

2. "He who strikes his mother or father shall surely be put to death" (Exodus 21:15).

3. "He who curses his mother and father shall surely be put to death" (Exodus 21:17).

C. Parental authority and child training

1. When your children are young, lead them by your _____.

2. When your children are teens, lead them by the power of your relational _____.

3. The transition
   a. From obedience to _____
   b. From obligation of doing right to _____ of doing right
   c. From duty to _____

4. Devotional Honor vs. Duty Honor

Key Principle: Parenting in the mind of God is a Kingdom issue.

6

Respect for Authority and Parents

I n our last chapter, we discussed the mechanics of the conscience and the role the conscience plays in moral training. This chapter serves a two-fold purpose. First, it introduces Christian parents to the Kingdom purpose behind moral character training. Second, it brings into perspective the practical side of moral training. What does living out biblical values look like every day? We start by defining character.

To understand what character is, we need to state first what it is not. Character is not a person's temperament or personality. We believe temperament is inborn, serving as the foundation upon which personality is built. In contrast, character is the quality of craftsmanship that went into building the personality. Character is the combination of virtues embroidered on the moral fabric of a person's life.[a] When we speak of Christian character, we are referring to moral and social excellence. God calls His people to a divine standard, not the moral mediocrity found in the mainstream of our society.[b] That higher standard requires action on the part of individuals, and more specifically, on the part of parents to communicate biblical values to their children.

CHARACTER TRAINING HAS A HOLY PURPOSE

God desires to be made known to the world, so He chose a people on Earth to represent Him to all nations. In times past, the nation of Israel was given that privilege. "And you shall be to Me a kingdom of priests and a holy nation" (Exodus 19:6). "For you are a holy people to the Lord your God; and the Lord has chosen you to be a people for His own possession out of all the peoples who are on the face of the earth" (Deuteronomy 14:2).

With Israel's rejection of the Messiah, the Church was called out of the world to be God's earthly representative. To the Church, the apostle Peter wrote, "But you are a chosen people, a royal priesthood, a Holy Nation, a people belonging to God" (1 Peter 2:9). What is God's purpose for calling the Church? The verse continues, "That you may declare the praise of Him who called you out of darkness into His wonderful light."

Declaring God to the world is the reason Israel existed and is now the purpose of the Church. For the New Testament saint, God wants our behavior to be distinctively different—not different simply for the sake of difference, but distinctively reflective of His character, which is in fact the means by which we, God's people, declare His praises, and in so doing, His presence in the world. But what does distinctive living look like every day, and what is the means by

a. Moral character is the quality of a person's personality and the moral restraint or encouragement of his temperament; it is the outward reflection of the inner man. Our morality defines character, and our character reflects our morality. Moral training and character development are synonymous concepts.

b. Character is never developed in a vacuum. You cannot develop kindness if you do not know what it is or how and when it is to be shown. It is only through the convicting work of the Holy Spirit, the practical application of biblical principles, and the patient training of parents, that good character will begin to evolve. You will have the joy of seeing it happen, especially in a atmosphere of encouragement, enthusiasm, and love. ('What Every Child Should Know Along the Way' by Gail Martin, pg 44)

References / Notes

c. The church and the family are insepa-rably linked together in God's kingdom purpose. When the Christian family is no longer what it ought to be, everything else that the church does is weakened, if not destroyed; for what we are as a family is what we are as a church. What is the church but a family of families and a household of households?

d. "Moral law?" Isn't that Old Testa-ment stuff? Aren't we New Testament people, living in the Age of Grace? These questions are often provoked by the word "law." Like grace, the moral law of God is timeless, just as the character of God is timeless (Hebrew 13:8). It is derived from both the Old and New Testaments.

e. Holiness for the Christian and Chris-tian family is not something we are, as much as something we do. It is a call to distinctive living and moral account-ability. Right moral behavior ought never to attract attention to itself, but point the way to Christ. The apostle Paul told the early church that, "Therefore, whether you eat or drink, or whatever you do, do all to the glory of God." (1 Corinthians 10:31) In its simplest form, the word glory means, "to make bigger, to magnify." We make something bigger so more people can see it. How do we make God bigger to the world? Jesus said it very simply. "Let your light so shine before men, that they may see your good works and glorify your Father in heaven." (Matthew 5:16) Our good works governed by the moral law of God are the most concrete form of Christian witness and is the means by which we define God to the world and help the world find God.

f. "But you are a chosen generation, a royal priesthood, a holy nation, His own special people, that you may proclaim the praises of Him who called you out of darkness into His marvelous light" (1 Peter 2:9).

which God extends Himself to the world?[c] We believe the family is the most fundamental social unit in God's world for Kingdom-building purposes. That is because the family is the place where children learn the values that will govern their behavior the rest of their lives. That was true in the old covenant with Israel and it is true with the new covenant and the church. That is why parenting, in the mind of God, is a Kingdom issue of great importance.

The primary focus of Christian parenting should be defining God to our children, and we believe that task is best accomplished by introducing our children to and guiding them by God's character. His character is revealed through the Scriptures and found in His moral precepts and directives. These are often referred to as the moral law of God.[d] When we refer to God's moral law, we are not referring to the codified laws given to Israel by Moses, although many of God's moral precepts are found in the Mosaic Law. Rather, we are speaking of the relational commands of God that reflect His heart, will, and character. The moral law of God is a relational prescription for a healthy life, a prescription that starts in the family and is passed on from generation to generation through God's kingdom builders—parents.

But there's much more. Enjoying wonderful relationships within our fami-lies and communities is not the ultimate purpose of character training. Biblical virtues and values, the building blocks of God's moral law, lived out in the Christian family and community serve a greater purpose. The essential purpose of a holy lifestyle is that, by our behavior, we are to help define God to a world that does not know Him.[e]

This is why moral training in the Christian community and the Christian home is so important. The results of morally beautiful behavior reflective of Christ become a compelling testimony, declaring "the praise of Him who called [us] out of darkness into His wonderful light" (1 Peter 2:9).[f] Therefore, we passionately teach our children about the preciousness of others, how to show kindness, gentleness, and preference for others, and all the other virtues that make up God's character. *Growing Kids God's Way* teaches that a child's holiness is more important than his or her happiness. In parenting, the moral law of God is not only a standard and means by which we restrain habits of sin, but it is the means by which we demonstrate to our children God's love, mercy, and justice. Not only are we defining God to the world, we are defining God to our children–a worthy task for each generation. Get the holiness and you give your children something far greater than happiness; they learn a lifestyle of moral contentment.

THE BASIS OF CHARACTER

The quality of your character and that of your children is best exemplified by the presence or absence of three attributes: respect, honor, and honesty. These are action terms. Having an attitude of respect, honor, and honesty is not enough; there must be an ongoing demonstration of the three. To respect our fellow man is to honor him, and to honor him is to live honestly before him. The parent's job is to take the intangible concepts of respect, honor, and honesty and make them tangible–to take their abstract meanings and make them concrete. They must show their children what moral truth looks like.[g]

There are six natural relationships that are foundational to every society because they are fundamental to all human relationships. Man interacts with:

1. Authority
2. Parents
3. Elders
4. Peers and siblings
5. Property of others
6. Nature

These six relationships provide the basis for all character training. By way of analogy, you can view these six relationships as a precious diamond that sparkles on all sides. The name of the diamond is, "Esteem for others" (Philippians 2:3). Like a diamond, these relationships have a single preciousness but many sides of appreciation.[h] Not to appreciate one side means to devalue the whole diamond. Parents who hope to raise morally responsible and biblically responsive children must be cognitive of these six relationships. Respect, honor, and honesty are like the hub of a wagon wheel. They give strength to each relational spoke. This chapter focuses on the first two relationships. Chapter 7 relates to respect for age, and Chapter 8 addresses the final three relationships.

RESPECT FOR AUTHORITY

Authority is not a foreign concept in Scripture. Hebrews 13:17a says, "Obey those who have rule over you." Romans 13:1 says, "Let every soul be subject to the governing authorities. For there is no authority except from God, and those which exist are appointed by God." First Peter 2:13-14 says, "Therefore, submit yourselves to every ordinance of man for the Lord's sake whether to the king as supreme or to governors, as to those who are sent by him for the punishment of evildoers and for the praise of those who do good." First Peter 2:17 says, "Honor all people. Love the brotherhood. Fear God. Honor the king."[i]

These verses relate to a believer's response to authority not to authority's responsibility to its constituents. That distinction must be made because all authority is governed by biblical imperatives. The theories of the divine right of kings or divine right of parents are unacceptable. Biblical authority has moral boundaries and is limited by biblical law and precept. When a man acts presumptuously and assumes the right to alter God's moral law, he no longer represents biblical authority. Biblical authority, whether parental, church, or governmental, must be exercised within the context of biblical ethics. When authority stops being ethical, it stops being biblical.[j]

Man, by nature, does not like authority. Our fallen natures are self-legislative, and authority challenges that state. Yet biblical ethics requires that we live in accordance with authority and live and play by the rules. When you play by the rules, you honor those outside of self; when you cheat in life, you dishonor others.

God wants His people to respect authority (Romans 13:2-3) and to train

References / Notes

g. *Respect is a habit that is developed daily in little ways. When we, as parents, take time to offer respect to others, our behavior will encourage other family members to practice this small but significant habit. ('Character Matters' by John and Susan Alexander Yates, pg. 97)*

h. *An individual with a servant's heart is one who genuinely seeks 'to love his neighbor as himself,' that is, to see ourselves as responsible for the care of others. We are not our own, rather we belong to God, and His desire is for us to actively, thoughtfully, graciously care for others. ('Character Matters' by John and Susan Alexander Yates, pg. 88)*

i. *Authority is not the law itself, but the power to represent and enforce the law. Although there are many different forms of authority, all of them originate from God. (Romans 13:1) Biblical authority includes pastoral and parental authority. Other powers include federal, state, county, city, and village authorities. Authority governs you when you drive your car, fly in a plane, walk across the street, or eat in a restaurant.*

j. *Whether governmental, societal, or parental, the discipline of respect for authority is on the decline. ('Heaven Help the Home Today' by Howard Hendricks, pg. 83) Therefore, to teach our children to respect any authority could be an uphill battle, with parents getting little or no support from the people they know. God does not let us off the hook, however. It must be done and parents must step up and get it done with their children.*

References / Notes

k. "Consequently, he who rebels against the authority is rebelling against what God has instituted, and those who do so will bring judgment on themselves. For rulers hold no terror for those who do right, but for those who do wrong. Do you want to be free from fear of the one in authority? Then do what is right and he will commend you." (Romans 13:2-3) "Children, obey your parents in the Lord, for this is right. "Honor your father and mother,' which is the first commandment with a promise, 'that it may be well with you and you may live long on the earth." And you, fathers, do not provoke your children to wrath, but bring them up in the training and admonition of the Lord." (Ephesians 6:1-4)

l. Not all rules are for health and safety concerns; some rules are for mutual and public benefit. One example of this is the leash law in public parks. Many parks have leash laws posted at the entrance. One reason is to protect your family from roaming dogs. The last thing you want is a stranger's dog joining you for lunch or frightening your children. Obeying the leash law shows respect for authority. However, the greater intent is to honor all that share the park. A second reason for this law is so owners will "scoop up" after their dogs. A park with unleashed dogs is no place for others to spread out a blanket and have a picnic. Here then is the moral principle. Keeping your dog on a leash is a way of respecting the authority that the sign represents. More importantly, we base our motivation for compliance on the higher principles of fair play and act on the preciousness of others, not the fear of a financial penalty. Our submission to authority means respecting those with whom we share the park.

our children to do the same (Ephesians 6:1-4).[k] Why did He put some people in positions of authority? There are a few obvious reasons. Without authority, there would be chaos, confusion, and destruction. If there were no authority governing the flow of traffic, every intersection would become a death trap. If there were no authority, who would punish the evildoers and bring them to justice (Romans 13:4)? Who would protect the innocent? Who would make sure that milk is really pasteurized, or that the food we eat is really safe? Who would protect your rights, your savings, and your investments? Authority is necessary for consistency of order and our submitting to authority is another way of keeping everything fair.[l]

There are hundreds of laws that govern man's behavior. Unfortunately, the more a society moves away from biblical morality and intrinsic motivation, the more dependent it becomes on controlling outward behavior by extrinsic means—more codes, more laws, more fines, and more punishment. What is the higher moral ground? It is doing right out of a mutual sense of respect for each other. When I yield to authority, I place value on you. I am indirectly acknowledging your preciousness by restraining my selfish motivations.

Authority and Your Child

How do you respond to forms of authority in front of your children? When a sign says, "Keep off the grass," do you ignore it? When a warning notice comes home from school, do you criticize the teacher in front of your child for sending it? What do you do with your gum wrapper? Do you toss it when no one is looking, or do you put it in your pocket to be disposed of later? The way adults respond to authority sets patterns their children will follow. As is the case with all phases of child training, parental example reinforces parental instruction. Our example gives credibility to our instruction. Many times we undo all of our good teaching by our failure to respond properly to authority. How we personally respond to authority sets the acceptable parameters for our children. If we constantly live below the standard, they will interpret our behavior as the standard.

Finally, keep in mind that our submission to authority is more than an act of outward compliance; it is an attitude accepting that, by divine appointment, this person was placed over me. Often a bitter attitude towards authority is a bitter attitude against God.

RESPECT FOR PARENTS

The second side of the diamond is respect and honor for parents. Teaching children to respect and honor their parents is basic to teaching them how to show respect for others. It starts with the parents. Do not underestimate the importance of the fifth commandment given to Moses on Mt. Sinai. It is a simple statement. "Honor your father and your mother, that your days may be long upon the land which the Lord your God is giving you" (Exodus 20:12). Maybe the simplicity of that statement is the very reason so many parents have become lax in putting into practice the true meaning of it. When we contrast this commandment with the other nine, we find that it is more closely associated

References / Notes

with the first four commandments, which deal with man's relationship to God, than with the latter five commandments, which deal with man's relationship to man. There is something special about the role you serve as a parent. For that reason, we give this warning. Do not allow your children to mock your position as their guardian by their impulsive thoughts, words, and deeds. When they do, they also mock God.[m]

Parent as Governor

Are you actively or even passively raising a child that mocks you—a child whose activities are characterized by disobedient behavior or even cursing? You should understand that the fifth commandment begins with the parent. Your children will not automatically obey, respect, or honor you. These activities run contrary to their natures. They must receive training and guidance from you. Although the Scriptures have called for obedience to princes, masters, pastors, and other superiors, the fifth commandment names only fathers and mothers, because they are the first governors to which a child's obedience is obligated. Do not underestimate the importance of your position.

THE AUTHORITY EXCHANGE

Mankind has always struggled with authority, but authority is absolutely essential because law and order for the family and society are dependent on their proper administration. In the Christian family, the Bible not only provides the basis of all authority but also the ethics that govern how it should be used.[n] Certainly, parental authority can be taken to extremes (and obviously at times it is). Too much authority leads to totalitarianism, while too little leads to injustice and social chaos. This is true for nations; it is also true for families.

As your children grow older, significant changes will occur for you and your children. Perhaps the greatest transition you will experience is that of learning to use less of your authority and more of your influence to motivate your children as they grow older and become more responsible. Here is a basic truism to consider. *When a child is young, lead by the strength of your authority. When he or she is a preteen and teen, lead by the strength of your relational influence.* (Please note this exchange in our diagram.)

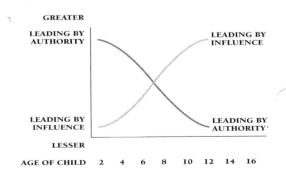

GREATER

LEADING BY AUTHORITY

LEADING BY INFLUENCE

LEADING BY INFLUENCE

LEADING BY AUTHORITY

LESSER

AGE OF CHILD   2   4   6   8   10   12   14   16

Between the two points, the need for parental authority should decline as your child begins to exercise moral self-control. By the time your child hits pre- and early adolescence, you will have exchanged rule-centered leader-

" Respecting my parents means honoring both of them (in word and deed) in their position of authority and their maturity of wisdom with which God has endowed them. I try to serve those in authority with cheerfulness, because all service to authority is ultimately a service of giving to God Himself, who loves a cheerful giver." – Christopher, age 20

m. *The commandment, "Honor thy father and mother," is so special that it has a promise attached to it. "Honor your father and your mother, that your days may be long upon the land which the Lord your God is giving you."*

n. *The Bible not only provides the basis of all authority but also the ethics governing the exercise of authority. Biblical authority is beautiful because it is morally focused. Similar to the character of love (1 Corinthians 13:5-7), biblical authority is not presumptuous, proud, unkind, or unfair but full of integrity, gentle, consistent, and gracious. It is motivated by love and used only when needed. Its purpose is to guide by encouragement and restraint. Authority is necessary because law and order for the family and the society is dependent on its proper administration. But authority can be taken to extremes. Too much authority leads to totalitarianism, while insufficient authority leads to injustice and social chaos.*

References / Notes

o. *Consider for a moment how you once controlled everything about your child's day. During his infancy, you determined when your child ate, slept, stayed awake, had a bath, played on the blanket, or went for a stroller ride. Such tight supervision is absolutely necessary during the early years, since a child does not know how to regulate his own day for his own good. But as children grow, they become more responsible. At five, you will no longer control or direct your child's day to the same extent you do in the earlier years. At five, children can come and go from the back yard, pick out their own board games, play with their hamsters, or go to their rooms and play with a puzzle. Because they continually demonstrate responsible behavior in these areas, parental policing is no longer necessary. Our point is this: although parental authority is still a considerable influence in a five-year-old's life, it is not as sweeping in its control as it was a few years earlier. The same holds true of a ten-year-old. With the increase of self-rule, there is a direct decrease in the amount of parental policing required. It is not that Mom and Dad's authority is no longer valid, but that the need for outside control is diminishing. Gradually, parental control is being replaced by parental influence.*

" Looking at my friends and the relationships they have with their parents, I am grateful that my mom and dad applied GKGW principles in our home. Relationships are the main priority of our family. I know I can share my thoughts with my parents and count on their wisdom. Although not equals, we do share a mutual trust in each other and that is a wonderful place to be as a teen." – Ashley, age 13

ship for principle-centered leadership because your children now know and understand what biblical virtues are and have been putting them into practice for many years.[o]

At the end of one of our parenting classes, Carla, a young mother of three, approached Anne Marie with a question. She listened attentively to Anne Marie's response, reluctantly agreed to try what she had suggested, and went home. When she returned to class the next week, she shared enthusiastically the following results. Here is a transcript of her conversation as she spoke to an audience of her peers.

"I have three girls. Whitney is ten; Brenda, seven; and Carissa is four. Like most parents, I have a real fear about this next phase of parenting, especially with my ten-year-old. I had a little talk with Anne Marie last week about an incident involving Whitney and sharing.

I explained to Anne Marie that Whitney had a bag of popcorn and Brenda asked for some. Whitney said no. This really bothered me because my seven-year-old is so generous with her sister, almost to a fault. So I intervened and told Whitney that she had to share. She finally did.

When I thought through the incident, I knew I had not done the right thing, but I did not know what I did wrong, so I asked Anne Marie what she thought I should do. I was surprised when she told me to think about not always intervening with my authority and forcing my kids to share with each other. This was a frightening prospect for me. I said to Anne Marie, "How long will I be doing this? What if this goes on forever?" Anne Marie assured me it would not but asked that I try this for several weeks and see what happens.

In God's perfect timing, the next day another incident took place. Whitney had some mints and Brenda asked for some. Whitney said, "No," and Brenda immediately looked to me for help. I told Brenda, "If Whitney doesn't want to share with you that's fine. God wants sharing to come from our hearts or it is not real sharing." Brenda protested for a few moments, and I went about my business.

A little later my ten-year-old came to me and asked, "It is okay if I do not share, Mom? Is that what you said?" I said, "Yes, that's what I said." Whitney left, but in that very moment, I could see something had changed in her heart. Five minutes later she was generously sharing all her mints with Brenda.

The next day, all I heard from the two girls was, "Can I borrow your this, can I play with your that?" I was shocked! Non-coercive sharing was foreign to my children–and to me!

So I called my ten-year-old aside and asked, "Whitney, why are you so willing to share all of a sudden?" And this is what she told me. "Mom, this is how I always felt, but you never let me do it without telling me I had to. I wanted to show you how I feel, but you never let me do it without making me. I want to show you that I know how to make a wise decision and do the things you and Daddy taught us."

I went home last week and gave up trying to control all the outcomes by using my authority. In a very marginal way, I started to use the power of my influence by speaking truth in love with my kids. I can tell you in one week's time, Whitney has become a different child–mostly because she has a different mom. And while I am still using my authority with Brenda, I can see why I need less and less of it to guide Whitney.

There is one more thing I learned through this experience. In the past when I tried to control all outcomes, I was actually robbing my kids of the joy of doing right. I can see that now. At Whitney's age, there is no joy in doing right when the actions required are always tied to my authority."

Can you relate to Carla's story? We sure can. We remember similar situations that occurred during our preteen parenting days. Please note what Carla did not do; she did not abandon her God-given authority. What she did do was start the process of giving up her power to control all outcomes with her oldest daughter while still maintaining the use of authority with the youngest. Knowing what to expect and when to expect it is the key to the healthy balance between leading by authority and leading by influence.

It all comes down to this simple principle: External motivations that once governed the child's life are replaced by internal beliefs that rule from the heart. Moral maturity emancipates the child, allowing him to direct his own behavior in harmony with family values. Take just a moment to consider: where are you right now in the process of authority exchange? Are you in the early years, middle years, or nearing the teen years? What does authority look like in your family?

OBEDIENCE, SUBMISSION, AND HONOR

We are commonly asked, "As adults, do we still have to obey our parents?" or, "At what age do I no longer have to obey my parents?" These are two legitimate questions. Before we answer them, we first need to distinguish between obedience, submission, and honor.

Obedience and Parenting

The duty of parents is to rightly exercise their authority and know when to exchange it for leadership by influence. The duty of our children is to obey and submit to our authority and leadership. In all of the New Testament, only two passages speak directly to children in this matter: Ephesians 6:1-3 and Colossians 3:20.[p] In the Ephesians passage, children are instructed to obey their parents, and then Paul moves to honoring parents, which we address in Chapter 9. We will not give a comprehensive review of obedience at this point. However, we will investigate the time-frame and purpose of obedience for children and the temporary nature of required obedience.

In child training, parents must help their children exchange obedience for submission.[q] The untrained heart of a child reflects self-centeredness and a lack of self-control. Obedience is needed to help shape the child's behavior and developing belief system. The obligation required by obedience serves the child as a teaching device. Obedience acts as a type of schoolmaster. As the law was the schoolmaster until Christ came (Galatians 3:24)[r] so obedience is the schoolmaster that leads a child to ultimate freedom. Freedom means obeying for the sake of doing right and not out of fear of reproof. Obedience is only the starting point of honoring, not the end of it.

What then is the purpose of obedience? It is to be a temporary teacher[s]

References / Notes

p. "Children, obey your parents in all things, for this is well pleasing to the Lord." (Colossians 3:20)

q. There is a difference between biblical obedience (which calls for the use of parental authority) and submission (which signals a voluntary yielding). Obedience is from the Greek word, "hupakouo." meaning "to line up under." It is used in Scripture for children, slaves, soldiers, and servants. It is an implied mandate – a moral obligation. Obedience is something you have to do, a duty. Submission is something you want to do. The word submission, from the Greek word, "hupotasso," also means "to line up under," but represents a different motive: compliance out of devotion. It speaks of a devotional submission. Establishing right motives for right behavior is one of the primary goals of child training. You want to move your child to the place where he or she responds out of a devotion to principle (virtue) rather than out of duty to parents.

r. "Therefore the law was our tutor to bring us to Christ, that we might be justified by faith." (Galatians 3:24)

References / Notes

s. Obedience teaches children to have self-control in all matters of life. Obedience moves children from extrinsic motivation to intrinsic control. Eventually, a child will no longer need a fence on the outside for his own protection, because his parents have helped him place a moral and ethical fence on the inside, which happens when obedience is replaced by submission.

t. As the term is used in Scripture, honoring a parent implies a deep respect given with love. Love and devotion legitimize honor. This love is based on time, knowledge, experience, and appreciation for all that your parents have done for you and with you. It is love that spills over to honoring out of devotion. In some cultures, the honoring of parents is a social/cultural mandate. This type of honor is not out of love or devotion, but is a forced honor out of duty. Being forced does not nullify honor, but it nullifies the sanctity of honor and God's original intent for honor. The child does not truly revere his parents; he only socially acknowledges them. That duty falls seriously short of honor that flows from a pure heart.

❧

" My parents trained me to respect all authority, including them. This training has helped me learn to respect those over me, such as my teachers at school. Showing them respect helps foster a relationship with them." - Russell, age 16

that brings a child to compliance by extrinsic means until he is morally ready to comply with intrinsic controls. In time, a child must exchange obedience for submission. Submission to parents means doing what is right out of devotion to the parents. This attitude comes when a child begins to accept God as his ultimate authority. He then obeys to please God, which includes submitting to his parents' headship.

After a child marries, the only thing required of him is to honor his parents according to the ethical mandate of Scripture. When that event takes place, the parent-mediator is no longer needed. The transition from obedience to submission was completed successfully. Once there is a leaving and a cleaving, a new authority structure is created by the departure of the child. Obedience and submission take their leave and the honor due to parents remains. The next question is: How will your children honor you? Out of devotion or duty?

Honor and Devotion

Adult children are called to honor their parents.[t] For some, this will be a pleasant experience; for others, it will be very difficult. Some realize how precious their parents are. They see God's blessing in their life and realize that it is the result of their parents' diligent care and nurturing. The closer they draw to God in their adult life, the more they appreciate and adore their parents, realizing all that they are is the result of their parents' godly attention in their lives.

In contrast, there are those who have suffered under the hand of abuse. The pain of the past, the lack of trust, or the current lack of any meaningful relationship reduces the act of honoring to a duty not a devotion. For these people, the commandment to honor their father and mother becomes a difficult commandment rather than a verse of blessing.

Yet the Bible still calls for a minimum amount of respect and honor. Regardless of how bad life might have been in the past, you cannot speak evil of your parents, slander them, let them go hungry, or ignore them in time of need; they are at worst reduced to being your neighbor, whom you should love as yourself (Mark 12:31). What is missing, however, is the joy of honoring.

What legacy will you leave your children? Will they honor you out of pure devotion or will it be a burdensome duty? There are very few things in this life that are more beautiful than to have your children move into adulthood and grow in their appreciation, love, and honor for you. Honor is a joy for them.

Joyful honor must be the legacy every Christian parent passes on to their children. It does not matter what type of relationship you had with your own parents. The only question from this point forward is: what kind of relationship will you have with your children? God requires them to honor you, but you will determine if that honor comes out of duty or out of devotion by the way you parent them now. Do not rob them of the joy of honoring you.

SUMMARY

In this session, we introduced two sides of the diamond–respect for authority and respect for parents. We suggested that respect for authority should be understood as fair play. When we all play fair and by the rules of life, we are in fact esteeming others higher than ourselves. Abiding by the rules means we do not allow our personal impulses to take advantage of other people.

We also introduced the second side of the diamond–respect for parents. Although obedience is the starting point for a child to honor his parents, it is not the ending point. Parents need to move the child from the mandate of obedience to willful and joyful submission. When that happens, the joy of honoring will be in the life of both parent and child.

Questions for Review

1. Read Romans 13:1. Based on this verse, why should parents train their children to respect authority?

2. Why is submitting to authority a natural struggle for children and adults?

3. Explain the purpose of obedience in the life of a child.

4. Explain the difference between honoring parents out of duty and honoring out of devotion.

This Week at Home

1. Offenses against authority take place all around us. Be prepared to give a couple of examples of blatant offenses observed during the week at work, while shopping, or while driving down the road.

2. Evaluate with your spouse your own relationship with your parents. Do you honor them out of duty or devotion? Evaluate why and be prepared to share your thoughts in class.

"I can never remember a time in my life when I was not required to show all those in positions of authority respect. It is second-nature for me to do so, although it is hard sometimes to respect a person who is in authority over you because of a lack of integrity in their personal life. It helped when my parents explained the difference between respecting the person and respecting the position. I can always respect a position of authority out of a sense of duty. When I respect someone in authority because of the way they conduct their life, I am honoring them out of a sense of devotion. Understanding the difference between "duty" and "devotion" helps me always respect authority figures." – Amy, age 19

Session Seven Outline
and Chapter Seven

Respect for Age

I.   Introduction

II. Respect for Age
A. The Commands
1. "Thou shalt rise up before the gray-headed and honor the aged one, and you shall revere your God, I am the Lord" (Leviticus 19:32).

The literal rendering of this verse is this: In the face of gray hairs, you shall rise and you shall honor the face of the old man and thus fear your God.

2. "For wisdom is with aged men; longer life is with understanding" (Job 12:12).

3. Every virtuous act toward age is credited as a virtuous act toward _____.

B. Back to basics
1. Offering your _____ to the elderly

2. Open the _____

3. Honoring age at _____ lines

C. What is the biblical justification for not spitting on the sidewalk or chewing like a barn animal?
1. Teach your children 1 Corinthians 13:5b and Titus 3:2.

"Love is not _____."

"Be _____ to all men."

2. The Interrupt Rule
a. It becomes a vehicle for the child to demonstrate and place

honor on _____, while at the same time communicating a need to the parent.

b. The child learns to _____ the parent that his or her needs will be met in an orderly way.

c. It helps the child gain the self-discipline of patience.

d. It reinforces the positive side of the child's conscience; thus confirmation comes from within the heart of the child as well as from without.

e. It communicates to the third party involved the standards of respect and honor you as a _____ are living by. (Remember, when you honor age you honor God.)

3. Push your _____ in when leaving the table.

4. Honor visiting guests in your home by teaching your children to _____.

D. Whatever happened to "Mr. and Mrs."?

Key Principle: Love is not rude.

7

Respect for Age

This chapter covers the third side of the "esteem for others" diamond—respect for elders. Parents should give attention in the training process to this attribute. The very fact that God made man relational requires moral sensitivity toward other members of our society, especially our elders. Leviticus 19:32 states, "Rise in the presence of the aged, show respect for the elderly and revere your God. I am the Lord."[a] The literal rendering of this verse is in the face of the aged person, you shall rise and you shall honor him, and thus show respect for your God. There is a link between man's relationship with man and man's relationship with God. In this passage, giving reverence to the old means giving reverence to God.

The ancient Hebrews believed that, "He who receives and takes care of an old man is rewarded as if he were taking care of God Himself." Job said, "Wisdom is with aged men, and with length of days, understanding" (Job 12:12). The message from both verses is clear; to honor age is to honor God. Begin your training with this confidence. Training children to honor and respect age is training them to honor God. It is that basic. We are all precious to God, and therefore respect is due. Yet, some among us are older, and a greater portion of honor should be directed to them.

BELIEFS AND ACTIONS

In Chapter Five, we used the example of 2-year-old Becky and her springtime walk in the public park. At that age, she was trained not to pick the flowers. Her actions, although guided by the fear of reproof, were morally correct even though she did not initially understand the moral reason behind her actions. With young children (under five years of age), the pattern of right behavior should precede the knowledge of right behavior.[b] Do not wait until your child is old enough to understand right from wrong to encourage him to do right and avoid wrong.

Before parents can require right actions, they themselves must possess right beliefs. As a parent, do you understand the principle of honor derived from Leviticus 19:32 and Job 12:12? Right parental attitude must lead to action and application. You cannot tell a child, "Be kind," without providing a vehicle for kindness. You cannot tell a child, "Be gentle," without showing what gentleness is. You cannot teach respect for age without knowing and showing what that virtue looks like every day.

TEACHING THE BASICS

Respecting age is a biblical mandate. Children need vehicles to help them achieve

" I believe honoring those who have gone on before me is very important, not only because God has made it so, but because they have already walked where I as a younger person have not. They have a legacy of experience and wisdom to pass on to us that is invaluable. It is doubly important not to lose this treasure because our culture so often rejects it." – Emily, age 19

a. A practical application to this verse is to stand to greet an aged person when they come to you. The simple act of standing shows respect. More importantly, it is one way to demonstrate our commitment to those things God has declared important to Himself.

b. For adults, beliefs usually precede actions; for children, actions usually precede beliefs. The actions of young children, especially under three years of age are naturally impulsive. They need guidance and direction in the otherness principles of life. Because the natural inclination of a child is oriented toward self and self alone, parents should not wait until their child develops a comprehensive knowledge of biblical virtues to begin requiring right behavior. Parents should require a proper response even though the child may not understand the "why" behind his actions. With children, actions precede beliefs.

7

c. When the word "vehicle" is used, it means this is a way a principle can be put into action. There are many cultures in the world and sub-cultures in America. What one culture or society use as moral vehicles may not transcend to another. But the principles from Scripture are the same for every culture. Principles allow your family to move between cultures and still treat those around them respectfully and with the preciousness that God would desire us to use to show Him.

d. The greatest influence on outcome is parental resolve and a willingness to teach and instill basic courtesies into the life of your child. A child's willful choice to ignore an adult extending a courtesy is one problem, but parents who dismiss the importance of directing a child's right moral response is another. Remember, respecting others is another way of honoring God.

e. Parents should help their children understand the moral mandates derived from Scripture are actions to be done, not just nice ideas to learn. For example, for energetic 4-year-old Leighton, gentleness is learning to hug his little sister without knocking her over. Or for boisterous 6-year-old Eli, kindness is learning to speak softly to others. Helping your children learn how to show in action a specific character truly demonstrates that Love, indeed, is not rude!

❦

" I listen to elderly people when they want to talk. Listening to someone who is elderly gives you a chance to learn things you would never know otherwise." - Ashley, age 13

the principle. Here are a few examples of age-respecting vehicles.[c]

Youth and Age

When an adult and a youth reach the door at the same time, what should be the response? Youth should honor age by allowing the adult to go first or by opening the door as a courtesy. These are simple gestures, but they reflect an attitude of respect for age that honors God. Here is another example. At the church or family buffet, invite the elders among you to go first through the buffet line. It is a simple gesture that sends a wonderful message. Teach your children to honor age by giving up their seats when there are no other seats left, such as on the bus, in a crowded auditorium, or in your living room.

These are the simple gestures with which most parents grew up. Pass them on to your children. Respecting age in this manner is not old-fashioned. It is a type of moral example that is never out of vogue. Insisting upon these actions and teaching the principles behind the lesson help in the process of cultivating right actions and beliefs in your children.

Love is not Rude / Be Courteous to all Men

Some of God's moral laws are very specific in their application. "Do not steal" (Exodus 20:15); "Do not bear false witness" (Exodus 20:16); "Do not lie to one another" (Colossians 3:9); "Do not show partiality among yourselves" (James 2:4). Some verses are tied to specific behaviors, while other biblical decrees are broader in application. For example, what is the biblical justification for not spitting on the sidewalk or chewing like a barn animal at the dinner table? While these behaviors may not be addressed specifically, they are addressed in a general context of courtesies drawn from the Scriptures.

First Corinthians 13:5b says, "Love is not rude," and Titus 3:2 instructs us to, "be courteous to all men." These are general commands that speak to a broad range of behavior. Why shouldn't children chew their food like a barn animal or spit on the sidewalk? Why should children respond when spoken to? Because love is not rude. Why should we push our chairs in when we get up from the dinner table, whether we are at home or at a restaurant? Because God asks that we be courteous to all men, and that involves giving consideration to those coming behind us.[d] A simple way of demonstrating this truth is by pushing our chairs in so those walking by do not have to work through a maze of obstacles in their way. Please note that putting your chair in is not the moral law but a means by which the law of courtesy is communicated.[e] The principle, "Love is not rude," and the command, "Be courteous to all men," can be seen in our next example.

The Interrupt Courtesy

Teaching your children how to properly interrupt a conversation is another practical way of showing respect to others. There are not many disrespectful actions worse than having a conversation rudely interrupted by a demanding child jerking on Mom or Dad's arm, insisting on an immediate audience and totally disregarding the context into which he is stepping. The child's behavior is only half of the problem. The other half is the parent who drops the conversation immediately in total disregard for the other person. It is difficult to justify that behavior in light of the moral description of love which does not act rudely.

There is a much better way. Teach your children how to interrupt your conversation politely. How can this be done? If your son needs to interrupt you for a pressing need, have him rest his hand on your side or your shoulder and wait calmly until you acknowledge him. He should not pull, tap, or shake you for attention. Rather, he should simply stand patiently with a hand on your side, knowing that in a few moments, you will find a place in the conversation to politely say, "Excuse me," to the person with whom you are speaking. Then, you can take care of your child's needs. Such an action reinforces in the mind of the child that he shares this world with other people. This response directs him towards the preciousness of others. This gesture beautifully displays respect for you and the one to whom you are speaking.[f]

Also, when your child puts his hand on your side, you might consider taking your hand and placing it gently on his. This lets him know that you know he is there. Often, the reason a child pulls on the parent and verbally interrupts, insisting on attention, is because he has not been acknowledged. Your hand on his affirms awareness of his presence. Teaching a child the appropriate way to interrupt your conversation with a third party is a gesture of honor and respect. It also demonstrates that love is kind and love is patient.

Review your general parenting practice. If your son or daughter has never had to wait for anything, then waiting to interrupt properly will be difficult. Therefore, work on waiting at other times. For example, when our grandchildren get out of the car in a parking lot of a grocery store, they are instructed to stand with a hand on the car until Mom or Dad is ready to move away from the car. Here, waiting is a health and safety issue, and it helps facilitate the discipline of patience.

Waiting is a self-control discipline affecting all aspects of developmental growth. Therefore, work on "waiting" in general and keep in mind all the different ways this discipline intersects with life, such as is the case with the interrupt courtesy.

Shyness and Respect

Shyness itself is not morally right or wrong, but it does have moral limits. It cannot be used as an excuse to dismiss disrespect since temperamental strengths and weaknesses do not exempt children from proper responses. If someone says, "Hi," to your child, the correct and minimal response back should be, "Hi." Such a simple greeting is the moral minimum required. If someone compliments your daughter's dress, the response of, "Thank you," is appropriate. Train your children to be courteous. Before you leave for a social gathering, inform your children of the probability of receiving a compliment on their hair, dress, or new shoes. Teach them beforehand how to respond properly. If you find yourself in a situation in which your child refuses to say, "Hi," do not make any excuses; just humbly say to that person on behalf of the child, "I'm sorry; we're working on this courtesy." And when you get home, work on it.[g]

References / Notes

f. *Benefits of the Interrupt Courtesy:*

1. It becomes a vehicle for the child to show honor to others while at the same time communicate his need to the parent.

2. The child learns to trust that his or her needs will be met by their parents in an orderly way.

3. It helps the child to grow in the virtue of patience.

4. It reinforces the positive side of the child's conscience. Thus confirmation comes from within the heart of the child as well as from other people.

5. It communicates to the third party involved the standards of respect and honor by which you as a family are living.

" When I'm in a conversation and my parents use the interrupt courtesy with me, I feel respected. When they do this it helps me understand why respect is so important in relationships." Nathan, age 13

g. *Often parents pick that moment for a battle in public. Nine times out of ten, it will be the wrong moment. Wait until you get home to work through the consequences and the associated teaching.*

h. *What do the titles of Mr. and Mrs. communicate culturally and individually? Culturally, such titles are social markers that pledge for the future that the youngest generation of the populace is committed to those who have gone before them. Individually, when a child applies the titles of Mr. and Mrs., he acknowledges that time has not allowed them to be equal. Although equal in a court of law and before God, they are not equal in societal responsibility. The use of the titles Mr. and Mrs. is the child's acknowledgement that he is still young and in need of wisdom and life's experiences. He is still growing intellectually and needs the benefits offered by adults. Those reasons are legitimate and virtuous ones for honoring age.*

" I do not feel addressing adults by ' Mr. or Mrs.' puts any barrier between me and them. If anything, it prevents barriers by showing that I am not their equal and it shows that I respect them."
– Donovan, age 15

i. *Addressing adults by their first name does not strengthen relationships or make a child feel any more secure. This only confuses societal roles. Children need to be children and adults need to be adults. There is no security in that relationship for the children. Nature itself demonstrates that fact. What species of adult animal are not seen by its young as the protector of the whole pack? In what social order in the animal kingdom are the children equal to the adults? None. Children, by nature, are not looking for adult friends; they seek adults who will guide and show them a safe way to go.*

Whatever Happened to Mr. and Mrs.?

It is morally correct for children to show respect when addressing adults. Titles such as Mr. and Mrs., or when appropriate, Sir and Ma'am, and terms of endearment such as Mom, Dad, Grandpa, Grandma, Aunt, and Uncle serve as age-appropriate vehicles to promote the "esteem for others" principle. These terms signify special relationships. Mr. and Mrs. represent social titles, while terms of endearment represent family relationships. The titles keep the lines of responsibility and obligation from blurring. Titles separate peers from adults, family from strangers, and loved ones from acquaintances.[h]

But Children Will Feel Closer, Won't They?

Using the titles of Mr. and Mrs. is not for adults, it is for the child. This is the most basic way for a child to show respect and honor to adults who are not relatives. Many teachers, parents, and youth workers have innocently accepted the opinion that by dropping these titles, a child will feel closer to the adult. It is theorized that somehow calling an adult "Bill," instead of "Mr. Jones," helps a child relate better and breaks down barriers between generations. What barriers? If closeness comes by establishing a peer relationship by using the first name, then why not go one step further? Have all children call adults "Mom" or "Dad". After all, terms of endearment speak to the closest of all relationships. Yet, we all realize that do so does not make sense. Neither does the connection between calling adults by their first name and children feeling closer to them as a result.[i]

Legitimate closeness is built on a number of relational factors, but the use of first names is not one of them. The depth of my relationship with any child is measured by the demonstration of kindness, patience, gentleness, a legitimate interest in what they say, respect, and much more. Not one of these is tied to the presence or absence of titles. The use of the titles of Mr. and Mrs. does not make one a wonderful and caring adult, and the use of first names without a title does not make children feel any closer or any more loved by an adult. The titles provide a vehicle to help children honor and respect age.

Is Attitude Enough?

We previously stated that *respect* and *honor* are action words. That means that having an attitude of respect without action does not go far enough. If attitude were enough, why make a child say, "I'm sorry"? The attitude of sorrow should satisfy. Why insist saying "Thank you"? A thankful attitude should be enough. Why have your children pay back something they have taken wrongfully? Should not just possessing the attitude of wanting to make it right be sufficient? But attitude is not enough; it must lead to action and application. Trying to teach your child an attitude of respect without providing a vehicle to demonstrate it exasperates the child. We recommend that you teach your children to respect age by using the titles of honor, Mr. and Mrs. It is a friendly tool for parent and child.

SUMMARY

We can restate Galatians 6:7 in a societal context without nullifying its true meaning: Whatsoever a society sows, that also is what it will reap. If you sow disregard for age, that is also what you will reap. There will come a generation that will vote on your old-age legislation. That generation will be raised with either the right or the wrong understanding of Leviticus 19:32. Respect for age is another side of the diamond that you do not want to chip away and dismiss as being unimportant; it is critically important.

How much more can be said? When building a right perspective of self, we must begin with a right view of others. A right view of others begins with God's claim on them. He created them, He owns them, and He died for them. They have precious value. Because of that truth, I am to order my life accordingly. When it comes to respecting age, God calls us to a precious response.

Questions for Review

1. Why are parents not to wait until their child develops a comprehensive knowledge of biblical virtues before requiring right behavior?

2. Why can't shyness be used as a legitimate excuse for disrespect?

3. As it relates to Mr. and Mrs., what is meant by the statement, "Time has not allowed a child to be equal"?

4. Read Appendix Three, "Questions and Answers About Mr. and Mrs."

This Week at Home

1. At home this week, teach your child to use the Interrupt Courtesy. Be prepared to share with the class how long it took for your child to routinely begin using it.

2. Be prepared to share an act of kindness or respect demonstrated by one of your children to an elder without prompting.

References / Notes

"It makes a difference to me that I show respect and honor when no one else my age does. When we are honoring to someone, we are not only showing the love of Jesus, but we are glorifying God. He has also instructed us to honor the elderly, and my parents have taught me the practical ways to do this. For that I am thankful." – Bryan, age 16

Session Eight Outline

and Chapter Eight

Respect for Peers, Property, and Nature

I. Respect for Siblings and Peers
    A. Peers defined
        When we refer to peer relationships, we do so from the broadest definition. A peer is one of the same age or dignity. By this definition, your child's peers are those who have common association. Brothers and sisters are included, as well as friends and classmates.

    B. How do you show respect, honor, and honesty to your peers?
        1. The Ten Commandments (Exodus 20)
        2   " ...esteem and regard others higher" (Philippians 2:3)
        3. " ...forbearing with one another" (Colossians 3:13)
        4. " ...live honestly before one another" (Romans 12:17)

    C. Where should you begin?
        1. "Do not seek revenge or bear a grudge against one of your people, but love your neighbor as yourself. I am the Lord" (Leviticus 19:18).

        2. "Whatever other commandment there may be, it is summed up in this one rule: Love your neighbor as yourself" (Romans 13:9).

        3. Jesus said to love God with all your heart, with all your understanding, and with all your strength, and to love your neighbor as yourself is more important than all burnt offerings and sacrifices (Mark 12:33).

    D. What does loving your neighbor look like for your child?
        1. Do not allow unkind _____.

        2. Encourage your children to be happy when something _____ happens to a sibling.

        3. Teach your children to respect each other's _____.

Notes

4. Teach your children _____.

5. Teach your children that they are each other's best _____.

II. Respect for Property
   A. Ex. 20:15–"Thou shall not steal."
   This verse is a commentary on _____ property. What does it include?

   1. Do not steal another's _____.

   2. Do not take advantage of a person's _____.

   3. Do not steal someone else's _____.

   4. Do not steal someone else's good _____.

   B. The object of respect
   The object of respect is not the property itself. The object of respect is always first and foremost the _____ who owns the property.

   C. Property vs. Dominion
   1. Property defined: That which is tangible and physical and within my _____.

   2. Dominion defined: That which I am responsible over both in the physical and non-physical realms. It includes property, time, space, and personal rights.

   3. Dominion is the _____ side of ownership; selfishness is the _____ side of ownership.

   4. Dominion sensor

   5. Starting with your children at home

   D. Teach the value of property

   The only benchmark measuring the value of any commodity is _____. Labor defines value.

   Labor can be divided into two categories:
   1. _____ labor

2. _____ labor

III. Respect for Nature
   A. Man's eye for beauty

   B. Three reasons to respect nature
      1. Because _____ made it

      2. Because of Genesis 1:28–Man is to take _____

      3. Because of the _____ of others

Key Principle: Labor defines value.

8

Respect for Peers, Property, and Nature

The fourth side of the "esteeming others" diamond is respect for peers and siblings. How do we teach our children to be sensitive to their peers and to act properly toward their siblings? When we refer to peer relationships, we do so from the broadest definition: a peer is someone of the same rank or dignity. By this definition, your child's peers come from common association. This may include brothers and sisters as well as friends and classmates. For adults, the definition would be the same. Our peers are the people with whom we play and work.

How can you show respect, honor, and honesty to them? There are basic guidelines stated in Scripture. For example, we can start with the last half of the Ten Commandments (Exodus 20:13-17).

Six:	Thou shalt not kill.[a]
Seven:	Thou shalt not commit adultery.
Eight:	Thou shalt not steal.
Nine:	Thou shalt not bear false witness against thy neighbor.
Ten:	Thou shalt not covet the possessions of your neighbor.

These laws represent man's relationship to man. They are the guidelines for behavior serving as the moral restraint and encouragement of our actions toward those around us. Our peers make up the greatest population throughout each stage of our lives.

The Old Testament law is not the only source of direction. The New Testament also speaks to us on this subject. Certainly, the one-anothers of the New Testament epistles direct us to proper conduct. Philippians 2:3 tells us that Christians are to esteem and regard others higher than themselves. Colossians 3:13 instructs us to be, "Forbearing with one another." Romans 12:9 says, "In honor giving preference to one another." Romans 13:8 instructs us to, "Love one another."[b] You can search this thought in a concordance and find plenty of support for respecting one another. It is a basic theme of Christianity and a necessary element for a healthy community.

Work positively with your children and their relationship with siblings and friends. Here are a few suggestions. Encourage them to be happy when something wonderful happens to a sibling, such as when one receives an award, wins a board game, or has an opportunity that the others do not have. Your constant encouragement in this area can make the difference between ongoing bicker-

" My relationship with my siblings is amazing. My parents worked hard when we were young to get us to be best friends. If we could not get along with each other, we were not allowed to spend time with our other friends until we did. I am grateful for that now. My two siblings live several hours away, so the time I get to have with them is precious. Yet we call and email each other often during the week. My brother and his wife invited me to go on vacation with them this summer. I cannot imagine him thinking of doing that if my parents hadn't worked on making us get along all those years ago." – Amy, age 19

a. The Hebrew language employs several words to express the idea "to kill," but the verb used here is a special word, which means "murder", and always indicates intentional slaying. A proper rendering of this commandment is, "Thou shall not murder."

b. Love is always gracious. When somebody needs help with something, somebody else must give up what he wants to do in order to help. Somebody is having a hard experience. Others must learn how to put themselves in his place, how to comfort and sympathize. Doing the little things nobody thinks are fun but that have to be done by somebody – these are opportunities for self-giving and sacrifice. ('The Shaping of a Christian Family' by Elisabeth Elliot, pg 134)

References / Notes

c. For more proactive helps in dealing with sibling conflict, please see Mom's Notes presentation, "Dealing with Sibling Conflict", Part 1, 2)

" What my parents learned in Growing Kids God's Way made a great difference in my relationships with my siblings. I know teens, even Christian ones, who seem to hate their own siblings, always putting them down and never wanting to be around them. My family is not like that. We genuinely love each other, and although we have the occasional clash now and then (as everyone does), we are always able to restore the relationships due to the principles we have been raised with."
– Kara, age 14

d. Pastor Henry Blackaby writes: The person who serves selflessly, lovingly, without complaint, and without seeking recognition is highly regarded in the kingdom of God. Christians like to refer to ourselves as servants, but we are seldom content to be treated as servants! We are tempted to adopt the world's evaluation of importance. But when we look to Jesus as our model, we see that it takes a far more noble character to serve than to be served. (We look to Jesus and our kids look to us.) The world will estimate your importance by the number of people serving you. God is more concerned with the number of people you are serving. Luke 22:27 (Experiencing God Day-by-Day, pg. 175)

" Rejoicing with someone means you are excited for them, not because there is any gain or reward for you, but because the other person is important to you. This fulfills Romans 12:15. This is simply being "others-centered" – asking "How can I bless this person and let them feel the love of Christ."
– Kristen, age 17

ing between siblings and a peaceful house.[c] When it is one child's birthday, the siblings do not need to receive a gift also. That only robs the birthday child of his special day. It teaches the siblings to selfishly look forward to a day of gifts rather than a day of celebrating the birth of a brother or sister. Mothers will often say, "I do not want anyone to feel bad because they did not get a gift." But they will all receive a gift–each one on their own birthday.

Continually remind your children that they are each other's best friends. They must learn how to take care of each other. Sibling relationships are the first peer relationships most children will know.

REACHING OUT TO OTHERS

How do you cultivate a servant's attitude in your children?[d] How do you instill an "otherness" sensitivity? Certainly, parental example and instruction play a big part in the formation of proper habits. In addition, you must place your child in an environment that will encourage service to others. Take household chores for example. Researchers from Toronto, Canada and from Macquarie University in Australia studied children from families who were given daily chores and those who were not. Their research pointed toward some interesting conclusions.

Children who performed household chores showed more compassion for their siblings and other family members than children who did not share in family responsibility. Even more interesting was the fact that not all chores are equal. The kids who did family-care chores like setting the table, feeding the cat, or bringing in firewood, showed more concern for the welfare of others than children who had only self-care responsibilities, such as making their own bed and hanging up their own clothes.

Such research validates the obvious. Whenever children participate in the care of others, they grow sensitive to human need. Include your children, to whatever extent possible given their age, in helping to secure the welfare of your family. That may mean bringing firewood in every day after school, helping out with the weeding of the garden, or setting or clearing the table. Whatever it may look like in your home, include your children in the experience of serving others daily.

How sensitive is your child towards others? That question takes us right back to Leviticus 19:18, which says, "You shall love your neighbor as yourself." When your child's neighbor is thirsty, will your child offer him a drink? When your child's neighbor is hungry, will he give of his food? When your child's neighbor is cold, will he give of his warmth? When your child's neighbor is alone, will he give of his friendship? How in touch is your child to the feelings, hurts, pains, and needs of other children? To be warm and friendly to the new child in the class is a caring and compassionate gesture. To have your son or daughter reach out to another child for no other reason than the love of kindness brings God's confirmation to the heart. In that moment, your child's kindness touches the throne of God because his actions please God.

Not all children are given the same measure of gracefulness, skills, abilities, and talents in every area of life. Do your children realize what God has given them is to be used to build up and edify those children around them? Children,

References / Notes

by nature, can be the cruelest members of any society. But children whose hearts are properly shaped can be vessels of honor used by God, bringing mercy to those who know no mercy and grace to those who know no grace.[e]

Life Is Not Fair!

Often, parents confuse the terms fairness and justice. Justice is legal equality; fairness is not. Life is unfair. How many times as parents have we heard or said this statement ourselves? One mother shared her daughter's sense of unfairness and asked how she could help her daughter deal with it. Life for her was unfair on the playground, in the classroom, and sometimes at home. The fact is "life is not fair." But that declaration has a context that qualifies its meaning.

Unfairness is relative to our own circumstances. Most understand fairness by what we are missing, not by what we are possessing. Therefore be prudent and teach your children how to be content. Point out to them just how much they have that others lack. Only when you learn to be thankful for what you have will you learn to be content.[f]

RESPECT FOR PROPERTY

The fifth natural relationship man has with his fellow man is linked to private ownership. Respect for the property rights of others is another facet of moral training. The Bible speaks of private ownership from its onset. Both Cain and Abel brought the fruit of their labors (i.e., private property) as offerings to God (Genesis 4:3-4).[g] Old Testament provides statements protecting man's right of ownership. Jesus encouraged the proper use of these laws and often used money and possessions as objects of teaching.

"You shall not steal" (Exodus 20:15) is the eighth commandment. The verse implies the following: first, you are not to steal another man's money or possessions. Second, you are not to steal from him by defrauding or preventing him from receiving what is due. The basis for this commandment implies private ownership, since you cannot take from a man that which he does not own. Man's property rights do not in any way take away from God's universal title, for He owns all the cattle on all the hills (Psalm 50:10). On the contrary, our privilege of ownership is a result of His benevolent sovereignty toward man. Private property is for man's sake. It is the reward of labor and is to be enjoyed (Ecclesiastes 5:18-19).[h]

Respect for Property is a Societal Need

Teaching respect for property begins at home and should be considered part of a social contract. When our children were very young, we took seriously the task of training them to respect the property of others. We started in our living room. As they became increasingly mobile, we set boundaries both for their welfare and for our peace of mind. Certain household items were off limits to their little hands (television knobs, stereo buttons, knickknacks, and other things). We did not worry about bruising their psyche or stifling their creativity. To us, moral correctness was more important than a presumed, psychological correctness.

e. Teaching your child how to respond in a sensitive way toward the feelings of his peers is a greater act of godliness than just getting him to control his hostile behavior. The hitting, pushing, and little scrapes our children get into during the growing years are not as much of a concern as is developing a genuine sensitivity to the feelings of others. Socially hostile behavior will be brought under control; society will see to that if parents do not. Respect for peers, however, is more than restraining the dark side of our natures. It also means reaching out in times of need to help others.

f. Thankfulness is the secret to human contentment. Taking inventory and realizing how much God has lavishly provided us can only produce a thankful heart. In contrast, discontentment keeps a person focused on self; when you look to self, you limit your ability to meet Scripture's moral mandate of looking to the preciousness of others.

g. Genesis 4:3-4: And in the process of time it came to pass that Cain brought an offering of the fruit of the ground to the LORD. Abel also brought of the firstborn of his flock and of their fat. And the LORD respected Abel and his offering.

h. Ecclesiastes 5:18-19: Here is what I have seen to be good and fitting: to eat, to drink and enjoy oneself in all one's labor in which he toils under the sun during the few years of his life which God has given him; for this is his reward. Furthermore, as for every man to whom God has given riches and wealth, He has also empowered him to eat from them and to receive his reward and rejoice in his labor; this is the gift of God.

References / Notes

i. *This type of training was not a quirk of the Ezzo family. It was a generational response—a socially understood, accepted, and expected standard of training. Respect for property was a visible virtue of our time. Because young children are not morally mature, parents in the past would restrict any behavior that would be morally offensive. The rights of others not to have their property inappropriately touched by untrained children was more important than allowing a child's impulsive desire to touch to be satisfied. The child's desire would be satisfied at the right time under the appropriate conditions, not at a neighbor's house.*

"My parents taught us to show respect for things that belonged to others (and our own things) at an early age. I shared a room with my sister for many years. My Dad made each of us a shelf that was kept by our beds. My Mom told us that what we kept on our shelf was our special things, and no one could touch them without permission. She said the things that were put in the toy box were "community property", meaning anyone could use them at any time. Because my parents showed respect for our things, we would follow their example."
– Briana, age 21

When visiting friends, we did not rearrange their living room claiming that the items were too much temptation for our children. Our children did not explore bedrooms or open cabinets, the refrigerator, or dresser drawers. They did not climb on anyone's furniture or carry their cat, slinging it from its neck. They did not do those things because we had trained them not to. Our training was motivated by our ethical responsibility to respect the property of others. We didn't child-proof our house; we house-proofed our children.[i]

Value the Person or the Property?

The duty of every parent is to instill a high degree of respect for the property rights of others. That process begins by respecting the person. The object of ownership is not the basis of respect; the owner is. The object is merely the target of respect. Viewing the owner as the object of respect eliminates independent value judgments that lead to conditional respect. For example, the condition of your front lawn, whether it is beautifully groomed or terribly overgrown, has no bearing on my obligation to respect it. I should not toss my gum wrapper on another's property regardless of its condition, though it may go unnoticed in the yard's overgrown state. Ultimately, what evokes my respect is you the person, not your property.

Many wrongly assess the value of an item based on its use. Take a store shopping cart for example. In your estimation, how much value does a shopping cart have? That should not be the question. Rather, the question should be: "how much value does the shopping cart have to the store owner?" The answer is, "plenty!" How should I respond to his ownership and the rights of others to use it? When you are finished taking your groceries to the car, do you return your shopping cart to the appropriate place? If not, why not? We should not leave our shopping cart squeezed between two cars because when we drive off we have no control over that cart. What if the wind blows it out into the roadway or into another car? Imagine returning to your car only to find two carts pushed against it. How would you feel? Most likely violated and angry. Returning our shopping carts to cart racks or the front of the store is another way of being courteous to all men (Titus 3:2). Returning the cart is not the principle but the vehicle delivering the principle of respect for another's property.

Property and Dominion

The question that remains is: as a person who wants to do right according to the ethical mandates of Scripture, how should I treat the property and dominion of others? To answer that question, allow me to define the terms property and dominion. Property is that which is tangible, physical, and within one's ownership. Property may be owned privately, jointly, or in common. For example, privately I own my tie, as a congregation we jointly own our church building, and all of us own in common the roadways.

Dominion refers to those things for which I am responsible both in the physical and nonphysical realms, including property, time, space, rights, and privileges. Dominion relates to stewardship responsibilities. Dominion is the positive side of ownership, while selfishness is the negative side.

Every human being is sensitive to dominion violations. Each of us has a small sensor that warns us whenever there is an encroachment on our dominion. That sensor has all the characteristics of a natural, spontaneous reflex as illustrated by the following example. Ryan is walking toward you carrying a bag of candy. You get down to his eye level and ask gently, "Ryan, will you share some with me, please?" Normally, Ryan will graciously offer you his treats; but if you had approached him with the intent to forcefully take away his candy, his natural response would be to pull away and protect it.

Why the different responses? In the first example, nothing threatened Ryan's property. Because of that, he was more willing to share. In the second example, Ryan's property were threatened and his dominion sensor sent a message of warning. He intuitively pulled back to protect his property.[j] This is part of the nature of man.

Threats to your dominion produce real feelings. Those feelings are not selfish sensations but dominion violations. One reason we suspect God made man sensitive to his dominion would be to help all of us better appreciate and serve others. That conclusion is consistent with the otherness of biblical ethics. The dominion sensor is not so much a reminder of our possessions as it is respecting the possessions of others. Pass that truth on to your children.

Value Derived from Labor

In order to truly respect the property of another, a person must understand the relationship between labor and value.[k] We recommend appropriate labor be part of child training. Labor can be divided into two general categories—duty labor and purchasing labor. Laboring out of duty relates to an individual's responsibility to the family such as doing household chores like feeding the dog, bringing in firewood, setting the table, and doing the dishes. Duty labor is not done for money, but to help the team. Everyone does something in support of the family.

Purchasing labor is work done for financial compensation. This occurs when a child seeks a job with the goal of purchasing something specific. That type of labor gives real value to money. One year, our children desperately wanted a popular board game that cost $25. They were willing to work for it and asked if we had any jobs around the house. We offered to pay them $1 for every bucket of rocks they picked out of the garden and dumped on the rock pile 30 yards away.

They agreed to the entire project. At first, it seemed an easy way to earn money. By the time they filled the twenty-fifth bucket (two weeks later), they had a full appreciation of the value of $25. That experience and others prepared our children to be wise money-managers. More importantly, it taught them to be wise stewards of their property, because money now had meaning and relevance. Our children could equate it to labor. When they wanted a $20 pair of jeans, they knew that equated to 20 rugged trips to the rock pile. Their understanding of the value of a dollar (or $100) as a result of their labors forced a greater appreciation for their own toys, personal possessions, and the property of others.

j. There is something within man that desires to guard his property, space, and rights. Do not assume that such attentiveness is always a result of greed and selfishness. It is not! All of us have experienced threats to our dominion. When that happens, we feel violated. How many times have you waited in line to return a purchase and observed people attempting to bypass the line, hoping to maneuver their way to quicker service? You chose to abide by the rules of fair play, and now someone is attempting to skirt these rules at your expense. Someone is trying to take an unethical shortcut, and you feel violated. This is a normal response. What you do with that feeling of violation can get you a heavenly pat on the back or it can get you into trouble.

k. Labor defines value. Receiving an item without working for it limits a complete appreciation of any purchase. The child that labors to earn money to purchase a bike will have a greater appreciation for its value than the child that receives it as a gift. Predictably, the first child's sense of stewardship will be greater since the value of the bike is closely related to labor.

Teaching respect for property begins many years before a child is old enough to work for hire. Start with the basics. Do not let your children throw another child's toy, play behind your neighbor's curtains, jump on the furniture, or in any other way disrespect your or someone else's property. Respecting another's property and dominion requires that the training begin first with the parent. The next time there is a violation of your property, remember why God gave you a dominion sensor so you will not do the same to others.

RESPECT FOR NATURE
The sixth relationship all people share is with nature. There are three basic reasons to respect nature and become active, biblical environmentalists with our children.

We Should Respect Nature Because It was Created by God
God created both the flower and man, but He created the flower for man. The fact that God created man in His image and likeness is the central theme of man's identity. That fact separates him from the animals as much as from the plants. The objects of nature do not possess the same essence as man. But nature, like man, has inherent value as a result of the creation process. The man or woman who believes that nature exists by cosmic chance cannot assign value to nature, since the source of value, random chance, is valueless. There is no inherent value in chance. The elements of nature are not, in and of themselves, autonomous with respect to their value. In other words, the existence of a flower does not give it value, but the source of its existence does.[l] God is the source of all existence and value.[m] We find the value of creation in the source of creation, God Himself. That is the first reason we train our children to respect nature.

We Should Respect Nature Because of the Dominion Factor
God granted man dominion rights over creation from the beginning. The problem is not man's rights but the integrity with which he manages those rights. It is man's duty to be a steward of creation, and that implies protecting and nurturing it. When God made man, He endowed him with a sensitivity to beauty. He instructed Adam to take care of the garden and to take dominion over it (Genesis 1:28). Functioning as a gardener, his task was to maintain ecological harmony. To allow him to accomplish that task, God invested Adam with an eye for order and harmony. His senses had to be in tune with nature's harmony. God would not give Adam a command without giving him the capacity to fulfill it.

Man, in spite of his separation from God is still responsible to take care of the garden. But earth is now everyone's garden. We are to take from it what we need, but at the same time nurture and give back to it, so it will become fruitful again for now and for the generations to follow. Taking dominion of creation does not mean destroying nature; it means preserving it.

We Should Respect Nature Because of the Preciousness of Others
Our stewardship responsibility over creation starts with our vertical relationship with God but is worked out for the horizontal benefit of man. Any

l. *It is as Charlotte the spider said to Wilbur the pig, who was amazed at the intricacy of her web: "The greatest miracle is not the web itself, but what the web represents." ('Charlotte's Web' by E.B. White) Creation is God's external signature on earth.*

m. *God has a covenant with creation. (Romans 8:19-22). He deals with a plant as a plant, with an animal as an animal, and with a man as a man. He never violates His order of creation. God treats His creation with integrity and each element to its creative class according to the way He made it for its greater purpose. If God treats His creation with integrity, so should man.*

act of respecting nature must include an awareness of others. If consideration for others is not part of the formula, then we can legitimately justify throwing garbage from our cars, as long as that garbage is biodegradable. As it sits by the roadside, it will decay and put nutrients back into the soil.

Without an appreciation for those who come behind us, the above statement would be valid. But there is more to respecting nature than the use of biodegradable products. Respecting nature must include consideration for those coming behind us, standing by our side, or going before us. The choice not to litter the roadside should be based on the right of others to enjoy the beauty of the roadside without the stain of your garbage. Aesthetic appreciation for natural beauty is the moral consideration.

America's highway system has no lack of posted signs warning against littering, and there is a sad reason for that. The more our country moves away from intrinsic motivation, the more dependent social order becomes on extrinsic incentives. Highway signs warn against littering to restrain the selfish and lazy side of man's nature. They are for those who are not motivated intrinsically by moral principle.

The slogan "Keep America Beautiful" is a wonderful reminder of our collective responsibility. Add threats, fines, and imprisonment to it, and it becomes "Keep America Beautiful or Else." In this manner, doing right out of the fear of consequences replaces doing right out of a sense of moral purpose. The only reason your should restrain yourself from littering is because it an offense against nature, others and most importantly, God's image.[n]

SUMMARY

Moral children know how to respect the property of others and the gift of nature. They understand the parameters of authority, devotion to parents, honoring of age, and the love of peers. Moral children are a joy to be around because they are complete children, equipped with moral reason. They are not the product of chance or genetics but of parental training. They reflect in their actions humility of heart, which is what character training is all about. Christ became the ethical model for us. Although we cannot copy His perfection, miracles, redemptive work, or deity, we can copy His humility and His behavior motivated by the preciousness of others.

Questions for Review

1. Explain the difference between the terms fairness and justice.

2. How do most of us assess the fairness of life?

References / Notes

n. Rick's eyes were drawn toward the enormous windows that framed an exquisite view. "Lela," he called, "come and take a look at this." Against the sky, the distant marsh greeted the blue water. The surface laid perfectly calm and even from this distance; the tiniest movements of Atlantic Shad were visible, making the still surface shimmer in the morning sun. "It's like this nearly every morning in the summer," Auntie Anne said reflectively. "Beauty, splendor, and wonder come upon the tide water, creating this peaceful scene undisturbed by man." Auntie Anne spoke in an exquisite tone. "It always reminds me of the words of an old hymn by Horatio Spafford: "When peace like a river attendeth my way, it is well with my soul." Humming the hymn, Auntie Anne made her way into the kitchen while Rick and Lela stood side by side at the window, mesmerized by flocks of little white cranes and large blue herons flying over the wide expanse of water. In a few moments Auntie Anne appeared in the kitchen doorway carrying a tray with three glasses of chilled sweet tea and a basket of assorted crackers. "Please join me on the back porch." (Taken from the Auntie Anne series, Book Three.)

In this series of books Gary and Anne Marie departed from their traditional method of instruction, and turned to an older and more personal style of persuasion—sharing parenting principles in story-form. Stories are entertaining and provide a unique conduit for dispensing practical wisdom and moral truth that otherwise might be lost. As it relates to this chapter, spiritual lessons from God's marvelous creation are woven through each and every book. Read about this resource at www.GrowingFamiliesUSA.com.

References / Notes

" My parents always told us, "Your brothers and sisters are your best friends." Because we are all expected to reach the same family goals, we grew together. So many siblings we see around us are disconnected, and wonderful relationships that should last a lifetime never even take root." – Emily, age 19

3. Explain why property itself is not as significant as the owner of the property.

4. Describe the difference between property and dominion.

5. In your own words, explain how labor gives real meaning to the value of a dollar.

6. What should be the Christian's motivation for not littering?

This Week at Home

Take your shopping cart back to the front of the store and discuss how you felt about doing something that you know is right but very few are doing.

Session Nine Outline
and Chapter Nine

Principles of Obedience

I.   Defining Biblical Discipline
When the bible speaks about discipline, it implies one thing– _____
(_____). Biblical discipline is all about getting to the heart of a child.

II. What is Obedience?
   A. Text
      1. Ephesians 6:1 instructs children, "Obey your parents in the Lord for this is right."

      2. Colossians 3:20 instructs children, "Be obedient to your parents in all things for this is pleasing to the Lord."

   B. Obedience is absolutely essential to _____ government.

   C. What does obedience look like?

"Take now your son, your only son Isaac, whom you love and go to the land of Moriah and offer him there as a burnt offering on one of the mountains of which I shall show you. So Abraham rose early in the morning and saddled his donkey and took two of his young men with him and Isaac his son, and he split the wood for the burnt offering and arose and went to the place which God had told him" (Genesis 22:2-3).

   D. Abraham did three things.
      1. He rose up _____.

      2. He prepared himself.

      3. He did that which _____ commanded him.

   E. Four characteristics of biblical obedience
      1. It is to be _____

      2. It is to be _____

Notes

3. Without _____

4. Without _____

III. How Parents Wrongly Train to Obedience
   A. _____ /_____ parents

   B. _____ parent

   "A bribe blinds the discerning and perverts the words of the righteous" (Exodus 23:8).

IV. Principles of Instruction
   How do we communicate instructions?
   A. If you speak in a way which requires an answer or an action, you should _____ an immediate and complete response.

   B. When giving instructions, parents should _____ what they mean and _____ what they say. Never give an instruction that you do not intend to have _____.

      1. Understanding objective and subjective obedience
         a. When parents require the standard, the child alone determines when he will be _____. The consistency of God's moral standard makes obedience objective, since the parent does not react arbitrarily.

         b. Anything less than first-time obedience brings _____ punishment. The child is governed by his parents' present resolve, and that is what keeps the child in a state of continuing conflict, confusion, and insecurity.

            Obedience is no longer objective, but subjective. Consequences are no longer tied to _____, but to the mood and whim of the parent at any particular moment.

      2. Immediate obedience in time

         The aids

         a. "_____, Mom/Dad"

         b. _____ at your face

3. Timely compliance

The aid: "Children, this is your five-minute _____."

C. If I ask my child to do something and he disobeys, my child is in _____. If I am characterized by repeating myself in hopes that he will obey, then I am the one in _____ as a parent.

Key Principle: Calling a child to first-time obedience is not a problem for the child as much as it is for the parent. Such a standard calls parents to consistency.

9

Principles of Obedience

" I'm so thankful that my parents learned how to transition their leadership from rule-based parenting when I was young and needed concrete boundaries to principle-based parenting as I grew into my teen years. In this way external boundaries gave way to intrinsic principles, and a way of life. These are principles and virtues that will be with me for life." – Rebecca, age 17

I n the previous three chapters, we demonstrated the link between moral training and family harmony. The joy of parent-child and sibling relationships relates directly to the quality of moral virtue reigning in the heart of each family member. How should a parent govern in order to secure such virtuous behavior? This chapter will begin to answer that question.

Ephesians 6:1 instructs, "Children obey your parents in the Lord for this is right." Colossians 3:20 follows with, "Children, be obedient to your parents in all things, for this is well-pleasing to the Lord." Obedience is absolutely essential to proper family government. If your children lack obedience, your efforts are minimized, if not totally in vain. You may rock, hold, and sing to your precious children. You may lead them in devotions, praying for them and with them. You may be unwavering in your efforts to secure their happiness and to gain their affections. But if they are continually disobedient, you will be thwarted in your efforts to train their hearts. How is a young child able to fulfill the great command of Exodus 20:12, "Honor thy father and mother"? Honoring one's parents is a command that remains constant throughout a child's life and into adulthood.[a]

a. In the early years, children demonstrate honor by being obedient. What is the difference between obedience and submission? A child obeys out of duty because someone in authority is forcing him to, by giving consequences to him if he does not. A child submits out of a heart of devotion because he knows that doing what is right pleases God and others. Children need to be taught to obey first. (Mom's Notes presentation, "Finding the Balance in Biblical Parenting", Part 2 - 'Understanding First-time Obedience')

TRAINING TO THE STANDARD

There will be many times when your child will reject or strongly oppose your reasonable instructions. What should you do? Teach him to obey according to the character of true obedience–immediately, completely, without challenge, and without complaint. This task is not as difficult as it may seem. Actually, true obedience is often more difficult for the parent than for the child. The child often responds to the parents' resolve and nothing more. Therefore, parents should train, encourage, correct, and teach to a level pleasing to God.[b]

As obedience relates to children, Colossians 3:20 makes clear God's requirement, "Children obey your parents." However, a warning follows immediately in verse 21, "Fathers, do not exasperate your children, that they may not lose heart." Do these verses conflict? To be obedient in all things all the time will frustrate a child, for certainly there are times when the burden of obedience can be unfair, unjust, and untimely. But for a child not to be obedient violates the standard presented in verse 20.

The warning to parents in verse 21 does not compromise the standard presented for children in verse 20. Rather, it reminds parents that biblical authority is not cold, calloused, and arbitrary. Parents should not exercise their authority without thought. Biblical authority is not whimsical or inconsistent. The intent of parenting is not to avoid exasperation but to avoid unnecessary

b. What is the nature of God's standard? According to 1 Samuel 15:22-23, God requires obedience from His children above all else. Speaking to King Saul, the prophet Samuel said, "Has the Lord as great delight in burnt offerings and sacrifices as in obeying the voice of the Lord? Behold, to obey is better than sacrifice and to heed than the fat of rams. For rebellion is as the sin of witchcraft, and stubbornness (insubordination) is as iniquity and idolatry." God puts a premium on obedience.

c. If you need to say something twice you were probably being ignored. When we repeat, we tend to use the same words, but intensify the presentation a bit. If what you said the first time didn't register, why would you believe it will the second time? Get your child's attention by going to where your child is; speak softly and slowly, and you will likely be heard. (Be a Great Parent by Dr. H. Norman Wright, pg. 174)

d. Parents will find that when they are verbally reminding their children over a period of time regarding a certain behavior or attitude, they will see their children slide in other areas as well. Be cautious in your use of verbal reminders and warnings. They can be used appropriately, or they simply become the flip side of "threatening and repeating" parenting. Try to get into the habit of only giving one reminder or warning. (Mom's Notes presentation, "Understanding Freedoms" Part 1)

e. The failure of parents to maintain a consistent standard only serves to lure a child into sin by causing him to think that he will get away with anything. In the end, inconsistency in parental resolve brings contempt for the standard of obedience.

f. "Do not accept a bribe, for a bribe <u>blinds</u> those who see and twists the words of the righteous." (Exodus 23:8) The crow picks out the eyes of the dead after the eyes no longer serve a purpose, but bribery destroys the soul of the living by blinding their eyes.

exasperation. The very nature of obedience will often frustrate a child, just as it often frustrates adults. Does that mean we ignore the standard? Most certainly not! We are to train children to the standard and guard against unnecessarily exasperating them in the process.

How Do Parents Undermine the Process?

Should Christian parents train their children to be unresponsive to instruction the first time it is given? The answer, of course, is no. Yet in reality, many parents are guilty of such negative training. Desiring obedience, they actually teach disobedience. Here are three common ways parents undermine their own efforts of bringing their child to the standard.

1. Threatening and repeating
2. Bribing
3. Negotiating in conflict

Threatening/Repeating Parent

The mother who first coaxes, then threatens, then bargains, then pretends to punish, and finally punishes a little is only making a bad situation worse.[c] No child will respond to God's standard if parental resolve for true obedience is lacking. Lack of moral fortitude and resolution in the parents undermines true obedience. How is it that a child will obey the third time but not the first? The reason is that the parent is finally resolved to force conformity. If a child obeys by the third request, why not by the first?

Understanding the objective nature of first-time obedience is of great importance. When parents require the standard, the child alone determines when he will be corrected for failure to comply by his disobedience.[d] Anything less than first-time obedience brings subjective punishment. That is, consequences are no longer tied to disobedience, but to the mood and whim of the parent at any particular moment. The threatening and repeating parent fosters a fearful, subjective response.[e]

Bribing Parent

Bribing parents barter with their children in hopes of gaining obedience. They use bribes, threats, or even scare tactics to gain temporary control of their children's behavior. A bribe might sound like, "If you are a good boy in the store today, Mom will buy you a special treat." An example of a threat might be, "If you are not a good boy in the store today, Mom won't buy that special treat she promised you." An example of a scare tactic might sound like, "If you are not good in the store today, I will call up the police to come and get you!"

Such verbal statements establish a false and improper motivation for obedience, thus devaluing obedience. Some parents train their children to obey for a bribe, rather than out of obedience to them.[f] Their children respond because there is something in it for themselves. Children should be rewarded for their obedience but should not be obedient just to gain a reward. That distinction is important. What happens when a reward is no longer a substantial motivator?

You are left with a child who is not moral on the inside or on the outside.

Children of bribing parents demonstrate several character and behavior patterns. They develop self-oriented tendencies and learn to manipulate others. Because they seek to be rewarded, they limit their ability to serve others unless they receive gratification. These traits are certainly not characteristics that God would have us develop in our children.

Negotiating in Conflict

Many parents insist on the standard of complete obedience while giving instructions but are willing to negotiate the line of compliance once in the heat of conflict. When Nathan's mom asked him to pick up his toys and get ready for lunch, her request was met with a, "No, Mom, I'm going to play with them after lunch." "Nathan," Mom said, "after lunch you are taking a nap, so I want all the toys picked up now." "Mom, I will pick them up after lunch." "No, Nathan. All the toys must be put away before lunch." Nathan did what his mother asked but brought to the table two of his small trucks. Upon seeing the trucks, Mom again confronted Nathan about all the toys needing to be put away. Finally, the two came to agreement that Nathan can keep one of the trucks with him during lunch.[g]

The issue is not whether playing with a truck at lunch is right or wrong, but whether his mom is characterized by always negotiating something less than her original instructions. When parents become characterized by continually accepting a negotiated compromise, they undermine their attempts to bring their child to first-time obedience. If all is negotiable, then no instruction is absolute. When we negotiate the standard in the heat of battle, there is no true surrender, only an agreed upon suspension of conflict. Without a complete surrender, there will always be a member ready to wage war.

Choose your battles well; but once you do, be resolved to hold the line (unless the line was wrongly drawn in the first place). If you are continually giving in, then you are continually undermining any progress toward biblical obedience.

PRINCIPLES OF INSTRUCTION

We will now investigate how parents can establish the character of obedience in a child. This is not as difficult a task as some would fear, but it requires adherence to some basic principles of communication. When we consider the role of instruction in a child's life, there are a few facts and elementary principles that should be kept in mind. Following these basic guidelines can prevent stress and increase willful compliance; failure to comply can lead to power struggles and continuous, outright rebellion.

Principle One

When you speak to your child in a way that requires an answer or an action, you should expect an immediate and complete response. This principle speaks to the parents' level of expectation. Children will rise to whatever level is expected and encouraged. Too many parents expect little and receive exactly that. We

References / Notes

" If my parents had offered me a bribe for doing a good job with something they asked me to do, that would have enticed me to complete it, but not necessarily complete it correctly." – Timothy, age 16

g. Parents negotiate with their children because they want to avoid the nasty scene conflict can bring. Having to deal with fits children throw wears parents out. But so does negotiating. Parents need to be resolved to stick to their original instruction and deal with whatever reaction they get. Elisabeth Elliot shares this about her mother, "Mother's steadfast insistence on obedience was not for her personal victory over a strong willed young son, but rather to strengthen her son's will to enable him to will against himself, that is, to do the things he ought to do before doing the thing he wanted to do." (The Shaping of a Christian Family, pg. 143)

References / Notes

"The most important thing to improve your family's life is consistency. The one thing young children need to know more than anything is where the line is. If I get in trouble for something one time and then do not the next, I do not know if my parents really meant what they said, and I do not know what to do the next time around. When parents are consistent, it makes life for the kids much easier." – Donovan, age 15

h. *When we were first introduced to Growing Kids God's Way, our son Michael was in 2nd grade. When I called him, I used to count to 1-2-3, thinking he needed time to obey me. Taking time to choose to come at my call was not obedience. True obedience would have been his coming at the moment I called his name, whether he felt like it or not, whether he wanted to or not, whether it was convenient for him to or not. This is what it is supposed to look like - I want Michael to pick up his toys. I call his name. I wait for him to respond with "Yes Mom, I'm coming!" When Michael comes to me, I instruct him to pick up his toys, and I wait for his response of "Yes Mom, I will pick up my toys now." Training your children in this way makes a big difference in how fast they will learn First-time Obedience. (Mom's Notes presentation, "Finding the Balance in Biblical Parenting," Part 2 – 'Understanding First-time Obedience')*

have consistently found that the requirement of first-time obedience is far less of an adjustment problem for children than it is for their parents.

Principle Two

Never give a command unless you intend for it to be obeyed. Therefore, when giving instructions, be sure to say exactly what you mean and mean precisely what you say. This simple principle is so easily violated by parents. There is no better way to teach a child not to obey than to give him instructions that you have no intention of enforcing. A child quickly learns the habit of disregarding his parents' instruction. This habit may become so strong and contempt for instruction so confirmed, that all threats will go unheeded. Do you want your child to go to bed? If so, do not state your instructions as a question in the form of a choice. Instead, you should state your instruction as a command to be obeyed.

Parental instructions are either directive (telling a child what to do) or restrictive (telling a child what not to do). Both types require a response of immediate compliance, unless otherwise given in the instructions.[h] There are three ways to maximize the success of your communication. We suggest you provide an appropriate warning, provide a door of escape, and consider context.

PROVIDING A FIVE-MINUTE WARNING

Sometimes the timing of instruction is as important as the instruction itself. Parental instruction that interrupts or terminates an activity should often be preceded by a warning. We have all experienced the total absorption of various projects, and we know the frustration we have felt when forced to leave our efforts without warning. The same frustration is felt by children.

There are times when it is appropriate to provide a five-minute warning that instruction will soon be following. Such a benevolent act helps the child emotionally prepare to comply. For example, Ryan was finishing his favorite television program. His mother interrupted and informed him that in five minutes she would return with instructions for him to prepare the dinner table. That five-minute warning made obedience more attractive for Ryan. Such parental sensitivity reduces the shock of intrusion and alleviates the tension between the child's desire to continue with his activity and the need to comply with his mother's instruction.

Giving a five-minute warning is reasonable. However, what if the parent gives instructions and the child continues his activity beyond the time? Perhaps he watched television until the end of the program, then to the next commercial and into the next program. That is an act of disobedience. The child decided to accept his own preference instead of the fairness of his mother's command and is now taking advantage of her graciousness. Some parents say it is a minor thing that the child stretched his time. But open defiance is not a little fault, and the judicial parent should not turn his or her back on it.

Since parents are instructed in Colossians 3:21 not to exasperate their children, we admonish you not to tempt your children to disobey by forcing them to choose between the strong pleasures of the flesh and your instructions.

Avoiding exasperation does not mean compromising the standard, but working wisely with it, such as giving a five-minute warning.

PROVIDING A DOOR OF ESCAPE

God never allows us a temptation for which He does not provide us a door of escape (1 Corinthians 10:13). This same principle can be applied to our parenting. You should teach your children to look for the door of escape when challenged by sin. For example, when two siblings squabble over a toy, the older child may know the punishment for striking the younger. But, if he has been wronged, the temptation to bring justice by the use of force is great. His door of escape is to take his conflict to the one who can make things right and carry out justice–Mom.

REMEMBERING CONTEXT

Understanding context prevents first-time obedience from becoming legalistic. Please review Chapter One concerning the importance of looking into the context of the moment to determine how to make a moral judgment on a child's behavior. Unless parents give due consideration to the context, they may judge right actions wrongly and may not judge wrong actions at all.[i]

Principle Three

When a child continually disobeys, he is in sin. When parents continually reinforce that disobedience, they are in sin. Judicial parenting does not allow parents to reward sin by doing nothing about it. For small faults, wisdom may dictate that parents show patience or give a stern warning, but parents should not consider direct and willful defiance trivial. Obedience and disobedience are moral acts, not individual preferences. Encouraging and establishing right, moral behavior in children requires consistency and clarity of instruction. Unless your instructions are clear and consistent, your child is at a loss to know what to do.

EYE CONTACT AND VERBAL RESPONSES

Require eye contact when giving face-to-face instruction. Make it a standard practice to get your child to look you in the eyes when you are speaking. Eye contact is a focusing skill and helps any child process instruction. Processing instruction is half the battle in getting your child to follow instruction. The child that is allowed to look around the room rather than at Mom or Dad too often struggles with compliance partly because he has never learned to actually pay attention to your instructions.

Closely akin to eye contact is a verbal response. A verbal response such as, "Yes, Mom," or, "Yes, Dad," facilitates healthy, moral development by assisting the focusing and concentrating process. That happens because, when the mouth is speaking, the brain is speaking. Verbal responses confirm your instructions. A "Yes, Mom" lets you know that your child is either committing himself to obedience by taking the appropriate action or to disobedience by avoiding the action asked of him. If a child responds verbally when called but does not come,

References / Notes

i. *Context gives perspective. Do you have a new baby? Is Dad tense when he is home because of issues at work? Are you building a new house? Did you just move? When children feel as though the rug has been pulled out from underneath them, it shows in their behavior. In these situations, parents need to decide what they can let go until life settles down, and what they need to continue holding the standard on. Is your child forgetting to make his bed in the morning? Remind him (let it go for now). Is he challenging your authority? That requires a consequence (do not let the standard slide in your first-time obedience training). (Mom's Notes presentation, "Finding the Balance in Biblical Parenting," Part 1-'Fundamentals')*

When my parents taught us about eye contact & respect for authority, it was hard at first. But we have really benefitted from it by having other adults respect us more now. It is a great feeling when adults ask my opinion or treat me as another adult rather than thinking of me as a "teen". – Aimee, age 14

References / Notes

j. What about a child who is so wrapped up in what he is doing that he has to be called several times to get his attention? The concentration level of some children may be deeper than others. Sometimes the parent's voice tone needs to be adjusted in order for the child's thought process to be interrupted. Think of it this way. You are watching a program on television in a state of total concentration. All of a sudden, a voice interrupts your concentration and says, "We interrupt this program to bring you a special news report." That is exactly what should be happening in your child's mind when you speak. Your voice should interrupt his thought process for a special announcement.

k. The transition between a child's actions and understanding is, in part, what makes parenting young children so hectic. There are numerous antagonistic forces at work. For example, a child needs supervision, but also needs the freedom to explore his developing world. He needs boundaries, yet he needs ample opportunity to let his curiosity take him where it will lead. Equally, he needs to learn when you are read to teach him, but you must be ready to teach when he is ready to learn.

l. The "Mom's Notes" presentation, "It's All About Attitude" gives detailed information on ways parents can work with their children's attitudes.

he is still disobedient. This child is negligent in prompt obedience.[j]

Once in a while, we may repeat ourselves. Sometimes repeating may be legitimate, and other times it may not be. However, we should be working toward a pattern of consistency in first-time response without the need for repetition. This become easier as your child is able to wed parental expectations with understanding.[k] You can train your child to tune you in rather than tune you out! It is only a matter of your willingness to do the training.

THE GOAL OF SELF-GENERATED INITIATIVE

Initiative is the only legitimate and ethical way to get ahead. Children operate on one of four levels of initiative.

1. Self-Generated Initiative

The highest and most desirable level of initiative is self-generated initiative. At this level, a child responds to needs without prompting or instruction. When Nathan saw the laundry basket filled with clean clothes, he began to separate his personal items, fold them, and put them away so Mom or Dad did not have to do it later. For a younger child, it may be as simple as putting away a toy left out after playtime. When a child responds to needs without prior instruction or being asked, parents should give plenty of verbal and physical affirmation. In addition to affirming the child, parents may choose to reinforce the behavior with a reward. It does not have to be expensive. What the child finds value in is the appreciation that the reward represents.

2. Prompted Initiative

The second level of initiative is called prompted initiative. At this level, a child responds promptly, but he receives instruction first. Borrowing from our example above, Nathan's mom instructs him to gather his clean clothes, fold them, and put them away. The request is met with, "Yes, Mom," and his little feet hustle off to do as told. Level two is characterized by right action and attitude.

Attitude is important.[l] The attitude with which your child accepts instructions is a benchmark determining the extent to which he respects your authority and headship. Parents can force action, but they need to mold attitude. There are tasks we all wish we did not have to do. That is true with our children as well. The challenge is this: with what attitude do I accept my share of responsibilities? A child does not need to bubble over with enthusiasm when asked to take out the trash, but neither should his attitude be one of anger, whining or pouting.

3. Forced Initiative

The third level of initiative is called forced initiative. At this level, Nathan responds to instructions in a delayed fashion with murmuring. Outwardly, he is standing up to go fold his clothes, but he is sitting down on the inside. Level three is characterized by the right action but the wrong attitude. What difference is there in attitude between levels two and three? Although the job gets done, it is done under protest. Unfortunately, many parents reward their children for getting the job done, but do not consider the child's attitude. If a parent rewards a child for behavior only, the child will most likely stay at level three initiative. Level three requires a parent's full attention and correction.

4. Suppressed Initiative

The fourth and lowest level of initiative is called suppressed initiative. After receiving his instruction, Nathan played with his train set in his room instead of sorting his clothes and putting them away. He totally ignored his mother's instruction and found another pursuit.[m] Level four is characterized by wrong actions and wrong attitude. Unfortunately, the parents themselves often encourage this behavior. Rather than dealing with the child's disobedience, Mom gives up by folding and putting away the clothes for him. The reason for her actions is simple. Doing the task herself is much easier and faster than getting her child to do it. This decision also avoids conflict. The problem with her action is that it reinforces the child's disobedience and teaches the child that if he waits long enough, someone else will do it for him!

At which level of initiative is your child working? At what level do you live? Prompted initiative is very good; self-generated is better and should be the goal to which every parent strives. What parental response will help motivate the child to the first level of initiative? Rather than giving rewards for instructions carried out, parents should always affirm the child with either a hug or word of encouragement expressing satisfaction with the child's behavior. Verbal and physical affirmation go a long way when a child knows his actions please his parents. When your child senses how pleased you are, he is more prone to accept additional responsibility freely. That in turn motivates him toward level one behavior.

SUMMARY

Disobedient behavior in children is not a mystery. They are often led into insubordination by us, their loving caregivers. If our intrusion has no resolve behind it, our children will take advantage of our parental uncertainty and assert their own, unguided will.

A child's feeling of acceptance and sense of approval is directly related to the standard of behavior required by his parents. This is true for all areas of character development and is especially true with first-time obedience.[n] The child whose parents require first-time obedience and encourage him in the process has a greater sense of parental approval, love, and acceptance than a child in a permissive or authoritarian household. Permissive parents tend to ignore the standard for obedience, while authoritarian parents eliminate the need to affirm their children.

When a child meets a high, established standard and receives parental approval, obedience becomes attractive, and the child knows his parents accept him. The higher the standard, the greater the confirmation and sense of approval. The lower the standard, the weaker the sense of approval and, ultimately, the weaker the parent-child relationship.

Training your child to respond to your voice the first time you speak means

m. Our goal in discipline should be two-fold: to train in self-discipline and to teach obedience. When our children learn self-discipline at an early age, they will be more likely to withstand the temptations of sin as they grow up. They will also have the personal discipline to be productive adults. Obedience to God is first learned when a child is taught obedience to his parents. If a child does not learn to obey his parents whom he sees, how can he be expected to obey a God whom he cannot see? ('And Then I Had Kids' by Susan Alexander Yates, pg. 102)

n. In Genesis 7 we find an incredible conflict between family identity and peer pressure. When Noah invited them to spend the next hundred years building an ark in obedience to a word from God, Noah's sons had to choose whether to believe those around them or to trust their father. They chose to join their father. As Henry Blackaby writes: "What a wonderful testimony to Noah's godly influence in his home! How fortunate for his sons that Noah refused to compromise his integrity, even though everyone else in his society had done so. As the world tries to persuade people to follow its standard, your life should stand in stark contrast as an example of a righteous person. Do not underestimate the positive effect that your obedience will have upon those close to you." (Experiencing God Day-by-Day by Henry and Richard Blackaby, pg. 167)

" When I was younger, ninety percent of the time I obeyed because I was afraid of getting in trouble. Now, I obey (most of the time) because it is the right thing to do, and I understand the ' why' behind Mom and Dad's instructions." - Kelsey, age 13

training him in God's standard of obedience. Although we all fail to consistently live up to that standard in our own lives, it remains the standard of God's pleasure. The obedience factor is very important in your child's development.

Questions for Review

1. What does Colossians 3:21 remind parents not to do? Explain.

2. List and briefly describe three ways parents undermine training in obedience.
   a.

   b.

   c.

3. What is the benefit of a five-minute warning?

4. Why is a verbal response important?

5. What is self-generated initiative?

This Week at Home

1. Take time this week and make a game out of your child coming the first time he is called with a, "Yes, Mom," or, "Yes, Dad." Be prepared to share with the class the results of your efforts.

2. Be prepared to share with the class how the five-minute warning helped you and your child.

3. Did you gain any victory from being a threatening/repeating parent? Be prepared to share that.

Session Ten Outline
and Chapter Ten

Discipline with Encouragement

I. Introduction

Instruction: Everything in child training starts here.

A. If you do not verbally instruct your children, how will they ever know what is _____ ?

B. If you do not live to the standard of your own instructions, then how much can it really _____ to you?

C. What is required to help children internalize values?

1. _____ knowledge

2. Parental _____

D. Parents need to separate <u>moral</u> behavior from <u>non-moral</u> behavior. Not all activities in your child's day are moral in nature-that is, behavior flowing out of the heart. Some activities are skill-based.

S1 _____

S2 _____

a. Link to _____-and-_____ behavior

b. Link with _____

S3 _____

a. Use goal incentives to motivate actions associated with _____ behavior.

Notes

b. Goal incentives used to motivate behavior are not goal incentives at all; they're _____ .

Why are bribes wrong?

1. Because God says they are wrong. "Bribes blind the discerning and pervert the works of the righteous" (Exodus 23:8).

2. You are appealing to the lust of the flesh, the lust of the eyes, and the pride of life (1 John 2:16).

B1 _____

a. We are defining behavior as actions that proceed from the _____.

b. Parents motivate heart behavior by _____ their children and by _____ their children.

B2 _____

E1 _____

E2 _____ reminder

You are encouraging your child to do right by reminding him of what is _____.

E3 _____ questions

The goal of this form of encouragement is to get your children to tell you what is _____.

E4 _____ words

As often as possible, use _____ words to encourage, not negative words to _____.

1. Instead of, "Do not _____ your cereal on the way to the table," consider saying, "See how carefully you can carry your bowl of cereal to the table."

2. Instead of, "Do not _____ out of bed," consider saying, "Obey mommy and stay in bed."

3. Instead of, "Do not _____ your sister," consider saying, "You need to show kindness to your sister."

4. Instead of, "Do not _____ so much," consider saying, "You need to learn to be a better listener."

E5 _____-activity Encouragement

E6 _____ affirmation

E7 _____ behavior

   a. Rewards are used to _____ behavior not to stimulate behavior.

   b. Rewards are, "_____ you were good in the store today," not, "_____ you will be good in the store today."

   c. Rewards can be tangible and non-tangible.

   D. Children should be rewarded for their obedience but not obedient for a _____.

   E. Beware of the condition of reward _____.

B3 Correction

Key Principle: Encouragement takes a quantum leap when you add physical touch to your words of praise. It is even more meaningful when Dad does this.

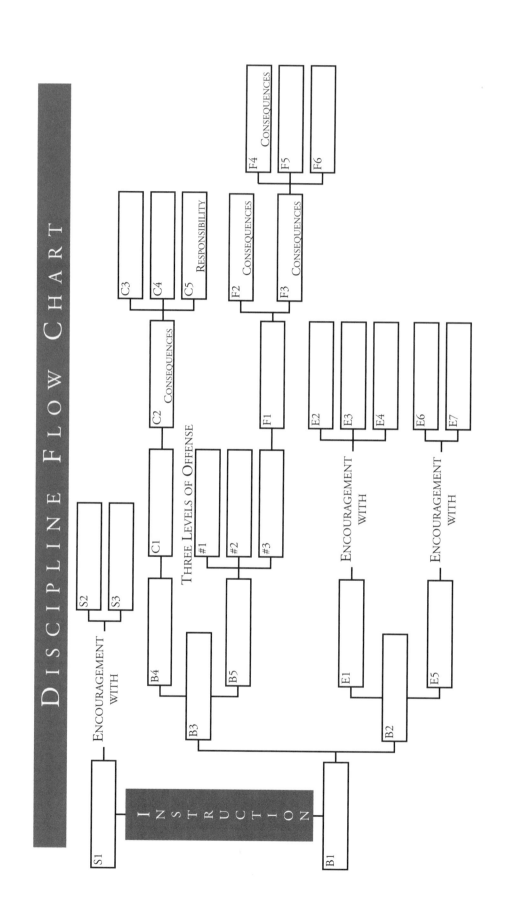

Discipline Flow Chart

10

Discipline with Encouragement

References / Notes

" Words of encouragement from someone you respect makes an enormous difference in attitude towards doing things well and giving it my best. In other words, when my parents encourage me for a yard, I can go a mile." – Kristen, age 17

While growing up in a Christian home, I often heard the catchy phrase, "Spare the rod and spoil the child." It was a universal phrase quoted with divine authority by all adults. Only after becoming a parent did I discover the passage from which that phrase originated. I was surprised to find out that it was not Solomon who penned those words, but Benjamin Franklin when writing Poor Richard's Almanac.

That misunderstanding raises a serious question about biblical discipline.[a] How many Christians base their disciplinary habits on cultural perceptions of biblical truth? The answer, unfortunately, is too many. The Bible exhorts parents to discipline their children. Unfortunately, our English understanding of the word discipline and our cultural practice do not line up with the intended meaning of Scripture. For example, a child who disobeys may hear his mother say, "Mom will have to discipline you for that." That is a common, but misused, application of the term. Today, we socially define discipline to mean spanking or punishment, but true biblical discipline refers to one thing–heart training. There is something in a child's heart that parents need to reach. What is there according to the Bible? Proverbs 22:15a says, "Foolishness is bound up in the heart of a child." Scripture never refers to a child as a fool but says that the untrained heart of a child contains foolishness.

Parents who consistently put effort into true biblical discipline and into shaping their child's heart and character do not have to concentrate as much on reshaping the child's outward behavior.

Biblical discipline consists of a number of essential principles and actions, some encouraging and some corrective. Various forms of encouragement that complement the biblical process include affirmation, goal incentives, praise, and rewards. The corrective side of biblical discipline consists of verbal reproof, natural consequences, isolation, restrictions, loss of privileges, and when appropriate, chastisement. Each activity has purpose, meaning, and a legitimate place in the overall process.[b]

a. Discipline is not action taken in moments of correction but an ongoing relationship with a mentor and student, or parent and child. Discipline is a process of training and learning that fosters moral development. It comes from the same word as disciple–one who is a learner. No child is endowed from birth with self-control, nor has he experienced enough in life to know how to discipline himself (Proverbs 29:15b). Parents fulfill that role as teachers, while children are disciples who learn from them a way of life (Proverbs 1:8-9).

b. Since the principal function of discipline is to teach morally responsible behavior, biblical discipline achieves that end more successfully than permissive or authoritarian parenting styles. The positive aspects of biblical discipline are synonymous with education and guidance in that they emphasize inner growth, personal responsibility, and self-control. All of these qualities lead to behavior motivated from within the child's heart (Proverbs 4:23).

SUMMARY OF ACTIVITIES

The Bible provides sufficient principles for child-rearing, but as stated earlier, it does not give us a detailed blueprint for every action. In order to maintain biblical harmony in the training process, the following guidelines are foundational to our thoughts: all activities of discipline, both positive and negative, must be compatible with biblical theology. No activity can be antagonistic to general biblical revelation. Guiding principles result either from expressed biblical statements or biblical examples. From these assumptions, we generated a Discipline Flow Chart (located in your outline).

The chart diagrams a number of disciplinary concepts compatible with the biblical design for child-rearing. The process begins with parental instruction, which is reinforced by a combination of positive and negative activities. Over the next three chapters, we will summarize the purpose of each activity and its relationship to the overall strategy of biblical discipline. This chapter starts with the encouragement side of discipline. Chapters Eleven and Twelve discuss the corrective side of discipline.

INSTRUCTION

Learning how to effectively communicate instruction to our children is essential to proper parenting. When Solomon penned the book of Proverbs, he referred to instruction approximately 100 times directly and indirectly. From the beginning of Proverbs to its end, instruction is the starting point of moral exhortation.[c] In the opening verses of Chapter 1, Solomon unfolds for his readers the purpose of this book. In verse 2, he says that the objective in life is to know wisdom and instruction and to discern the sayings of understanding. In verse 3, he adds that our goal should be to receive instruction in wise behavior and to learn how to live righteously, in justice, and in equity. Verse 4 indicates that instruction is also given to help one move from naivete to wisdom. In verses 5-7, Solomon gives a warning. In verse 5, he says, "A wise man will hear and increase in learning and a man of understanding will acquire wise counsel." Then, in verse 7, he contrasts the fool with the wise man through the warning, "Fools despise wisdom and they despise instructions."[d]

Some decisions and activities of life have no moral rightness or wrongness attached to them, such as the development of basic skills and natural talents. Learning to swim, tie a shoelace, ride a bike, kick a ball, climb a rope, play the piano, and memorize the multiplication tables are non-moral activities. They are skills associated with natural gifts, talents, and mental attributes. Recognizing the difference between moral and morally neutral behavior is important. The types of instruction, encouragement, and correction necessary to develop skills differ from those of modifying behavior. Motivation plays a big part in discerning between the non-moral and moral. With the first, you are working with talents, skills and natural abilities. With the second, you are shaping a human heart that has propensities toward resistance.

S-1 SKILLS, TALENTS, AND GIFTEDNESS

Skills, talents, and giftedness differ from one another. Skills are basic to all human beings like riding a bike, learning to swim, and throwing a ball. Natural talents are gifts from God. They differ from skills in that they are not universally given to all. Everyone has talents but not necessarily the same talents. Giftedness is a magnified talent. There are many naturally talented musicians, but Mozart was gifted.

A child's natural skills, talents, and gifts are often in need of training.

c. If you do not instruct your children, how will they ever know what is required? If you do not live the virtue you are communicating, how much can it really mean? Moral knowledge and parental example are absolutely necessary to help children internalize values.

d. In Proverbs 29:17, he says, "Correct your son and he shall give you rest. He will give delight to your soul." In this context, "correct" means "to educate". Correction, in this context does not mean to punish, but to train. Proverbs 22:6 says, "Train up a child in the way he should go and when he is old he will not depart from it." So to "train" means to "initiate learning, to cause one to learn, to instruct". If parents are going to cause their child to learn, they are going to need to ensure that circumstances are ideal so learning can take place. Teaching children when they are fed and rested are ideal circumstances for moral learning. So is teaching children in times of non-conflict. "Causing one to learn" may also mean parents need to reinforce the learning they want to take place with discipline. Proverbs 19:18 says, "Chasten your son while there is hope. And do not set your heart on his destruction." Destruction, in this context, means to "destroy a child's soul by the lack of training and instruction."

Learning to ride a bike is a skill, but riding a bike in such a way as to not hurt someone is behavioral. Learning to swim is a skill, but bullying other children in the water is wayward behavior. We contrast skills and behavior because it is important to understand their differences. It is wrong to treat a moral act as a skill, and it is equally wrong to treat deficiencies in skills as moral weaknesses.

There are three essential elements required in the development of skills–patience, guidance, and motivation. For a child to be willing to invest time and effort into the practice essential to the development of a skill, there must be some source of satisfaction to provide the motivation.[e] That motivation comes by way of parental praise and goal incentives.

S-2 VERBAL PRAISE

A common source of motivation for a child's development of skills is the personal satisfaction obtained from the verbal praise received (Proverbs 15:23b, 25:11). For example, "Great job catching the ball, Ryan. I can see how much your practice has helped you," or, "Jennifer, I'm listening to you play the piano. I can hear how much you have improved over last week by just adding five minutes more to your practice time." Link your words of encouragement to the cause and effect of your child's efforts. In both of these illustrations, the praise was tied to gains made as a result of practice. Linking your encouragement to a specific activity helps the child measure the value of his practice and encourages him to continue his effort.

Children will often share their little successes with their parents for the purpose of hearing praise. Such confirmation encourages their hearts. For example, when Becky walked over to show her mom the picture she colored, her mother complimented her neatness by saying, "What a good job of staying in the lines, Becky." Yet, we have found that the most effective praise motivating a skill comes when the child is not expecting it. For example, if Becky's mom had unexpectedly noticed how well she had stayed within the lines and then praised her, it would have meant even more (Proverbs 27:2).[f] Because the praise was unexpected, it will be remembered each time the activity is repeated. Unexpected praise becomes a motivator for achievement.[g]

S-3 GOAL INCENTIVES

A second way to encourage children is with goal incentives. Goal incentives are tangible, external rewards used to motivate a child to try harder in a particular developmental area. Parents can use goal incentives to help train a child to ride a bike, color a picture, improve a grade, or learn to type. All of these morally neutral activities are worthy of incentives, but not all morally neutral activities are skill related. For example, eating potato chips on the couch is morally neutral, but it has nothing to do with developing a skill.

Living near a lake, we wanted our children to develop water safety by learning how to swim. To facilitate Amy's learning, we offered her a goal incentive by saying, "Amy, if you learn to swim this summer from Grandpa's dock to the yellow buoy, we'll buy you the snorkel set you saw in the store." That summer, she made learning to swim a priority. Her motivation was heightened by the

e. We often praise our children when they do something well. We need to praise them for the effort they put into what they do as well, sometimes regardless of the outcome. Praising children for their efforts will teach them the value of hard work.

f. "Let another praise you, and not your own mouth; someone else, and not your own lips." (Proverbs 27:2)

g. A word of caution. The overly praised child will be more inclined toward image maintenance than moral maintenance. "How I look on the outside" becomes greater than "what I am on the inside."

References / Notes

h. Parents use goal incentives to motivate actions associated with skills, talents, and natural physical attributes but not for changing behavior. Skills and talents are non-moral elements of the child's life. Where a bribe is wrongly used to motivate behavior, goal incentives are rightly used to help a child develop skills.

⁓⁓⁓

" When my parents give me encouragement when they think I have done something well, it gives me incentive to work harder." – Anthony, age 14

i. Webster's Dictionary defines "encourage" as "to inspire with courage, to cheer on or up." When our children feel that there is nothing they can do right, that is the moment we need to inspire them with courage. How can you do that? First, when training in biblical virtues, work with them on one thing at a time and at a pace they can handle so they do not get overwhelmed or discouraged. Second, be willing at a moment when your child is in despair, to step in and help him achieve victory. We can do this by offering assistance, backing off on our demands to give them time to regroup, or just be there with them while they work things through. (For more practical helps see Mom's Notes presentation, "Finding the Balance in Biblical Training," Part 1 – 'Fundamentals,' and "Using the Bible in the Instruction and Training of Your Children.")

incentive. She worked diligently, learned to swim to the buoy, and received her bright yellow snorkel. If she had not met her goal, she would have received praise for trying but not the goal incentive.

Be careful not to overuse goal incentives or to use them to a child's discouragement. That happens when a parent expects more from the child than is reasonable for his or her age. At four years of age, Amy learned to swim an appropriate distance, but she was not yet ready to swim the length of the lake. Such a demand would have defeated the purpose and the benefit of a goal incentive.[h]

B-1 BEHAVIOR

As stated earlier, a child's actions are either moral or morally neutral. Skills and talents are morally neutral activities in and of themselves. Behavior is associated with the duties of the heart; parents motivate the heart by encouragement and correction. Both activities are important, and neither one is truly effective without the other.

B-2 ENCOURAGEMENT

True encouragement motivates right behavior.[i] Each of us enjoys receiving a pat on the back or hearing, "Well done," from someone of influence. We find appreciation in hearing how our actions pleased or helped another. Our children are no different. They are encouraged when justified praise comes their way. Unfortunately, this is an area in which many parents fail, particularly during the early years. During that time, parents are so preoccupied with getting things under control by continually correcting their children that they forget to encourage them. And, of course, we all know from personal experience that the absence of encouragement is discouragement.

E-1 PRE-ACTIVITY ENCOURAGEMENT

Pre-activity encouragement comes verbally before a required behavior is expected. This is accomplished through the use of verbal reminders, dialogue questions, and positive words.

E-2 VERBAL REMINDER

Parents should encourage right behavior with verbal reminders such as, "Ryan, Mrs. Brown is coming over for lunch today. Be sure to say hello to her when she comes in. That would be very respectful," or, "Stevie, remember there is to be no running in the church. That is where we worship God." In both of these examples, the parent reminds the child verbally of what he expects and the reason why he expects it.

E-3 DIALOGUE QUESTIONS

Parents can also accomplish pre-activity encouragement through dialogue questions. With verbal reminders, you tell the child what is required; with the dialogue method, the child tells you what is expected. This method is primarily (but not exclusively) used with children under five years of age. Driving to the grocery store, a mother may ask, "Who can tell me the rules for the store?" A child might respond, "No running, no touching the displays, and we have to stay by your side." Mom responds with encouraging words of praise for the correct answers.

Young children are more apt to take ownership of their behavior when they hear themselves verbalize the rules of conduct and receive praise for the right answers.

E-4 POSITIVE WORDS

In Chapter One, we talked about the fact that parents tend to spend more time and energy suppressing wayward behavior in their children than elevating good behavior. We spend more time restraining wrong than advancing right. While words of restraint are necessary throughout the training process, we must retrain ourselves to communicate the positive. This will take self-discipline, but the efforts will pay great dividends. When communicating with your children, attempt to speak as often as possible in the positive not the negative. If there is something you do not want your child to do, then communicate your desire for restraint by speaking in favor of what you want done.

Here are a few examples to help you get started. Instead of saying, "Do not spill your cereal on your way to the table," consider saying, "See how carefully you can carry your cereal to the table." Instead of saying, "Do not get out of bed," consider, "Obey mommy and stay in bed." Instead of saying, "Do not talk so much," consider, "You need to learn to become a better listener." Instead of saying, "Do not leave a mess for everyone else to clean up," consider, "Be responsible and clean up after yourself."

With young children, there will be plenty of justifiable "do nots." "Do not touch the knives." "Do not play with the stereo." "Do not hit the dog." Such prohibitions are appropriate with young children. But as they mature, they need positive direction. Consider the transfer from negative to positive speech a good habit to get into.[j] Proverbs 26:24 speaks of the care we should take in selecting positive words. "*Pleasant words are like a honeycomb. Sweetness to the soul and healthy to the bones.*"

E-5 POST-ACTIVITY ENCOURAGEMENT

Post-activity encouragement reinforces behavior after the fact. It is done through the proper use of rewards and verbal praise.

E-6 AFFIRMATION

In healthy relationships, verbal affirmation is never redundant. If we are not verbalizing our encouragement, what message are we sending? Verbally encourage your kids in the little things and the big. It is easier to catch their big efforts, but many times it is the daily stuff that makes or breaks relationships. Sometimes a simple, "Thank you," can go a long way.

Another way to verbally encourage a child is to say, "I need your help," instead of, "I want it," or just, "Do this." The humility it takes to ask for help by expressing sincere needs elevates the other person. If you are just getting started

References / Notes

" It is because of my parents training and routine words of encouragement that we are a family of best friends. My parents are so positive about our relationships, my brothers and sisters are my best friends. Many of my peers cannot stand to be around their siblings and long for the day when they turn 18 and can leave home and get away from who should be their best friends. Instead, my siblings and I jest about who is going to get to live with whom when we grow up....because we want to stay close forever." – Kristin, age 18

j. *Why are encouraging words so important? Because they facilitate a teachable spirit. According to John and Susan Yates, "A teachable spirit begins with the realization that one is incomplete – intellectually, morally, and spiritually. None of us is all that we can be or need to be. The wise person wants to learn from his mistakes rather that seek to justify them, and doesn't resent it when his errors or shortcomings are revealed. He goes through life with an underlying sense of thankfulness to God which enables God to develop in him the qualities of Christ-likeness. ('Character Matters,' pgs. 34-35)*

" When my parents are working on something with me, expecting me to improve my behavior or standards, it makes me feel like I am on the right path and I want to keep working on it when they encourage me." – Ashley, age 13

k. Recognition of their progress in positive behaviors goes a very long way to insure that the right attitudes and right actions will continue. Be careful not to sandwich your compliments with criticism, correction, or ideas for improvement. It can be de-motivating to hear, "You have done a nice job, but…" This is especially true when they have worked hard and feel that they have done their best. ('What Every Child Should Know Along the Way' by Gail Martin, pg. 84)

" I would not try to do my best if my parents rewarded me when I didn't give my best effort, because if my 'not so best' is good enough for an reward, then I do not have a good motive to do any better than that."
- Lindsay, age 13

on the encouragement side of your relationship, be careful not to qualify your encouragement. Do not say, "Thanks for doing the dishes tonight. Miracles never cease," or, "It looked like you started out preparing a great meal. Too bad you burnt it." Such qualified encouragement is not encouragement at all.[k]

Encourage with touch by simply placing a hand on the son's or daughter's shoulder and saying, "Great game," "Great job," or, "Thank you." Verbal affirmation combined with physical touch is an unbeatable combination and is highly effective with children of all ages–even with spouses.

E-7 REWARDS

Rewards are either tangible (a pack of gum) or intangible (a trip to the park). They are offered to reinforce behavior, not to stimulate it. Verbal praise and encouragement will stimulate behavior, but the purpose of a reward is to confirm and reinforce behavior. Ryan's mother might say, "Ryan, because you were so good in the store today, Mom wants to buy you a special treat." This is an example of rewarding a child. She called attention to his good conduct in the store and showed her appreciation for it. Offering your children something in exchange for good behavior before you get to the store is a bribe, not a reward. It is a manipulative appeal to the child's lust of the flesh and eyes (1 John 2:16a). Children should be rewarded for their obedience, but not be obedient for a reward.

When parents overuse rewards, the child becomes conditioned, even dependent, on receiving them. When that happens, the child may only go through the motions of good behavior, demonstrating outward but not inward conformity. Like a trained seal, the child has learned to perform his tricks just to get a prize at the end of his performance. In this case, the child bases his obedience on external stimuli and not on anything internal. Bribing a child produces temporary results. Properly rewarding a child motivates him from the heart, a place you want to influence.

Questions for Review

1. What is biblical discipline? What is God's purpose for it?

2. Explain the difference between moral and morally neutral behavior.

3. Explain the purpose of goal incentives. What are they used to motivate?

4. What is the difference between a goal incentive and a bribe?

5. What is the purpose of a reward? What is it used to reinforce?

This Week at Home

Take time this week to encourage your child both verbally and physically at the same time as discussed in this lesson. Be prepared to share with the class the results of this form of encouragement.

Session Eleven Outline
and Chapter Eleven

Discipline with Correction

I.   Introduction

B3 _____

   A. General Principles
      1. In the early, years you are putting _____ into your child.

      2. You are exchanging _____ for foolishness.

      3. A child by nature is self-oriented; biblical ethics is other-oriented. The tension between the two produces _____.

   B. Three Periods of Conflict
      1. Phase One: _____ months

      2. Phase Two: The Years _____

      3. Phase Three: _____ years old

   C. Specific Principles
      1. The first principle of correction: The type of correction depends on the presence or absence of _____ intent.

      2. When making an assessment on a child's actions, parents should ask, Were my child's actions accidental or intentional? A mistake or malicious intent?

B4 _____
Childishness defined:

C1 _____
Admonishment means to _____.

   C2 _____ Consequences

      C3 _____

      C4 _____

      C5 _____ responsibility.

B5 _____

Foolishness defined: Willful defiance and open rebellion are what the Bible calls _____.

A. About Foolishness:
1. A child is not acting childish if he is disobedient; he is acting _____. Foolish behavior needs correcting, but parents should not correct all foolish behavior the same way or with the same strength of consequence.

2. The second principle of correction is this: The punishment or consequences must fit the crime, because punishment sets a _____ on an offense.

B. Because a child's sense of justice is established through punishment, not rewards, parents must be aware of the two sins of punishment:
1. _____-punishing

2. _____-punishing

C. Parents should consider the following four factors before rendering a judicial decision.
1. The frequency of the _____

2. The _____ of the moment

3. The child's _____

4. The overall characterization of the child's _____

D. The Three Levels of Offense:
1. _____

2. _____ and action.

3. _____ punishment

F1 _____

Key Principle: The first principle of correction is this: the type of correction depends on the presence or absence of evil motive. When making an assessment on a child's actions, parents should ask, "Were my child's actions accidental or intentional? A mistake or malicious intent?"

11

~~~~~~

Discipline with Correction

There are ere are days when our children make us proud. They follow through on your expectations, saying "Thank you," just at the right time, comfort a sibling in need, and shake hands with the new neighbor while saying, "Very nice to meet you." There are also days when our children willfully fall short. They make mistakes, misbehave, and choose wrong over right. As for meeting the new neighbor, all you hear is a grunt, instead of "Hello" and feel your face flushing red. While it is easy to encourage the "good" moments, how do you correct the unpleasant ones?

In this and the following chapters we'll take up the challenges associated with the correction side of training. Anxious parents have frequently asked why we present a subject of such great importance at the end, and not the beginning of the series. It is placed here because correction is not part of the moral, emotional or intellectual building process, but rather part of behavioral management and maintenance. It is what parents do to keep their children on track and moving forward. Correction is the constant process of restoring children back to a level of expectation and a way of life that benefits them and those with whom they interact.

Any conversation relating to discipline and correction cannot take place without first encouraging the relational, moral, emotional, and intellectual components of training.[a] If these foundational components are deficient, then parental correction can easily become a type of tyranny, rather than an expression of love and education.

To our way of thinking, correction is a way of rescuing children from decisions made out of their immaturity or lack of wisdom, and sometimes from those moments when they choose wrong over right and disobedience over obedience. However, the corrective side of training is not all about fixing undesirable or wayward behavior, because parents must also pay attention to the preventative components of training that reduce the amount of correction needed in the first place and the developmental components that are continually changing.[b]

Training in the early years requires a basic understanding of what is going on in the developing mind of your child. Life expands very rapidly for young children and becomes more complex for older ones. Conflict is a normal part of learning, but there are greater and lesser periods of conflict. However, parents will always have a choice. They can train proactively to prevent poor or undesirable behavior placing a greater emphasis on building into a child's character habits of the heart that are good and nutritive, and that promote healthy growth. The other is a reactive approach that takes notice of unwanted behaviors, after they have already sprouted. In the latter case, a greater emphasis is placed on

References / Notes

a. Most parents think only of punishment when they think of discipline or correction, but true biblical discipline is the process of training and learning that fosters a way of life reflective of God's character. The purpose of Biblical discipline is to teach morally responsible behavior, shaping Christ-like keepers of God's moral mandates, kingdom-builders who live out the fruits of the Spirit and touch others with the character of Jesus.

b. There are several transitions children and parents will pass through during the pilgrimage from the toddler months straight to the teen years. The word transition implies a process of maturing where old ways of doing things give way to new understanding and improved patterns of conduct. The six major transitions starting in toddlerhood include:

Nature to Will Transition: A child does wrong as a result of his nature versus the child choosing wrong with an understanding why his behavior is wrong.

Training to Educating Transition: Training teaches the how of behavior, (what right responses look like). Educating teaches the why of behavior after a child is old enough to gain understanding.

Boundaries to Freedom Transition: The establishment of external limitations that are gradually replaced by self-restraint.

Compliance to Obedience Transition: Following instructions simply because authority said so, versus yielding because of a growing appreciation of the virtue of obedience.

External to Internal Transition: Applying outward pressure to conform a child is eventually replaced by internalized principles that motivate him to do the right thing.

Authority to Influence Transition: The process by which leading by parental authority gradually transitions to leading a child by parental influence.

References / Notes

c. In 'On Becoming Toddlerwise', Gary Ezzo and Dr. Robert Bucknam introduce the developmental concept of _capacity_ and _desire_. This concept states that childhood correction must align itself with age readiness. For example, in Chapter Five, we learned the higher conscience of a three-year-old begins developing and the child is intellectually ready to understand the "otherness" meaning of simple instructions such as: "Do not hit," "Do not steal," and "Do not lie." As he matures, his parents begin to expand their moral explanation.

Parents working with child younger than three years of age will predominately work on outward behavior. That is, they help the child become familiar with right actions even though he is months away from understanding the moral implications of his behavior. What are the developmental implications of these factors? It means that a child under two years of age is acting out of his nature and not from a moral sense of right and wrong. He clearly demonstrates a capacity to do wrong, but does not have the relational knowledge to know why it is wrong. Nonetheless, if he takes a toy from another child in the nursery, correction is still necessary, for such correction sets the patterns of his little heart.

By three years of age he reaches a moral phase in which his behavior becomes values-driven. He now has the moral capacity to understand right from wrong and makes many decisions with that knowledge. It is during this age that his parents must pay as much attention to the issues of the heart that drive his behavior, as they do the behavior itself.

removing, rather than preventing, unwanted behaviors. This is like spot treating weeds in the lawn. While this approach will work, it is very temporary. A few weeks later you will find yourself going after a new set of behavioral "weeds."

We can assure you, proactively encouraging behaviors that help children stay on track is indeed a wiser and more effective strategy than simply reacting in a moment of crisis, when trying to fix an unwelcomed behavior takes center stage. Yet, there is truth in the cliché, "Children will be children," and correction will be necessary along the way.[c] What will that correction look like? What corrective options work and which ones should parents avoid? How will a parent know if he or she is punishing too little or too much? These and many more questions will come into focus as we move through the Discipline Flow Chart.

B-3 CORRECTION

Let's face it: life is full of temptations, and that is why young lives require training. Part of the training comes from encouraging right behavior, and part comes by correcting wrong and inappropriate behavior. Correction means to bring back from error, or to align an unacceptable deviation back to the standard. While parental encouragement keeps children on track and moving forward, the objective of correction is to get them back on track.

It is natural for parents to react spontaneously to negative behavior. They see defiance and jump on it. However, before responding, parents should first stop and think about what just happened and then filter what they saw or heard through two governing precepts related to correction.

The first one is this: _The type of correction depends on the presence or absence of malicious intent._ Where do you draw the line between the mistakes associated with innocent play and purposeful mischief? When does curiosity cross the line to snooping? At what point does a misdemeanor become a felony?

In life and certainly in parenting, there are two realms of wrong. The first realm is called, "childishness," and represents the unintentional and non-malicious mistakes made in life. With children, it is often the result of a lack of knowledge or lack of understanding. Your son or daughter does something wrong, but he/she did not know it was wrong. There was no intent to do wrong.

In the second realm, a child knowingly and intentionally chooses to act in defiance without regard to consequence or injury to self or others. The child knows that he is doing wrong, and continues anyway. This is referred to in scripture as, "Foolishness" a heart condition we'll expand on later in this presentation. One of the more common mistakes parents make in the correction process is failing to recognize the difference between childishness and foolishness, thereby treating all wrong the same way. That is neither fair to the child nor a wise way to parent. While wrongful acts of childishness and foolishness need correction, what separates the two realms is motive and intent. There is a difference between the mistakes of childhood and purposeful disobedience. Spilling a glass of water is childishness. Intentionally spilling a glass of water on a sibling is a foolish wrong.

When assessing behaviors in need of correction, parents should ask themselves, "Was my child's wrongful action born out of childishness or foolishness?"

How that question is answered will determine what happens next. Both child-ishness and foolishness require correction, but not the same type of correction.

The second rule of correction is this: *The punishment/consequences must fit the crime.* If correction is to be meaningful, then it has to be fair, balanced, and weighed properly against the child's wrong. Punishment serves a specific purpose within the correction process. It is the means by which parents establish the value of an offence against another person or their property. It teaches a child how a particular action or behavior is viewed, whether it is a minor infraction or a serious offence.

For example, when a six-year-old is told to sit for five minutes in his room as punishment for hitting his sister with a plastic bat, resulting in bruising, the parent established in the mind of the offender and the offended a moral equivalent—willfully hurting your sibling is worth five minutes of confinement to a chair. Is that all the infliction of pain on a sibling is worth?

Whether it is with social policy or the privacy of your own home, under-punishment perverts justice, and so does over-punishment. When a parent says, "You left your light on in your room and for that, no computer or television time for a month," what message is that sending? Over-punishing children fosters exasperation, leading to more conflict, because over-punishment is calling for perfection, which no child can give their parent.

Parents are not being merciful to their children when a grievous offence is treated as a misdemeanor, nor are the needed lessons learned when a misdemeanor is treated as a grievous offence. Once again, under-punishment and over-punishment pervert a child's developing sense of justice, fairness, moral equity, and understanding of mercy and grace.

This is another reason Precept One is so important. Parents must first separate the unintentional wrong from the intentional wrong. Then, whatever direction that leads, Precept Two says make sure the punishment or consequence is fair, appropriate, and conveys the right value and message.[d]

B-4 CHILDISHNESS

As we just noted, childishness represents the unintentional and non-malicious mistakes or wrong decisions made in life.[e] Childishness can also be attributed to age and the lack of physical coordination. A four-year-old drips orange juice on the floor, because the glass was too full to carefully manage. Think of it this way Childishness is a head problem. The child has no intention of doing wrong, thus no sense that their present actions are wrong. Foolishness is a heart prob-lem. The child knows what they are doing is wrong, and continues to pursue it. Both childishness and foolishness require correction, but not the same type of correction. When dealing with childishness, we suggest the following.

C-1 ADMONISHMENT

Correcting childish behavior begins with admonishment (Ephesians 6:4). The word admonishment means to put into one's mind or to warn. Admonishment, then, is to warn the child that an action or lack of action is unwise and that it may bring calamity upon himself or others.

References / Notes

d. Natural and logical consequences are common forms of correction, but, unlike punishment, the primary objective is to train children in personal responsibility, not to punish them for an offense.

e. There is a distinction between the child who accidentally hurts his brother while playing, and the child who does so with the intention of inflicting pain. There is a difference between the child who accidentally damages property and the one who intentionally vandalizes. And there is a difference between bump-ing into a dwarf plum tree by accident and striking it with sticks to make the fruit fall to the ground.

The Ezzos once had a semi-dwarf grapefruit tree. It bears fruit once a year. In terms of size and color, the grapefruit look mature in November. However, in Southern climates they do not fully ripen until February and March. One Thanksgiving weekend, a group of three- and four-year-olds were playing in the back yard. One child saw all the yellow grapefruit and thought he would help Mr. Ezzo by picking them. After all, last week he had helped his uncle harvest grape-fruit (which came from a year-round producing tree), so he knew all about it. All the children joined in and picked a half-bushel of unripe grapefruit.

The children had no knowledge regarding the ripening process of dwarf grapefruit. It was the lack of knowledge, not a malicious intent of the heart, that drove their behavior. In fact, their intent was noble—to help Mr. Ezzo. Their actions were simply childish. What they did was wrong, but they didn't do it to be wrong. That afternoon, they received a lecture from their parents about touching even ripe-looking fruit on trees without asking permission.

f. Considering the circumstances and the child's characterization of behavior, any applied consequence greater than a warning could be potentially devastating to a child whose motivation was not evil. Children become exasperated when parents pursue perfection instead of excellence, especially since the parents are not perfect in giving instructions and encouragement.

⟨⟨⟨⟨◆⟩⟩⟩⟩

"To have Mom and Dad come down on me for a small offense makes me angry, frustrated, and confused."
– Nathan, age 13

For example, Ryan is conscientious and usually parks his bike in the garage when he is finished riding it. But one day, in a rush to share some news with his mom, he dropped his bike in the front yard and ran into the house. He forgot about it. When his father came home, he found the bike in the front yard.

Was Ryan wrong for leaving his bike on the front lawn? Yes. Was it done with the motive to disobey? No. It was a childish act–maybe not smart, but certainly not evil. For that rare offense, his dad admonished him to be sure to put the bike in a safe place each time he finished riding. That warning served to encourage Ryan to be responsible.[f] If Ryan's dad were to find the bicycle in the front yard the next day, he might apply certain consequences related to Ryan's failure to behave responsibly.

C-2 RELATED CONSEQUENCES

Some mistakes bypass the warning stage and require immediate consequences. Those consequences need to be logical and related to the mistake. The purpose of consequences is to encourage good stewardship and to cause the child to accept responsibility for non-rebellious yet unwise actions. When mistakes come, they are usually associated with property, privileges, and personal behavior. Children need to learn the association between their decisions and the consequences that come from their decisions.

C-3 PROPERTY

Teaching a child how to be a good steward of possessions will help him or her be responsible with the property of others. Let's return to our story of Ryan and his bike. A couple of days after the first incident, Ryan left his bike near the front porch while he went into the house to retrieve his jacket, he thought. Once inside, he got caught in an unexpected phone conversation. Ryan hadn't realized how easy it is to get sidetracked!

He didn't intend to ignore his father's counsel from two days earlier, but he took an unwise chance, believing he would be in the house for only a minute. When his dad arrived home and found the bike, he took it away for a couple of days; he had moved to the second level of correction by applying related consequences. That response helped Ryan learn that with the privilege of owning a bicycle comes the responsibility of taking care of it.

Explanations should always accompany stewardship training. As your child grows, however, the explanations should get briefer. By the time Ryan is nine years old, more than likely, he already knows his bike could get stolen or rust in bad weather if left out. Dad does not need to go into these in depth. All he needs to say is something such as, "Ryan, you are forgetting that your bike could be taken or ruined if left outside. To help remind you of your responsibility, I will be putting your bike up for a few days."

C-4 PRIVILEGE

A parent can also structure related consequences to help a child be responsible with a privilege. For example, Cheryl asked if she could feed peanuts to the blue jays. Her mom gave a qualified yes. She gave Cheryl instructions to break the shells on the grass and not on the patio like she had done last time. When Cheryl's mom found her standing on the patio with shells underfoot, she applied a consequence. Since Cheryl had not exercised responsible behavior according to the instructions given, her mother denied the privilege of feeding the blue jays for a couple of weeks. She was also responsible for cleaning up her mess.

C-5 PERSONAL RESPONSIBILITY

Parents should hold children personally responsible for their non-rebellious accidents that affect other people or property. One day, my daughter was playing hide-and-seek in the house and accidentally tripped on the lamp cord, pulling it off its stand. Although it was not intentional, she was still responsible for her mistake. Although she did not mean to break it, the damage was done. We implemented related consequences to teach her to accept responsibility for her mistakes and to help her learn to make things right. The consequence was not given as a punishment but to help her understand that personal responsibility is a prerequisite to freedom.

Based on her age, we required her to do additional chores around the house to earn enough money to help pay for her mistake. Making restitution was part of the consequences. We required payment from her so that she would understand the concepts of labor, money, property value, and personal responsibility.

For review purposes, the first principle of correction determines motive of the heart. A parent can ask, "Were my child's actions childish or foolish?" If foolish, then what punishment will fit the crime?

B-5 FOOLISHNESS

A child is not acting childishly when he is disobedient; he is acting foolishly. The word foolish means deceptiveness, trickery, and deceit. It is a variant of the word folly. Folly means stupidity, emptiness, thick-headedness, senselessness, and disobedience. The Scriptures describe a fool as one who has reached adulthood whose parents have never trained the foolishness out of him. The job of a parent is to transform the heart from what it is to what it should be. Parents must gear their efforts toward one common goal of taking the foolishness that is bound up in the heart of a child and replacing it with wisdom.

Foolishness is rebellion, and rebellion shows itself either directly or indirectly. Disobeying, talking back, refusing to accept correction, and rejecting any form of authority are all expressions of direct, willful defiance. The haughty look, pretending not to hear, pleading ignorance to the obvious after being caught in a misdeed, doing something good or cute to get out of doing what was instructed, and constantly saying, "I forgot," are various forms of the more passive, indirect forms of defiance.[g] (In this last situation, the problem is not only in the child's characterization of failing to remember the instruction, but in his failure to put any effort into learning the lesson.)

Sulking, pouting, and whining may be other subtle forms of passive rebellion. Too often, parents ignore these forms, thereby teaching their child that they will tolerate some types of rebellion and not others. That reaction sends a mixed signal to the child, thus undermining any character training taking place. Foolish

References / Notes

g. *The passively rebellious child will tell you that she "forgot" or "didn't remember" because you back off from giving her a consequence for not following through on what you asked her to do when she says these things. Most likely the child didn't "forget" but rather chose not to remember. If you evaluate her over a period of time, you will see that she is perfectly capable of remembering what is important to her, and not remember the things she just doesn't want to do. The following are some helpful ways to work with a child who is characterized by "forgetting" and "not remembering".*

• *Do not remind her. Instead, have her sit in a chair until she "does remember" what she was instructed to do. She may cry, whine, pout, plead and beg you to tell her again what her instructions were. Resist the temptation to give in, unless you are absolutely sure she does not remember.*

• *If she concentrates hard enough, she will remember. Initially, you may have to work with her with some prompting such as, "When you came home from school you asked me if you could watch television, and I told you that you could as soon as you did what?*

• *Most importantly, once the child remembers, she still receives a consequence for not following your instructions. It may be losing the freedom of watching television for a night, since that is what she did instead of "remembering" to do what you asked.*

If you are consistent with this, you will be amazed at what your passively rebellious, "I forgot" child will start "remembering."

References / Notes

h. *Understanding temperaments will help parents gain insight as to why their child shows his rebellion in a particular way. Children with the Choleric and Sanguine temperaments, for example, will demonstrate their rebellion in ways that cannot be overlooked. They will argue, yell, cry, whine and even tell a fib. Children with the Melancholy and Phelgmatic temperaments will rebel in quiet ways. They pout, whine, withdraw or become aloof. No matter how they show it, their hearts are the same – defiant and rebellious. The best resources we know of on temperaments are: 'Spirit-Controlled Temperament' by Tim LaHaye, 'The Treasure Tree' by John Trent and Gary Smalley, and the Mom's Notes presentations, "Working with Your Child's Besetting Sin," Parts 1,2,3.*

"The 'Growing Kids God's Way' emphasis on self-control was a favorite principle for my parents. As a teenager, I can fully appreciate the emphasis Mom and Dad placed on this and realize how valuable of a gift it really is. I currently attend a public high school in California, so I have a suspicion as to what I would have been like if my parents did not teach me the basics; such as how to listen when spoken to and how to follow directions the first time. It is horrifying (and frustrating) to see the number of times my teachers must stop lessons to repeat their instructions to my peers. I cannot imagine life without this training.
- Victoria, age 17

behavior needs correction, but parents should not correct all foolishness the same way or with the same strength of consequences.[h] Parents should consider the following four factors when rendering a judicial decision about a child's foolish actions:

1. The frequency of the offense
2. The age of the child
3. The context of the moment
4. The overall characterization of behavior

Once parents identify foolish or rebellious behavior and consider these four factors, they should then determine the appropriate level of consequence. When considering the consequence, parents should also consider the first rule of correction–the punishment must fit the crime. Too harsh a punishment exasperates the child; too lenient a punishment fails to put a correct value on the offense.

Since we know offenses range from infrequent and minor infractions to open defiance, correction should reflect the degree of the offense. Generally speaking, a child's foolishness falls into one of three levels:

1. Minor infractions that call for verbal correction
2. Infractions that need some action and which call for more than a verbal reprimand
3. Offenses that require the full weight of parental law

These three levels are not sequential. That is, they do not necessarily follow in order. In fact, in the early years, level three is used more than levels one or two. Parents should reserve levels one and two, the warnings and mild reprimands, for borderline cases that are less common.

LEVEL 1: VERBAL ADMONISHMENT

The first level of offense calls for a warning. The warning does not reduce the significance of and need for first-time obedience. You would not punish a child for a single infraction if he is normally characterized by immediate compliance. Although his infraction may be rebellious according to the letter of the law, it does not require the full weight of punishment, but the fair weight of justice. You should consider his actions a first level of offense given his normal behavior. Admonishment is the proper consequence in this context.

Warnings do not need to be repeated every day. With the earlier illustration, Ryan received a warning for leaving his bike out, not chastisement. He was not characterized by disobedience or by poor stewardship. But, if a child repeats the same behavior daily, his actions go far beyond level one or level two offenses.

LEVEL 2: VERBAL ADMONISHMENT AND ACTION

Level two offenses include new (but unacceptable) behaviors that are becoming more common, old habits that are reemerging, or yesterday's warning that has not been heeded. The consequence can be a swat on the hand or on the bottom and a general rebuke.

Parents can also use what we label a reflective timeout or reflective sit time.[i] The goal of a reflective sit time is to help a child become prudent, foresee evil, and avoid punishment by doing what is right. Proverbs 22:3 states, "A prudent man foresees evil and hides himself. But the simple pass on and are punished."

Here is an example of a level two offense and how a reflective sit time is used. Becky, Ryan, and Nathan were playing kickball in the backyard. Their mom, Mrs. Jones, approached them and gave the children a warning to be cautious and not kick the ball into the newly planted garden. While observing from the kitchen window, Mrs. Jones noticed Becky's lack of caution, as evidenced by the number of times the ball made it to the edge of the garden before being stopped. Before Becky got herself into serious trouble, Mrs. Jones assigned her to a patio chair for five minutes, not as a punishment, but to help her settle down and gain self-control.

Becky's careless kicking was foolishness because she did not take her mother's warning seriously. Although the ball never actually made it into the garden, it was clear that caution was not part of Becky's play. The instructions given by Mrs. Jones dealt as much with caution as they dealt with keeping the ball out of the garden. Her offense called for more than a warning, but less than a level three consequence. Becky's mom used a reflective sit-time when she assigned Becky to the patio chair. She was instructed to sit, not as a punishment, but as a time to gain control of her thoughts and actions, and to think about the course she was on, before it leads to greater consequences.

When used in this manner, reflective sit times become the last stop before crossing the bridge to trouble. The idea is to get this child to ask herself, "Do I really want to go in this direction?" Whether it involves a new behavior or a reemerging old habit, you are calling attention to the behavior and letting the child make the decision to do what is right. If the child fails to respond properly, her behavior automatically defaults to a level three offense.

Using a "time-out" as commonly practiced in our society, is not an effective substitute for repeated offenses that call for correction, especially with children younger than three years-of-age. In fact, contrary to popular opinion, using time-outs as a primary method of correction, or punishment is one of the least effective methods for this age group. There are two reasons behind this statement.

First, the child seldom associates sitting in a chair with the act for which he is being punished since the frustration of the parent is usually a more dominant factor in the situation than the act itself. As a result, the child tends to associate parental frustration with time-outs rather than with the wrong deed itself. The child is not sitting in a chair contemplating the benefits of a virtuous life, nor is he beating his chest and chanting, "Oh, what a sinner I am."

Second, there is little to no punishment-equivalent. A five-minute timeout for hitting his sister with his hard plastic bat sets the wrong value on the offense. The child equates the pain and bruising to his sister with sitting five minutes. Under and over punishments perverts the true meaning of biblical justice.

i. *Reflective sit time should not be confused with the discipline tool of isolation. While appearing similar, there is a difference between the two. Reflective sit time serves a three-fold purpose. It is a preventative strategy used to control physical or emotional energy. This is used in those moments when a child needs to be protected from a surplus of energy. Reflective sit times can be used as a maintenance strategy to help a child realign his thinking and gain self-control over current or potential wrong behavior and think toward wise behavior. (An example is provided in the main text.) Third, a reflective sit time can be used as a corrective strategy assisting a parent in bringing a child to repentance, forgiveness, and restoration. This is the sit time when a child reflects on matters of the heart. Isolation is used as a consequence to inappropriate behavior. We will discuss isolation in our next chapter.*

References / Notes

❦

"During the reflection phase of discipline I would (and do) often struggle not to wallow in self-pity and self-justification. Usually, I didn't or chose not to understand the root issue and the hidden and subtle path of destruction on which I was headed because of similar "minor" offenses. I had to come to the point where I stopped measuring my sin by my man-made scale, and recognize the heart issue that was offensive to a Holy God. I would never have understood the preciousness of the moment if my parents were slack or inconsistent with the corrective side of my training." – Mollie, age 18

j. Keeping your child on track is the goal of discipline and bringing him back to where he should be is the role of correction. For his protection, welfare and the welfare of others, parents must be proactive. Your child needs direction and yes, correction, both are a demonstration of necessary love.

LEVEL 3: CONSEQUENTIAL PUNISHMENT

This level of offense refers to routine acts and attitudes of rebellion, both active and passive, and to moral violations against others, including siblings, peers, parents, and others in authority.

The following scenarios will bring clarity to some of these points. After the workers hung new French doors in my office, my two-year-old granddaughter found it amusing to open the door, walk through, shut the door, and then repeat the action again from the other side. Her father instructed her to stop playing with Grandpa's new doors. Her compliance lasted only fifteen minutes before she tested her father's instruction. Her rebellion was active and direct, requiring level three correction. She did not require any additional warnings, since her father had just instructed her. In contrast, let's assume Ashley had complied with her father's instruction. For that, her father would have offered her encouragement and praise.

Three weeks passed before Ashley came to visit again, and she soon rediscovered the new doors. As her little hand touched the brass knob, she heard her father say, "Ashley, Dad is going to give you a warning; do not play with Grandpa's office doors." Because of the time that had passed since her previous warning and given her age, her father correctly gave her a level one warning. He admonished her to do right, even though he had instructed her three weeks earlier. She complied with the warning and went to her toy box for amusement.

In this case, the warning did not undermine the character of first-time obedience any more than when God told Cain that his first sacrifice was unacceptable and that he must offer a second one (Genesis 4:5-7). You are not waiving the requirement of obedience but judging potential disobedience in light of context, the child's age, and characterization of behavior.

The third level of offense refers to routine acts and attitudes of defiance that are both active and passive and to moral violations against others, including siblings, peers, parents, and those in authority. This third level of offense involves different types of applied consequences which brings into his life some form of attention getting discomfort.[j] Pain can come by way of natural and logical consequences, loss of privileges, restitution, and, when appropriate, chastisement. Discipline methods are the focal point of our next chapter.

Questions for Review

1. What are the two governing principles of correction?
   a.

   b.

2. Punishment serves a moral purpose. What does it communicate?

3. How does childishness differ from foolishness?

4. What four factors should parents consider when rendering a judicial decision about a child's foolish actions?

5. Summarize the three levels of offense.

This Week at Home

1. Using the definitions from Chapter 11, write out a scenario that you witnessed this week that illustrates childish and foolish behavior. How did you deal with each case?

2. From this week's experience, be prepared to give examples of the three levels of offenses, why you classified each act as you did, and how you responded.

<u>Session Twelve Outline</u>
and Chapter Twelve

Consequences and Punishment

I. Introduction

Contrasting Punishment and Consequences

Punishment is used more in the early years; natural and logical consequences more during the later years.

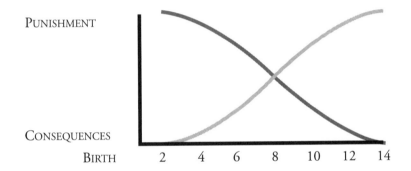

PUNISHMENT

CONSEQUENCES

BIRTH　2　4　6　8　10　12　14

F1 _____

F2 _____ consequences

F3 _____ consequences

F4 _____ consequences

Logical consequences need to be logically associated with the offense of the child.

F5 _____

Isolation pain is the loss of _____ contact.

F6 _____

II. About Chastisement

   A. Definition: Chastisement means to _____ pain with controlled force to amend an inner attitude.

   B. Differences between cultural spanking and biblical chastisement

Cultural spanking is something parents do _____ a child.
Biblical chastisement is something parents do for a child.

Cultural spanking is a reaction activated by _____.
Biblical chastisement is a response activated by rebellion.

Cultural spanking is used as a punishment of _____ resort.
Biblical chastisement is not an act of punishment but of love.

Cultural spanking attempts to change _____ behavior.
Biblical chastisement is used to change attitudes of the heart.

Cultural spanking is performed throughout a _____ life.
Biblical chastisement is nearly completed by the age of five.

Cultural spanking frustrates the _____.
Biblical chastisement clears the child's guilty conscience.

Cultural spanking has no long term _____ or effect.
Biblical chastisement molds lifelong character.

   C. The When of Chastisement
     1. Chastisement is a _____ matter.
     2. Chastisement should not be done in _____, nor should it be done out in _____.
     3. Chastisement should not be done in front of other _____.
     4. Chastisement should not be done on bare _____.
     5. Children should only be spanked on the _____.
     6. Avoid _____ resort spanking.
     7. If you're going to spank, you must be _____ with the standard and your spanking.
     8. The goal of chastisement is not to _____ or shame the child into right behavior, nor to intimidate the child by making the child a public example.

D. What is covered in the *Growing Kids God's Way* text
1. Chastisement and the scriptures
2. Chastisement: When and Why
3. Objective versus subjective spanking
4. Breaking the child's will or spirit?
5. Chastisement and the blended family
6. What to do before and after chastisement
7. Chastisement and your child's age
8. Why chastisement sometimes fails to work
9. Warning about child abuse

E. Summary

Key Principle: Punishment serves a moral purpose. It communicates to children the value of good and evil by the weight of punishment ascribed to each wrongful act.

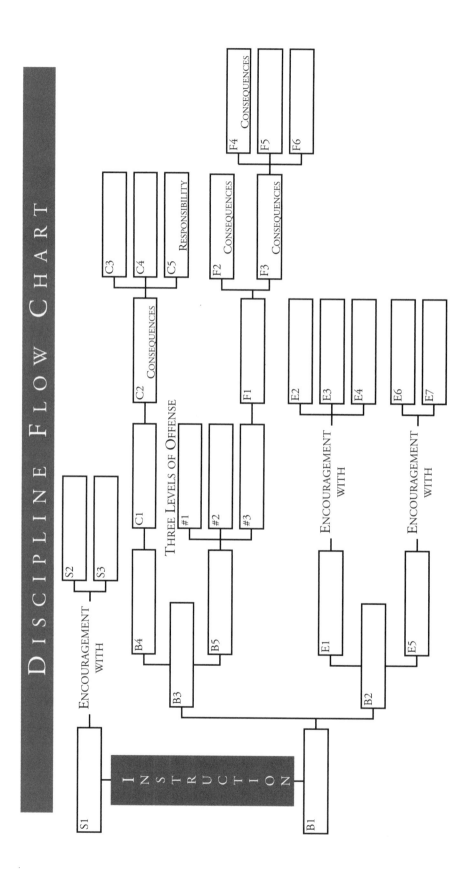

DISCIPLINE FLOW CHART

12

Consequences and Punishment

There are two goals to achieve in the correction process. The first is helping our children take ownership of their decisions, and the second is helping them learn how to make wise decisions. That, of course, comes with moral maturity and proper training. The most effective way to bring attention to poor decisions is to allow children to experience the consequences of their choices. Sometimes those choices result in pain.

Rebellious and defiant acts sometimes produce their own pain as a natural outcome. When they do not, parents then must structure an appropriate form of consequence to motivate change. In both cases, some form of pain gets the attention of children faster than anything else. Man may grow complacent with pleasure, but never with pain. Pain is an educator and comes in many different ways, including from isolation, rebuke, and various forms of consequences. It is one element contained in the overall scheme of biblical discipline.

F-1 PAIN

Pain is a gift from God, not the result of Adam's fall into sin. Pain warns us that something is not right and needs attention. In fact, in the human experience, nothing gets our attention as fast as pain. In the training process, the same axiom is true. Pain has one purpose: it is an educator of our children.[a] It helps a child focus and gain self-control over destructive behavior, whether it is disobeying, talking back, or an intentional discourtesy.

In childhood, the pain associated with discipline comes in one of two ways–by natural consequences or structured consequences. With the first, pain is the natural outcome of wrong behavior; with the second, it is brought into the child's life through some form of correction.

F-2 NATURAL CONSEQUENCES

Rebellious and defiant acts will sometimes produce their own pain as the natural outcome of foolish behavior. For example, Becky's mother instructed her to stop running on the sidewalk because of the danger of falling on the big cracks in the cement. Becky foolishly did not listen, and her disobedience resulted in scraped and bruised knees. In that case, Becky's mother would not spank her for her failure to listen. She would, however, use the pain of the natural consequence to draw her daughter's attention to the importance of obeying Mom.[b]

While serving a useful purpose, the use of natural consequences has limits. Do not let training by the use of natural or logical consequences disrupt or

a. One of the most basic goals of any corrections is that it should promote learning and understanding. Correction requires explanation. Without the why (explanation) of wrong there is no correction, just a random redirection of behavior. Whether a child's actions are innocent mistakes or malicious disobedience, explanatory teaching will always be necessary. The parent's job is to give verbal explanation that moves the child from what he did this time to what he should do next time. Whatever the wrong behavior, use it to impart knowledge. If you complete your talk and learning didn't take place, correction didn't happen.

b. Natural consequences are not effective when parents unintentionally override the effect of the pain incurred. Your daughter pulls the tail on the cat. He scratches her. While Mom comforts the little girl, she says, "Bad Kitty," instead of gently telling her child that this is why Mom told her not to pull the cat's tail. Are we saying that parent's should not comfort their children when they suffer a natural consequence? No, but be careful that your words do not convey the wrong message. (Mom's Notes presentation, "Finding the Balance in Biblical Parenting," Part 3 – 'Discipline Issues')

References / Notes

c. "Fathers, do not provoke your children, lest they become discouraged" Colossians 3:21. Discouragement can come to children many different ways and forms. The Silent-Delayed Parent Type is one example to be aware of.

Twelve-year-old Robby never intended to hurt his little friend with the Tetherball, but he saw how much fun six-year-old Blake derived from trying to catch the ball as it wrapped faster and faster around the pole. Robby's father was also observing the fun and games but offered no warnings about the most probable outcome. Someone was going to get hurt. Blake was out-matched by a boy twice his age, size, and strength. Of course someone always gets hurt when caution is thrown to the wind. What was Robby's father thinking? The silent / delayed parent does not provide guidance at a time when guidance is needed, nor does he warn of impending calamities. Rather, he waits for trouble to happen then reacts.

Silent or delayed, this parent-type does not direct but reacts. The child is not taught to think ahead, consider his context or the potential consequences of his actions. When a situation gets out of hand that could have been prevented the parent reacts impulsively, after-the-fact rather than taking the preventative initiative to caution the child. The long term result is a child who grows up always looking over his shoulder for something that will inevitable come crashing down on him. He may grow up lacking empathy or possessing the sensitivity to recognize the feelings of others. (The Parent-Type Summary Booklet, pg. 16)

control you or other family members. For example, your child loves to go to his preschool play group but twaddles in the morning causing you to rush him out the door, thereby creating a stressful situation. Here is our recommendation. If his play group starts at 9:00 a.m. and it takes ten minutes to get there, do not say to the child, "If you are not ready to go by 8:50 a.m., you will not go to play group today." That deadline only puts more pressure on you because you are left in a state of tension wondering whether the child is going to make it or not. Set the child's deadline for 8:30 a.m. If he is not ready by that time, he loses the privilege of going.

With this earlier deadline, you are not stressed out, wondering if you are going to make it on time. You can warn the child at 8:25 a.m. that he has five minutes left, but if he chooses by his actions to present himself ready at 8:35 a.m., the privilege of his play group should be withdrawn. Do not be a softy and go back on your established deadline, even if he shows up at 8:31 a.m. Children quickly develop contempt for wishy-washy authority. The child needs to learn that some things in life are very exact. An exception, however, occurs when a child is characterized by being ready on time but is late once. Withholding a privilege in this case would not be acceptable, as you may be violating the general principle of Colossians 3:21.[c]

F-3 STRUCTURED CONSEQUENCES

Foolish behavior does not always produce pain. When it does not come naturally, it needs to be created artificially through structured consequences. By structured consequences, we mean that parents will structure the best method of correction for the offense. This may include the loss of privileges, isolation, logical consequences, restitution and more.

F-4 LOGICAL CONSEQUENCES

One form of structured correction is the use of logical consequences. The title provides its definition. The consequence a parent employs to redirect a child's thinking and behavior should be logically associated with the offense.

In general, the purpose of correction is to help a child accept responsibility for his rebellious or non-rebellious actions. The type of consequence is subject to age consideration. It is one thing when a three-year-old child disobeys his mother's instruction and receives a few swats for his disobedience. Suppose an eight-year-old child does not come right home from playing with friends after school. How should that be dealt with? Although the act may be equally disobedient, the consequences may include a different corrective response because of his age. Since the purpose of correction is to help the child become self-governing according to moral principle, parents must choose a consequence that will best serve that purpose. With our last example, the loss of the privilege of staying after school to play may teach the eight-year-old the seriousness of his actions better than a spanking ever could. The reverse is usually true with younger children.

Logical consequences may take place in addition to, or independent of, chastisement. A parent must consider circumstances, the child's age, and the motive behind the action when deciding which punitive measures would be best for the child. Whichever consequence the parent employs, it should be logically associated with the offense.[d]

F-5 ISOLATION

Children are social beings. Isolation means temporarily taking away the privilege of social contact. For example, when one child becomes continually disruptive in group play, one option is to isolate him to play by himself. The pain comes by way of separation. In that case, the playtime is not taken away, but he has lost the privilege of playing with others. Isolation can also be used as a form of correction when a parent isolates a child to his room, not for play, but for contemplation. This approach should be used to draw attention to the more serious offenses.

Finally, isolation is not an "end all" discipline. Like other discipline elements, it can be very effective when used appropriately and ineffective when misused. Isolation as a structured consequence can begin with a child as young as nine months of age and can be used through the teen years. A child must learn that he is responsible for controlling his behavior in social settings. Isolation is a tool that helps the child gain self-control.

F-6 CHASTISEMENT

Spanking children is still a very common form of correction. *Chastisement* is the biblical term commonly associated with this method.[e] The word in its simplest form means to inflict discomfort on a child for the purpose of amending behavior. Thus, chastisement does not always mean spanking. Scriptural references for chastisement are found in Deuteronomy 8:5, Hebrews 12:6-7, 2 Samuel 7:14, Revelation 3:19, and Proverbs 19:18.

To Spank or Not to Spank?

When parents carry out discipline that is thought-out and appropriate to the offense, everyone benefits–children, parents, and society at-large. When parents abuse their children, whether by intent or neglect, humanity sinks deeper into its shame. Where does that leave parents in regard to spanking being thought of as abuse? Should they or should they not spank their children? If they spank their children, are they teaching violent behavior, or are they molding the will of the child for the child's and society's benefit? In this highly empirical day of science, are there any legitimate studies supporting the use of abandonment of spanking? Amazingly, there are none. The key word here is legitimate. The absence of such studies creates an intellectual vacuum too often filled by unchecked, passionate human opinion, which gives way to moral bullying and subjective reasoning on this topic.

Opponents of spanking seem to view any form of spanking as abuse. Any form of discipline taken to an extreme or carried out in anger is potentially abusive. Under such circumstances, time-outs are abusive. Opponents equate the terms "spanking" and "corporal punishment" with words like hitting, violence, cruelty, aggression, assault, lashing, beating, and whipping. Is a swat on the

References / Notes

d. The best form of correction is prevention. Children learn by gaining knowledge, but not all knowledge comes through textbooks or living room lectures. Sometimes we teach our kids what not to do by walking them through behaviors. In the Ezzos' vegetable garden there is a series of brick walkways that children like to playfully weave through. Sometimes, however, little three-year-old feet mindlessly leave the path. Usually young children have no knowledge of plants underfoot. This child would not understand a lecture on the recovery rate of crushed cucumber stems. Education in this case is facilitated by hands-on learning, taking the child for a walk on the bricks, pointing out where he can step and where he cannot. Make the education you give age-appropriate. Just be sure to give it.

e. When reflecting back on our early parenting, knowing all that we have learned and taught through the years, we certainly could have resolved many conflicts with our children without resorting to chastisement. While there were times when it was necessary, there were many times when reflective sit time and self examination would have brought about the "peaceable fruit of righteousness" just as well. Parents please be wise and prudent with your use of chastisement. Personally, our biggest regret back then was the fact that we did not have Growing Kids God's Way, nor a community of like-minded parents to help us parent. You have both! Take advantage of them.
~ Gary and Anne Marie

f. Within the tenor of our times, one might reasonably conclude that advocacy and opposition to corporal punishment is just another battle in the larger cultural war. By this we mean that the catalyst driving the debate finds its energy in the macro, social/ideological battles of our day as much as it does from the single, micro concern over spanking. For example, in the mind of one who begins with the rejection of a personal Creator, is spanking the first and foremost centerpiece of concern, or is the primary issue the fact that spanking is linked to the Bible and thus to God? Does an anti-God stance motivate the secularist to get rid of all perceived God-associated sanctions and prescriptions in order to move us, culturally speaking, toward a God-free society?

g. Can parents raise a loving, caring, and morally upright child without spanking? Yes, it can be done. There are circumstances where spanking would be prohibitive (foster care, ex-spouse will not allow it) so the other tools of correction would suffice. It is our experience that it takes a much longer period of time to get first-time obedience in young children without using spanking, but it is not impossible.

h. Spanking and withdrawing privileges are the two consequences to misbehavior that are the most effective. Unfortunately, some have taught that spanking is unloving and unwise. In fact, it is just the opposite. A two-year-old will not fully understand adult reasoning. He's not supposed to! He will, however, get the message that the spanking will bring. Spanking can be a positive force in teaching self-discipline and obedience. ('And Then I Had Kids' by Susan Alexander Yates, pg. 106)

backside of a three-year-old for running toward the busy street while ignoring his mother's warning really any of those things? Whether one aligns himself with the pro or con side of this debate, there are powerful cultural forces at work that make reasonable and honest dialogue difficult.[f] Wherever this debate lands in the future, it is important that the perspective of parents be directed toward the possibility of spanking being used in an abusive way. Most parents understand that it is not the sum total of biblical discipline but rather one of many tools available for helping parents train their children.

If parents choose to spank, however, it needs to be said that a parent should never spank when he/she is angry. If this is the case, the child should be instructed to go and sit on his bed while his parent goes to the parent's bedroom and prays, asking God to help him calm down. When the parent is calm, he/she can go to the child and administer the chastisement, or the parent can ask his/her spouse to administer the chastisement in his/her place. School teachers, doctors, and other professionals are "mandatory reporters," meaning that if they think a child is being abused because of spanking they are legally required to report that family to Children's Services. Anyone who is opposed to spanking can file a report as well. For this reason, it is recommended that parents never spank their children in public or threaten to do so.

As authors and teaching members within the Christian community, we do not believe the Bible explicitly commands spanking, but it does commend it (starting in the Old and continuing in the New Testament) in both the Old and New Testaments (Proverbs 13:24, 22:15, 23:13-14, 29:15; Hebrews 12:6, 12:11; 1 Corinthians. 4:21).[g] It is an optional form of correction, but not a biblical mandate. We support its use because it is part of the wisdom (literature) of Proverbs and is used in conjunction with righteous training. However, it is not the silver bullet that is meant to fix all child-rearing problems.

CULTURAL SPANKING AND BIBLICAL CHASTISEMENT

Swatting a child with the sole intent of bringing correction through reasonable pain is socially called spanking.[h] The Bible uses the word chastisement. Chastisement means to inflict pain with controlled force on an individual to amend an inner attitude. There is actually a difference between cultural spanking and biblical chastisement as it relates to motive, purpose and practice. Here are a few casual observations:

CULTURAL SPANKING	is something parents do to a child.
BIBLICAL CHASTISEMENT	is something parents do for a child.
CULTURAL SPANKING	is a last resort punishment.
BIBLICAL CHASTISEMENT	is an objective form of correction.
CULTURAL SPANKING	attempts to suppress outward behavior.
BIBLICAL CHASTISEMENT	is used to change heart attitudes.
CULTURAL SPANKING	is performed throughout a child's life.
BIBLICAL CHASTISEMENT	is nearly completed by the age of five.

| CULTURAL SPANKING | has no long-term positive effect. |
| BIBLICAL CHASTISEMENT | can help mold lifelong character. |

Chastisement: When and Why

Offenses that require chastisement should be limited to those related directly to open and continued defiance or conduct where a value must be placed on a behavior or response for the sake of the child. The sensation of pain draws attention to foolish decisions that lead to wrong behavior. Children are impulsive by nature. Chastisement may be viewed as a mentor to teach a child to gain proficiency over his foolish impulses and not be a slave to them.[i] Chastisement is by no means the only way of correction, but for some children it is the fast track to learning.

i. Hebrews 12:11: No discipline seems pleasant at the time, but painful. Later on, however, it produces a harvest of righteousness and peace for those who have been trained by it.

Objective and Subjective Spanking

Parents that train to first-time obedience tend to spank more at first but as willful defiance decreases so does the need for spanking. The higher standard forces objectivity by removing the guesswork for both parent and child. That is the nature of objective spanking. Once you mark a boundary, stay with it for the sake of the child. This way both parent and child know exactly when a spanking will result and why it is needed. The child is the one who ultimately determines whether a spanking will occur by what he does or does not do.[j]

Parents who are not consistent with obedience tend to spank subjectively. That is, the parents subjectively determine the time of correction. Unfortunately it is often based on their mood, whims, and other external factors that are sometimes totally unrelated to the child's behavior. There is no predictability or consistency as to when a spanking will come. The child is suspended in the fear of not knowing when or how his parent will judge his offenses. He tiptoes across the boundary, then dashes back in hopes of not getting caught.

j. If you employ spanking as a method of correction, please consider the dignity of the child. Chastisement should always be a private matter between parent and child. Do not spank on bare skin, nor swat your child in public, in front of adults, in front of unrelated children, and only rarely in front of siblings. The goal is not to embarrass your child into right behavior, nor to intimidate the child by making a public example of him or her.

Breaking the Child's Spirit or His Will?

Parents are often cautioned not to break their child's spirit, just the will to do wrong. Why break eighter? It is not the will that gets a child in trouble but the sinful expressions of the will. And it is not the spirit of a child that must be safeguarded but the dignity of the child. A mother will say, "If I insist on obedience, I fear that I will break my child's spirit." Not so. You do not break a child's spirit by training and correcting to God's standard; that only strengthens the child. But a child can be robed of his or her dignity through improper parenting. A child is made in the image and likeness of God. When human dignity is attacked through improper training, the image of God is attacked. A child is robbed of his dignity when called names (such as stupid, dumb, or imbecile) or, humiliated, screamed at, or belittled in front of others. These actions truly break the spirit of a child because they attack his dignity as a human being.

Chastisement and the Blended Family

There are guidelines to consider if you are in a stepchild relationship. First, if there is no memory of the biological parent, the stepparent will have more

References / Notes

k. What is an appropriate chastisement instrument? Context and common sense seems to point to the use of a neutral instrument that is flat and flexible and does not bruise the skin. An instrument that is stiff and unbending is not appropriate (such as a wooden spoon). Anything that causes tissue or muscle damage including overly flexible items such as a father's belt, extension cords, or anything that forms a whip-like motion, are not good choices either. Regardless of what you use, if you leave a mark or a welt on your child it is probably a mistake. Furthermore, if you are leaving marks and welts on your child routinely, they can and probably will be considered excessive punishment, regardless of how loving your intentions may have been. Excessive punishment of this type is akin to abusive punishment. Please exercise wisdom and caution.

l. Parents should use a balanced approach when training children. There is no one method that is more spiritual than another. Parents can misuse praying with the child, especially when the child does not truly have a repentant heart, and the parent still insists on praying. On the other hand, to never say anything after correction is just as wrong. Many times the child needs to have the reason for chastisement explained in order to learn the lesson. Communication with the child should take place before and after chastising. Beforehand, establish the child's guilt and have him accept responsibility for his own actions. That is accomplished by telling the child why he is being corrected. He needs to know what he did wrong. Never ask, "Why did you do it?" You will probably hear several reasons that, in the child's mind, justify his actions. Next comes restoration. Without restoration, correction is incomplete. This will be discussed in the next chapter.

freedom to chastise when needed. If, however, a child maintains contact with or has a memory of the absent biological parent, then the present biological parent should administer the majority of chastisement, with supportive verbal reinforcement and encouragement coming from the stepparent. These are suggestions to consider, not rules. There are many variables potentially associated with blended families that can cause the grey areas of corrective discipline to increase or would create a condition when chastisement would be completely inappropriate.[k]

WHAT TO DO AFTER CHASTISEMENT
What should you do after chastising your child? Here are the five most frequently offered suggestions.

1. Immediately after chastising, place the child on your lap (if age-appropriate). Talk to him about his actions, affirm your love, and pray with him.

2. After chastising, have the child sit quietly and think for a few minutes about what he did wrong. Then, talk with him about his actions.

3. After chastising, send the child to his room with instructions to remain there until you say he may come out.

4. After chastising, warn the child not to repeat the offense. Consider the matter closed.

5. After chastising, do and say little and consider the matter closed.

Which method listed is correct? Each of the five may be appropriate when used in context with the offense. Exclusive use of any one method will only leave the child frustrated. A parent, for example, who uses method one or two exclusively creates a dilemma. The parent will either go through the process for even the smallest offense, thereby exasperating the child, or will only chastise for major offenses, letting little offenses and acts of passive rebellion go by. Either choice may be detrimental to the child.[l]

Chastisement and Your Child's Age
One often-asked question deals with how many swats should be administered. That depends on the offence, the age of the child, and the meaningfulness of each swat. Between 24 months and 3 years of age, a child might receive 1 to 3 swats. It is about the same for a child between 3 and 5 years old. The point is this: swats may increase with older children and for more serious offences. One word of warning: any parent who is routinely bruising tissue as a result of spanking is spanking too hard or with the wrong instrument. On the other hand, when children smile or laugh at their parents after a spanking, that usually means the spanking failed to generate sufficient pain to get Mom or Dad's message across. That only embolden's a child's contempt for parental authority.

WHY CHASTISEMENT SOMETIMES FAILS TO WORK

The following list summarizes why chastisement may fail to be an effective tool of discipline:

1. Parents do not believe in its efficiency. They are carried along by cultural expectations rather than personal conviction.

2. Parents disproportionately correct wrong behavior instead of proactively teach morally or socially approved behavior.

3. Parents swat hard enough to get the child upset, but not sufficiently enough to outweigh the pleasure of wrong.

4. Parents use the wrong instrument or chastise through clothing that is too thick.[m]

5. Parents are inconsistent with their boundaries.

CHASTISEMENT AND ABUSIVE

What is abuse? Child abuse is any act of omission or commission that endangers or impairs a child's physical or emotional health and development. The point at which a parent inflicts injury, rather than inflicting discomfort that offsets a wrong, is where the line is crossed from physical punishment to abuse. When we look at the characteristics of abusive parents, five traits stand out:

1. Verbal aggression. Abusive parents tend to scream at their children, releasing their anger and frustration at the child.

2. Verbal assaults. Abusive parents tend to call their children names, express hatred towards them, or verbally assault them by degrading, belittling or shaming them.

3. Excessive physical punishment. Abusive parents have no starting or stopping point; they just continue to hit.

4. Uncontrolled emotions. Abusive parents communicate through body language, attitudes of anger, and hostility.

5. Absence of reasoning. Anything can set abusive parents off, including actions unrelated to the child. Because the parent lacks self-control to govern their own reactive impulses, the rest of the family walk on egg shells, fearing that something they say/do will set off the abusive controller.

If any of these behaviors manifest during correction then:

1. Stop spanking altogether because spanking abusively is symptomatic of a larger issue that needs attention.

References / Notes

m. The Bible refers to the "rod" of reproof. The word rod actually has several different meanings in the Old Testament. The rod referred to in the Bible came from a branch of a tree or from the stem of a bush. The context of each passage specifies which type of rod is implied. Just as the rod of "thy rod and thy staff" is not a thin offshoot of a bush, the "rod of correction" is not a five-pound branch. To David, it was a symbol of guidance and care. Psalm 23:4 says, "Thy rod and thy staff they comfort me." The rod was also a symbol of authority and rulership. "Moses took the rod of God" in Exodus 4:20 and held the rod of God in his hand against Amalek in Exodus 17:9. Many miracles were performed with rods (Exodus 8:5, 14:16; Numbers 20:11). The rod was also a symbol of God's anger and chastisement. References to the rod occur throughout Scripture (2 Samuel 7:14; Job 9:34, 21:9; Isaiah 9:4, 10:5, 30:31; Lamentations 3:1). Psalm 2:9 tells us that someday Jesus will rule the world with a rod of iron. In reference to child training, the rod is used as instrument of correction (Proverbs 22:15).

References / Notes

"Your child's respect for your position as a parent is closely linked to discipline. Never forget that you are the parent and he is the child. Do not try to be his buddy. It is infinitely more important for your child to respect you than to like you, although both are possible. He will quickly lose respect for you if he sees he has control over you. ('Parenting with Scripture' by Kara Durbin, pg. 173)

2. Seek wise counseling. Whatever that "anger trigger" might be, it has to be affecting other areas of life, and other relationships. If that is the case, we suggest parents employ non-physical corrective strategies.

While spanking is often administered out of genuine concern for the welfare of a child, any gains are nullified when anger rather than love becomes the driving force. When that happens, the benefits associated with correction are replaced with the damaging influence of abuse. Please don't let that happen in your family.

Questions for Review

1. What is the purpose of pain in the correction process?

2. Summarize the difference between *natural* and *logical* consequences.

3. Summarize the difference between a reflective time-out and isolation.

4. Summarize the difference between objective and subjective spanking.

5. According to the authors, when can spanking cross the line to overpunishment?

This Week at Home

Study the Discipline Flow Chart and be prepared next week to fill in the entire chart without the aid of any notes.

Session Thirteen Outline

and Chapter Thirteen

Repentance, Forgiveness, and Restoration

I. Introduction

   A. Defining Repentance

     "Now I rejoice not that you were made sorry, but that your sorrow led to repentance. For you were made sorry in a godly manner, that you might suffer loss from us in nothing. For godly sorrow produces repentance leading to salvation not to be regretted, but the sorrow of the world produces death" (2 Corinthians 7:9-10).

   B. Regret

     Repentance is not the same thing as regret.

     You cannot repent without regret, but you can regret without repentance.

   C. The doctrine of repentance must be understood in the context of _____.

   D. The object of repentance is not the _____ itself, but the effect sin had on the relationship.

   E. Repentance and Young Children
     Age Consideration

     1. The most ideal state of repentance for children over four years of age is relational repentance.

     2. For children under four years of age, regret is present, but relational repentance is difficult.

     3. Fellowship

II. Restoration

   A. Restoring the relationship closes the offense and _____ it.

   B. Without restoration, relationships continue in a state of _____.

Notes

III. Forgiveness
  A. Repentance begins with the _____.
     Forgiveness begins with the person _____.

  B. Forgiveness is the process which requires _____.

  C. Seeking forgiveness and saying, "I'm sorry"
     1. Asking forgiveness does not mean saying, "I'm _____."

     2. Saying, "I'm sorry," is to acknowledge an unintentional mistake.

     3. To ask forgiveness is to acknowledge the motive of the heart.

  D. Attach a confession. What is it that you have done?

IV. Restitution
  A. Restitution means to make things _____ .

  B. Restitution is an effective _____ measure.

V. Measuring Repentance
   Two Tests of Repentance
  A. The most obvious test of true repentance is whether the child goes _____ back doing that for which he was just punished.

     Why does this happen?

     1. Parents forget to give the _____ reason why.

     2. Parents give a half-hearted _____.

  B. The second test of true repentance is the child's _____.

VI. Training to a False Repentance

   What should a parent do if their child confesses before getting caught?

   Praise your child for his honesty, but punish him for the offense. You do not rightly deal with sin by swapping it for a _____ .

Key Principle: Repentance begins with the offender; forgiveness begins with the offended.

13

Repentance, Forgiveness, and Restoration

In child training, repentance is an essential component of correction. But what is repentance? How is it measured? Does it have to look, feel or sound a certain way? Some children cry just before correction is administered. Is that repentance, remorse, or just regret for getting caught?[a]

Many understand the term repentance to mean "turning from sin." However, that definition, common as it may be, is an adaptation of the actual meaning. The Greek word *metanoeo* is translated into English as *repent*. It speaks to the mind and heart being changed. However, in Scripture, that change has to do with how man thinks about God and salvation. When John the Baptist told his listeners to repent and be forgiven (Luke 3:3) he was trying to get them to change their minds about how salvation was coming—not through a conquering earthly king, but a heavenly king. Not for the salvation of a Nation but salvation for the individual. In Acts 2:36-28 Peter was persuading his listeners to change their minds about who Jesus is, and then called each listener to repent and be baptized in the Name of Jesus Christ. Biblical repentance is always tied to man's vertical relationship with God and redemption. However, within the message of repentance are principles governing the restoration of human relationships separated by sin. How do the principles of repentance apply to parenting?

Repentance and Parenting

Unfortunately, parents will often confuse regret with repentance. A person cannot repent without regret, but they can have feelings of regret without repentance. For example, little Stevie received clear instructions to stay away from the back fence when kicking his ball in the air. Twice he disregarded Mom's instructions. A few moments later, he accidentally kicked the ball over the fence and into the fast-moving river. He felt immediate regret, as he watched his ball float away. However, his regret was misdirected. The focus of his sorrow was over losing his ball and the way he kicked it—not on his disobedience that led to the incident. For a person to regret an action because of inconvenience is neither virtuous nor reflective of true repentance.

This is what the Apostle Paul described in 2 Corinthians 7:10 as a "worldly sorrow." Here, the object of sorrow is the loss of a momentary happiness, comfort or earthly peace. Yet, the Apostle Paul also said there is a "Godly sorrow" that has value beyond happiness, comfort and the status quo—it is a sorrow that leads to repentance and life.[b] It is a sorrow where God is present. That means Godly sorrow leading to repentance is not "object oriented", but "relationally

References / Notes

" My parents started Growing Kids God's Way when I was a teenager. Before that I do not ever remember a day of calm or harmony in our home. We only had peace when we weren't together and that was fine with me. The lesson that changed our family from being conflict-filled to conflict free was understanding repentance, forgiveness and restoration. Even though it has been a long and difficult journey, I sent Mr. and Mrs. Ezzo a thank-you note for the miracle that took place in my family. - Anthony, age 18

a. Children will often regret their actions when faced with the consequences of their choices. Sometimes they are embarrassed after their wrong is exposed, and only then do they feel sorrow as a result. Others feel remorse when they are not allowed to do what they want to do. Just because a person regrets his actions does not mean he has experienced repentance. Regret over an act and repentance because of the act are two different responses.

b. To repent means to stop going in one direction, to turn around completely, and to go the opposite way. Repentance involves a dramatic and decisive change of course. We have not repented if we continue in our sin. The evidence of repentance is not words of resolve, but a changed life. ('Experiencing God Day-by-Day' by Henry T. Blackaby and Richard Blackaby, pg. 155)

References / Notes

"When someone intentionally wrongs me I know that it is their responsibility to make it right, but I need to forgive them whether they apologize or not. That is not easy, but it is right." – Stephen, age 18

c. We bear a responsibility to our children and to others who are watching the way we live. What kind of legacy are you leaving for your children – and their children? If they take their cues from the way they see you respond to pain, disappointment, and loss, how will they respond to life's tragedies? How are your responses shaping their view of God? Have you considered the impact that your forgiving spirit (or your bitterness) will have on future generations? ('Choosing Forgiveness' by Nancy Leigh DeMoss, pg. 185)

"My parents spent more hours than I want to admit teaching me to repent and seek forgiveness. With my parents' training over the years, and the Word of God, I learned forgiveness is a command that can save years of hurt and bitterness. It is much better to forgive, restore a relationship and then enjoy that relationship than to hang on to a hurt and regret it years later." – Briana, age 21

focused." It considers how personal actions affect relationships.

When we sin against God, do we repent primarily over the act of sin or how our sin affected our fellowship with God? The latter is the correct answer. In the same way, when we sin against another person, in word or deed, repentance is validated, not just with a sincere regret of our actions, but how our actions brought injury to the relationship. It is nearly impossible to regret a wayward action and turn from it, if that action has no relational significance. That is why, helping children understand the relational component of repentance is as important as understanding the wrong of an action.

Age, Children, and Repentance

To understand repentance, forgiveness and the importance of restoration, children must reach a developmental age of understanding. For our two-year-old granddaughter, life is pretty clear-cut. Although she is old enough to understand wrong actions, she is not old enough to understand how those actions affect relationships. She may even regret her wrong actions, but only because of the associated consequences. At this stage of life, she does not have the moral maturity to understand the link between her actions and relationships. That comes, but not for a few more years, when her moral warehouse begins to fill up, and she begins to act in accordance to the regulating values of her heart.

REPENTANCE, FORGIVENESS, AND RESTORATION

The book of Judges records the cycle of sin better than any other book. The sin cycle includes separation, regret, repentance, forgiveness, and restoration. First, the children of Israel would commit sins against their God (Judges 3:7, 3:12, 4:1, 10:6, and 13:1). After the passing of time, they would turn their hearts back to God and would begin to "cry unto the Lord" (Judges 3:9, 15; 6:7; 10:10). God's response was always the same: He heard their cries, delivered His people, and restored them to Himself.

From those examples, three related concepts emerge—repentance, forgiveness, and restoration. Repentance begins with the offender. Desiring to have their relationship restored, the children of Israel would initiate the process by turning back to God. The same is true with our children. The first steps of repentance begin with them and their contrite hearts. Complete forgiveness is a process requiring agreement between two parties. It begins with the one offended, who offers it to the offender. Parents should not assume that, just because they have offered forgiveness, it automatically brings restoration. It does not! The very essence of restoration requires forgiveness on the part of the one offended and acceptance on the part of the offender. There is no restoration, if forgiveness is not accepted.

Christ's atonement sets before us an example of true and complete restoration. Jesus died on Calvary's cross, paid for our sin, and now offers forgiveness to "whosoever shall call upon His name" (Romans 10:13). Does that mean that God universally forgives everyone in the world? We do not believe so. While our heavenly Father stands ready to forgive all, it is man who must accept God's offer of forgiveness before true restoration can take place.

Take note of the two components. The offended party stands ready to forgive; the offender bears the obligation to seek forgiveness. Asking for forgiveness from another human being is an act of humility, because we are acknowledging and surrendering our wrong and seeking something another person has that can offset our wrong—forgiveness.[d]

Asking for forgiveness does not mean saying, "I'm sorry." That phrase is reserved for unintentional, childish mistakes. If Ryan unintentionally steps in Mrs. Brown's flower bed and uproots a new plant, he apologizes by saying, "I'm sorry." That is the appropriate response since his actions are childish and void of purposeful wrongdoing. However, if Ryan had received instructions not to play near the flowers, his actions would have been foolish and would require that he ask for her forgiveness. To say, "I'm sorry," is to acknowledge a mistake; to ask for forgiveness is to acknowledge motives of the heart.[e]

We believe this distinction is very important. When we intentionally offend another, we have an obligation to seek forgiveness by asking for it, rather than dictating how sorry we feel. To simply say, "I'm sorry," or, "I apologize," is not enough. Sorrow is subjective and can range from little to great. Forgiveness is objective and has no middle ground; it is absolute. That means, it is either offered or it is not. There is no such thing as partial forgiveness.

Restitution

Restitution is a biblical concept defined as repayment for lost, damaged, or stolen property. The principle of restitution was very much part of American Judeo/Christian ethics 30 years ago. If you broke a friend's cookie jar, you bought a new one. If your child uprooted the neighbor's plant, you replaced it. Whenever financial liability occurs as a result of mistakes or intentional wrongdoing, restitution should be part of the restoration process. Some scholars are of the opinion that within the Hebrew theocracy, forgiveness was not complete until the offender made restitution. Restitution was the outward sign of repentance. The Old Testament law required restitution when intentional or unintentional acts caused property damage or loss. In Exodus 22, Moses delineates how and why this method worked (verses 1, 3, 5, 6, and 12). Zacchaeus in his repentant statement to Jesus said, "If I have taken anything from any man by false accusation, I restore him fourfold" (Luke 19:8).

It all comes back to personal responsibility. Saying, "I'm sorry," and asking for forgiveness are not enough if you have created a financial liability accidentally or intentionally. Restitution must be part of the restoration process. If the child does not have the means to repay, the parent then serves as his proxy and should make restitution to the injured party on the child's behalf.

MEASURING REPENTANCE

How do you measure the legitimacy of repentance?[f] By words, by attitudes, or by deeds? Many children cry before receiving correction. Sometimes the tears are sincere; sometimes they're not. Some children will say, "I'm so sorry, Mom; I will never do that again," until they do it again the next time. Still other children play off the lighter side of their parents' emotions by making cute, little faces

References / Notes

d. Confession is a brief description of one's offense. "Will you forgive me, Mom for disobeying you?" replaces, "Will you forgive me, Mom?" Confession really is good for the soul.

e. The outcome of our lives is not determined by what happened to us but by how we respond to what happens to us. Our only hope lies in realizing that we do have a choice about how we respond to life's circumstances. Persistent unforgivingness is not an option. ('Choosing Forgiveness' by Nancy Leigh DeMoss, pg. 41)

f. An obvious test of true repentance is whether the child goes back to doing the action for which his parents chastised him. That usually happens for one of two reasons. First, parents sometimes forget to give the reason for chastisement. The child needs to know which boundary he overstepped and how he did it. The child should acknowledge his violation and explain why it was wrong. The second possible reason a child returns to his misbehavior is due to a halfhearted spanking. That is, he may have received some swats that were hard enough to get him upset but not hard enough to turn his heart from sin. For that child, the pleasure of the offense outweighed the punishment.

References / Notes

g. *Although true heart repentance should demonstrate a balance between emotions and intellect, there may be an occasional time when a child demonstrates only intellectual repentance. With emotional repentance, you usually see a change in the child's spirit. With intellectual repentance, the change may only be in the child's thinking. Intellectual repentance may take place when a child does not understand all the reasons which are keeping him from doing what he wants. He is willing to avoid wrongdoing based on an intellectual acceptance of the parent's facts, but not based on an emotional acceptance of wrongdoing. For example, a child may not agree with the reasoning behind parental correction, but he is willing to change for no other reason than because that is what Mom or Dad said. Although this should not be the norm, intellectual repentance in such cases is acceptable.*

h. *There are times when a verbal rebuke is a sufficient consequence, that is, when a child voluntarily confessed wrongdoing. That would be the exception, not the norm and would depend on two considerations—whether the child has been characterized by disobedient behavior in other areas and by the seriousness of the offense.*

"Things will go a lot smoother if you can learn to forgive or ask for forgiveness for something that went wrong. You will get along better with people if you learn to forgive."
– Kaylene, age 16

or gestures they found to work in the past. Yet, there should be consequences for wrong behavior. Parents have trained a child to a meaningless and false repentance when they continuously remove consequences on the basis that the child has confessed or appears repentant.

If your child confesses a wrongdoing before getting caught, praise him for his honesty. Honesty is a wonderful virtue; but it is not a substitute for justice or punishment. You do not deal rightly with sin by swapping it with a virtue. You do not justify stealing from the cash box because some of the money taken was given to a local charity. If a parent removes the consequence at every voluntary confession, the child will repent every time, whether or not he means it.[g]

Some people respond in protest to that conclusion by arguing that God does not punish us every time we sin. That is true, and there is a good reason for His mercy. Jesus Christ bore our shame, guilt, and punishment at Calvary. He paid the price and suffered the punishment for every one of our sins. Be careful not to confuse God's mercy with His grace. Mercy is not getting what you deserve; grace is getting something you do not deserve. Both operate in concert with biblical justice. Apart from justice, grace and mercy have no context and become meaningless attributes.[h]

The working of repentance takes us back to the life of King David. He confessed his sin and God forgave him. Yet all kinds of calamities occurred in David's life so that he could learn that repentance itself does not eliminate the consequences of sin.

Restoring without Frustrating

Parents can also frustrate their children by not allowing them the opportunity to surrender with dignity. Everything may be restored in Mom and Dad's thinking, but not necessarily with the child. Restoration is too important to be forced on a child, if a child is not ready.

Children communicate their desire to restore in different ways. Very young children often stretch their little arms upward. This is a signal that they desire to be restored with you, and, as God does with us, parents should allow immediate restoration. Older children demonstrate this principle by attitudes and actions.

For example, we had a friend, who, after administering correction, went out to wash his car. Ten minutes later, the son came out and asked: "Dad, can I help you?" The attitude that accompanied the action was a clear signal that everything was over and that the child wanted restoration. He wanted to be with the father in a right relationship and to enjoy the pleasures of his company. That completed the cycle—separation, regret, repentance, forgiveness, and the sweetness of restored fellowship. For this father and son, the division created by the offense was gone. That can be true for all of us. God has shown the way to deal with relationships separated by wrong—repentance, forgiveness and restoration. Each component must be in play if true restoration is to be achieved.

SUMMARY

Repentance is another aspect of parental discipline that cannot be neglected if family relationships are to be meaningful. It starts with the offender, who directs it towards the one offended. The one offended then needs to offer forgiveness in order to make restoration possible. Love for other family members is what makes repentance meaningful. Without these relationships, repentance diminishes to pointless regret.[i]

Questions for Review

1. Explain the difference between regret and repentance.

2. Explain this statement: "Hatred of sin is meaningless if we do not understand how it affects our fellowship with God."

3. When should you say, "I'm sorry"? When do you need to ask for forgiveness?

4. What is the purpose of restitution?

5. What will happen if parents continuously remove the consequences of a child's wrong behavior?

This Week at Home

1. Be prepared to share with the class examples contrasting regret and repentance. Draw your illustrations from your family, workplace relationships, news report, or a TV sitcom.

2. Was there a time this week when you required restitution from one of your children? If so, consider sharing with the class how you taught the principle of restitution.

References / Notes

i. Parents who faithfully applied the principles of Growing Kids God's Way have learned that by staying consistent with the three step process of repentance, forgiveness and restoration, that their children tend to acquire a deep, heart-led initiative to seek true restoration with the one they may have offended. (Mom's Notes presentation, "Understanding Freedoms," Part 2)

"I am so grateful that my parents taught me how to repent, seek forgiveness and restore relationships. Being able to walk through these steps has saved my closest friendships and I know it is something I will need to know how to do the rest of my life." – Sarah, age 22

14

Session Fourteen Outline

and Chapter Fourteen

Discipline Issues (Part One)

I. Introduction

A. Proverbs 26:4-5

"Do not answer a fool according to his folly lest you also be like him. Answer a fool according to his folly lest he be _____ in his own eyes."

"Do you see a man wise in his own eyes? There is more hope for a fool than that man" (Proverbs 26:12).

B. How parents wrongly encourage this condition

1. Parenting outside the funnel

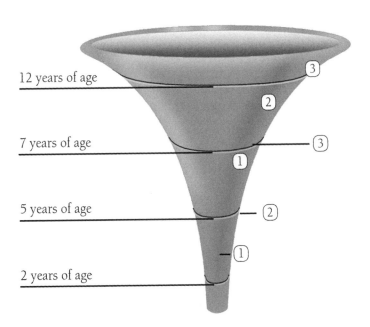

12 years of age ③ ②

7 years of age ③ ①

5 years of age ② ①

2 years of age

2. The three problem areas that make a child wise in his own eyes

a. Premature freedom in _____ making

b. Premature _____ freedoms

Notes

    c. Premature _____ freedoms

II. Understanding the Problem
    A. Premature freedom in decision making
        1. The problem is not giving your children choices, but giving your children too many choices before the establishment of the moral conscience, which is necessary to monitor and regulate the decision-making process.

        2. Young children cannot handle the _____ that is associated with decision making.

        3. If your child can handle not having a _____, that is when your child is ready for choices.

    B. Premature physical freedoms

    C. Premature verbal freedoms

III. Pulling in the Boundaries

    Key Principle: Children are ready for choices when they can handle not having any choices.

14

Discipline Issues (Part One)

Does this happen in your home? It is breakfast time, and four-year-old Jackson enters the kitchen. You have just poured orange juice in the red cup. When Jackson notices, he politely reminds you that his cup is the blue one with the starship. You smile and make the switch. He also informs you of his desire to have grape juice this morning instead of orange juice. "No problem," you think. "Both are healthy." You pour the orange juice in your glass and the grape juice in his. As you begin to butter Jackson's toast, he decides that today he would like jam instead of butter. Well, the buttered toast can be for Mom. You put another slice of bread into the toaster for Jackson. Putting jam on it is no big deal.

After breakfast, it is reading time. You say to Jackson, "Sit here near the light, and Mom wants to read you a story." But Jackson decides to sit near the big pillow. The big pillows are fun, so Mom joins Jackson. Next, you pick up a book and open it on your lap. Jackson, however, picks another story, his favorite, and then the two of you enjoy a fifteen-minute adventure. After reading time, your son informs you, "Mom, I'm going to play on my swing set," and off he goes. "Okay," you say as he disappears out the door. "Thanks for letting me know."

So far the morning has been rather easy—no conflicts or trials. Who said parenting was hard? At noon you instruct Jackson to put away his toys and get ready for lunch. "Mommy," Jackson says, "I decided to have lunch later. I'm playing with my trucks now."

You repeat your instructions in a firm voice. Jackson is equally firm. Things begin to escalate. Soon your little tempest becomes a raging storm - a small skirmish has now become a full-blown battle of the wills. Frustrated and discouraged, you ask yourself, "Why am I experiencing such behavior from my son? After all, have I not been fair with him all morning, meeting his needs and desires? Why am I getting such defiance and resistance to my instructions? This choice thing is not working like the experts said it would."[a]

Let's look back over the morning from another perspective. Who decided that it would be the blue cup and not the red cup? The child did. Who decided it would be grape juice and not orange juice? The child did. Who decided that it would be jam instead of butter? Again, the child made this decision. Who decided where he would sit and what he would read? The child. Who decided what happened after reading time? The child also made this decision.

Jackson has been making every decision for himself. He has gotten his way all day long. He is lord of all he surveys and master of his own destiny. Every

References / Notes

" When my parents saw the need to restrict my freedoms, it helped me to get my priorities back in order. It forced me to focus my attention on obeying and/or submitting my will under the authority of my parents, teaching my heart to recognize the importance of trustworthiness and the self-control of submission."
- Mollie, age 18

a. People will say that children need to have freedom of choice in most everything they do and to limit these choices is to hamper the emotional development of a child. Who cares if he wants the red cup or the blue cup? It does not matter. We are telling you it most certainly does matter. The product of redefining behaviors are children who will not do what you tell them unless you threaten them with dire consequences that they believe you will follow through with; children who whine, argue, debate, pout, sulk, throw fits of anger, refuse to do chores or anything else unless they want to; and children who expect their parents to wait on them hand and foot, giving in to their every whim and desire. If this is acceptable to you, go ahead and "go with the flow," because that is where the flow is going to take you. "Even a child is known by his actions, by whether his conduct is pure and right," Proverbs 20:11. ('Christian Parenting in the Information Age' by Dennis and Dawn Wilson, pgs. 83-90)

References / Notes

b. Proverbs 26:4-5 says, "Do not answer a fool according to his folly, lest you also be like him. Answer a fool according to his folly, lest he be wise in his own eyes." This 3000-year-old proverb is most appropriate for today. What does it mean to be "wise in our own eyes"? To be wise in your own eyes is not a compliment but a warning. It is a form of arrogance, thinking you know more than anyone else and you know how to do things better than anyone else. It is a self-sufficient wisdom that is lacking in the one who thinks they have it. We trust you can see the problem here when it concerns children. Proverbs 26:12 reinforces this point when it says, "Do you see a man wise in his own eyes? There is more hope for a fool than for him."

c. Throughout your child's life, two processes continue to dominate – growth and learning. These activities are interdependent but not interchangeable. Growth refers to the biological processes of life; learning refers to the mental processes, which include moral training and development. With both growth and learning, the building blocks are progressive. Each stage of development depends on the successful completion of the previous stage.

time Mom wants X, Jackson chooses Y, and so Mom changes to Y. Jackson may even change to Z. So why on earth should he think Mom had any voice in the matter whatsoever? Mom's desires for him are merely suggestions or points of departure. What's up with this directive to put away his toys?

For Jackson and children like him, having the final word is a way of life. Mom's instructions are an intrusion. At the ripe old age of four years, Jackson has become "wise in his own eyes."[b] He is so used to making all of the decisions in his life that any change on Mom's part is worthy of resistance. This false sense of empowerment and the accompanying feeling of self-reliance gets children into trouble. Children who are wise in their own eyes will tend to go places they should not go and say things they should not say.

At this age, Jackson is not able to discriminate between non-moral choices (the red cup versus the blue cup) and moral choices that require obedience. From his perspective, saying no to Mom's instruction to pick up his own toys is no different than saying no to her selection of juice. The privilege of refusing the orange juice is transferred to the right to refuse any of Mom's instructions. Consequently, Mom has a problem. The observation that "Absolute power corrupts absolutely" is true even in children.

GETTING TO THE ROOT OF THE PROBLEM

All too often, parents rush the process of growing up.[c] Too soon, Dad and Grandpa are signing R. J. up for junior hockey, simply because he was mesmerized by the latest ESPN commercial. He slides on the polished floor with a plastic sword as a makeshift hockey stick, and Dad has him at the ice rink three mornings a week. Never mind the fact that R. J. is only four years old and hates the cold. Dad is left coercing, correcting, pleading, and dealing with tears, while R. J. is clearly out of his league. R. J. simply does not care about a future contract in the NHL. Poor R. J.—none of this frustration needed to be in his life.

To summarize, R. J.'s dad placed him in a situation bigger than his four-year-old mental or physical capacities can manage. Dad wants him to be like the big kids on the ice and finds himself trying to correct a problem that should never have existed in the first place. R. J. is not interested in competitive hockey.

Maybe you have not rushed your child to the hockey rink lately, but have you rushed him in other behavioral activities that are way beyond his intellectual and social readiness or interest? Your eighteen-month-old points to a baboon on the T.V. screen and you are thinking how to best prepare him for zoological studies at Harvard. Before you rush to the primate section of the local library or rush your preschooler off to a week of math camp for the intellectually gifted, think about their readiness to learn.

While it is true that the brain grows best when challenged, it is also true that such challenges must be developmentally and age appropriate. Too often parents push their children into higher learning activities only to discover that their children's abilities are impaired because they were rushed. In our sophisticated society, we tend to rush our children (or more accurately in some cases, bulldoze them) beyond their developmental schedules. Children in our society are rushed morally, behaviorally, sexually, intellectually, and physically. We either give them too much information or too many freedoms of self-governance, far beyond their intellectual, moral, and behavioral readiness. Like R. J.'s Dad, many parents push their children into activities that are more often a parental fantasy than the child's dream. Three-year-old children playing organized soccer, complete with shin guards and body armor, is a bit much. In these cases, the driving force behind the competition comes almost entirely from the parents.

A second and more subtle way to push our children too quickly in development is to flood them with far too many choices and to give them too much freedom to make decisions. Jackson is a product of this type of parenting. He gets to choose when to snack, when to nap, when to play, what to watch, what to wear, when to come, and when to go. Such freedoms in self-governance are as dangerous as rushing children into sports or academic activities before their little brains and bodies are sufficiently organized to master the tasks.

Giving children too many choices too early allows them to have premature freedoms that they cannot handle.[d] This is evident in Jackson's life. Conflict results because he cannot handle the power associated with decision-making freedoms prior to the establishment of a self-regulating, moral conscience.

Why do some parents face greater behavioral deficits in their children than other parents do? Why do some children tend to bounce from one activity to another, never fulfilled with any? Why do some children challenge their parents on everything—morning, noon, and night? Before we blame ADD, ADHD, ODD, junk food, or bad genes, we might first consider if this child is being parented "outside the funnel." If this is the case, the good news is that there is a nonmedical cure. Such behavioral problems can be fixed.

PARENTING OUTSIDE THE FUNNEL

Childhood experts agree that when a child is at peace with his environment, his learning potential increases, learning disorders abate, and dysfunctional behaviors diminish. So what happens when a child is consistently placed in an environment that is not age-appropriate? What does it do to a child if she is always smaller than the chairs, the toilets, and the other kids? What does it do if she's always larger? What happens to a child who is given too many freedoms, too early? What about a child who is free to direct his own life without parental accountability?[e]

When talking about the funnel, we find it helpful to return to the funnel diagram introduced in *Preparation for the Toddler Years*, (next page). In this diagram the narrow stem represents the early stages of parenting, when the child is very young. The wider part represents the expanding growth, maturity, and gradual freedoms a child is able to handle.

In their all-too-complex worlds, parents tend to rush their children through childhood. In an effort to give the child confidence, parents sometimes allow their child behaviors or freedoms that are neither age-appropriate nor in harmony with the child's moral and intellectual capabilities. We call this "parenting outside the funnel."[f]

" When my parents give me more freedoms, I find that there is also more responsibility. I am glad for my parent's advice and counsel because they have a wealth of wisdom that I can acquire from them." - Aubrey, age 17

d. When parents allow their children freedoms prior to the development of age-appropriate self-control and age-appropriate moral understanding, they are parenting outside the funnel. By doing so, they are creating more parent-child conflict than is natural for the child's age and the child himself.

e. This entire presentation, in story form can be found in Book Two of the 'Let's Ask Auntie Anne' series. Discover the joy of learning through short stories and everyday parents asking the same questions as you. The 'Let's Ask Auntie Anne' series is explained in greater detail on our website at: *www.GrowingFamiliesUSA.com.*

f. Another helpful resource to compliment this lesson is found in 'On Becoming Preschoolwise' by Gary Ezzo and Dr. Robert Bucknam.

References / Notes

g. *Please note that the problem does not start with the child. It begins with the parents, who have thrust their child into a situation bigger than he can handle at his age. Often, parents do not realize they are allowing this to happen. Let's say that six-year-old Kyle wants to watch a cartoon on television that features high-kicking action super-heros. At six years of age, Kyle can handle the stimulation that comes from watching this type of show (for one half hour). Kyle's three-year-old brother, Tyler, wanders into the room and settles down to watch the same program. Soon, Mom is having to intervene as Tyler is now karate-kicking his brother in the face. Unless an older sibling is willing to watch a program geared towards a younger child, it is rare that it is appropriate for children in different phases of maturity to view television together. It is common for parents to miss this.*

h. *The permissive parent is not a lazy parent. To the contrary a parenting style without boundaries takes much laboring effort, for nothing is ever constant or absolute in their world or that of the child. The failed assumption that it is beneficial to allow a child unlimited freedom at a time in their life when they have no self-control to regulate self-gratifying impulses is nearly self-evident. Children need healthy boundaries starting at an early age. As they grow and internalize principles of responsible conduct, more freedoms are granted.*

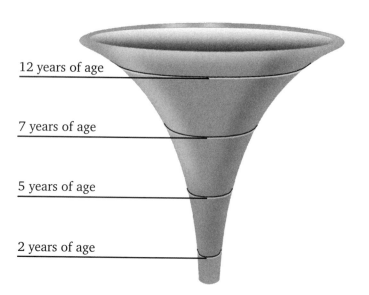

12 years of age

7 years of age

5 years of age

2 years of age

To allow a three-year-old child the freedoms appropriate to a six-year-old child, for example, is to parent outside the funnel.[g] It forces a child to carry an oversized burden he is not prepared to carry. Contrary to child-centered thinking, such freedoms do not facilitate healthy learning patterns. Instead, the permissive style encourages excessive freedoms and creates oversized problems for an undersized child.[h]

BIG BRITCHES AND WISE EYES

No concerned parent would give a three-year-old child a sharp knife and let him peel his own apple. But most parents would consider granting that freedom to their twelve-year-old. The difference, obviously, is in regard to the age and sense of responsibility in the children, because with responsibility comes freedom.

As parents, we are very protective of our children when it comes to health and safety issues. We would never let our four-year-old child climb a ladder leaning against the second-story window. Nor would we intentionally put our children in dangerous environments. We would not let our five-year-old child spray weed poison around the house just because it looks like fun. If we granted such freedoms on a regular basis, our children would probably assume a false sense of confidence in their own abilities and judgments. It is that unjustified confidence that can lead to reckless behavior and tragedy.

When was the last time you heard these clichés: "That kid is too big for his britches," or, "That child is a smarty-pants, and it is going to get her in trouble one of these days"? Beneath these less-than-complimentary statements is a legitimate concern that warns against creating the false impression in the mind of a child that she is able to do anything, say anything, and go anywhere without parental guidance or approval. Simply put, this is a child who has been granted too many freedoms of self-governance too early, and this is how children become "wise in their own eyes."

It is our firm conviction, based on our observations, that more conflicts arise out of this "wise in your own eyes" attitude than any other single factor in parenting. A child who acts "wise in his own eyes" is a child living above his age-appropriate level of freedom. He is living and playing outside the funnel, wrongly assuming rights of self-rule and direction.

How does it happen? What are some of the ways children become wise in their own eyes and thus acquire a false sense of security? Here are the three most common ways during the preschool years:

- Parents grant too many decision-making freedoms.

- Parents grant too many physical freedoms.

- Parents grant too many verbal freedoms.

DECISION-MAKING FREEDOMS—TOO MANY CHOICES TOO EARLY

The cry of our day revolves around choices. "Give children choices in the early years," says the theorist. "Let the child decide, and he will learn to make wise decisions when he grows up." However, that outcome may not be sustained by evidence. Contrary to the theorist's opinion, having choices and the freedom to be self-determining does not mean people will make the right choices.[i]

There is no question that children can be guided into good patterns of decision-making by learning how to make wise choices as children. Allowing a child to make his own decisions is both educational and rewarding. However, good decision-making skills do not rely on the natural inclination of the child, but instead upon careful parental guidance. It is crucial for parents to take leadership in this matter. Without guidance, the child will grow up making decisions based only on his natural inclinations: pursuing pleasure and avoiding pain.[j]

Here, too, parenting philosophies help or hinder the development of wise decision-making. Neither over-controlling nor under-controlling children's behaviors are helpful approaches for teaching choices. The first tends to deny the child sufficient opportunities to make choices. This suppresses the child's age-appropriate sense of control and the educational opportunities to learn through wise and unwise decisions. The second philosophy overindulges the child with too many choices, too early.

As it relates to decision-making freedoms, the majority of parents today are not guilty of overly suppressing a child's choices. On the contrary, most homes tend to go in the opposite direction. At a typical three-year-old child's birthday party, guests are offered multiple beverage selections before they even sit down. And then they have to choose where to sit, who to sit next to, the size of their piece of cake, and whether they want a corner or middle piece.

Please keep this in perspective. We are not saying you should hold back all choices from your children. We are suggesting that you guard against prematurely granting freedoms to decide on issues that your child is not developmentally, intellectually, or emotionally ready to handle. Let's face it, making decisions all day can be overwhelming to adults. Think how this affects children. They might be willing to go along with this freedom you have given them, but the stress it causes them will show up in a child's attitude. And think about this—if a child is ready to make choices about major life issues, why does he need Mom and Dad around?

References / Notes

i. Children need healthy boundaries starting at an early age. As they grow and internalize principles of responsible conduct, freedoms are increased. Also, please keep in mind that the child with age-appropriate self control is a content child. He is more relaxed and secure. As a result he grows in confidence and becomes less fearful of failure. Too many freedoms too early destroys confidence because the child cannot manage his world, and trouble tends to be around every corner.

j. There will be times when parents will need to recall a freedom that their child was not ready to handle responsibly. Recalling freedoms should not have to be done often. You can avoid this by carefully evaluating what you allow your child to play with and do, and by what decisions you allow him to make, given your child's age. Remember, it is easier for both parents and child to give freedoms that are earned rather than take away those that weren't. It is more difficult to pull in boundaries than to let them out.

References / Notes

k. *Parents tend to overindulge their children in two common ways. The most common is by way of nonessential material goods given during a time when the child is not able to understand or appreciate the "value" of those goods. A second more subtle form of indulgence comes when parents grant "too many freedoms" to a child before the child is developmental ready to handle such freedoms. In this case, the child is not able to comprehend the "value" of the freedom granted and it is relationship to personal responsibility. Too many indulgent freedoms negatively impacts a child's coping ability to handled disappointment. If your child is having a meltdown every time you say "No" to a request, you might want to review what your day looks like and who is making most of the decisions during the day on behalf of your child. Have you overindulged your child with too many freedoms?*

l. *A child who is addicted to choice cannot emotionally cope in life when no choice is available to him. That is what happened to Jackson. He recoiled when confronted with required behavior because he was addicted to self-determination. Therein lies the sad legacy of poorly thought-out parenting philosophies. Jackson's parents set him up for frustration and emotional danger while thinking they were helping him to succeed.*

m. *Avoid giving freedoms simply because he is a certain age. It is the combination of age and maturity that earns a child freedom. Just because all her friends get to spend their free time alone at the mall, this does not mean your 13-year-old daughter has the freedom to join them. A common mistake parents make is to say, "When you turn 13, you will get to do that." Try to remember age is only one factor that determines freedoms. Children need to be characterized by doing what they say they will do, by being trustworthy, not demanding their own way, and so forth before they earn age-appropriate freedoms. (Mom's Notes presentation, "Understanding Freedoms," Part 2)*

FREEDOMS FROM A CHILD'S PERSPECTIVE

Remember, the real problem is not in giving children choices, but doing so prematurely and to the point of overindulgence.[k] Is this true in your family? This can be easily measured with a simple question or two. Can your child handle not being given a choice of what to eat at breakfast? Will she have an emotional meltdown if she cannot pick her own play clothes for the day?

Parents can know if their child is addicted to choice by simply observing what happens when all choices are taken away. For example, if at breakfast Mom offers milk in a clear glass, cereal in a plain bowl, and a piece of buttered toast on a plate, would your child accept this without complaint? Try it tomorrow morning. If he comes to the table and accepts your meal decision without complaining or protesting, then your child is probably able to handle a degree of freedom in making decisions in this area. If, on the other hand, your child protests your breakfast selection, grumbles, complains, cries, or refuses to eat, you may have a problem. There is a strong possibility that you have a child who is addicted to choice.[l] How would you know?

Does your child fall apart when you deny him an impulsive desire? Does he debate you all the time—must he have the last word? Does he always have a better idea? When you give specific instructions, does your child struggle to submit, or give you less than you asked? Consider the possibility that he is addicted to deciding for himself—he is addicted to choice. You may have given him too many freedoms, too early. This is no way to prepare him for life. The real world will not bow to his every whim, nor will it always give choices. You are not doing anyone—yourself, the child, or society, any favors by allowing him to be addicted to choice.

MORE SIGNS OF TROUBLE—VERBAL AND PHYSICAL FREEDOMS

Do you let your three-year-old child go into the backyard to play without asking permission? Do you let your seven-year-old daughter decide for herself when she can go next door to play with her friend?[m] Think through your day. How many times do you hear your child say, "Mom, I'm going to..." rather than, "Mom, may I...?" Is your child asking your permission to do things, or just telling you what he is going to do?

How we speak to our children and how we allow them to speak to us greatly affect patterns of behavior. Again, remember that this chapter is devoted to prevention. We want to prevent poor behavior by what we do and say. What we say to our children and what we allow our child to say to us represents verbal definitions of the boundaries of the child's perception of self, including self-reliance and self-governance.

The child who customarily tells you what she is going to do is assuming a level of decision-making freedom that she may or may not ought to have. And if this continues, it is because you have allowed her to take this ground and hold it. Parents must evaluate whether the freedom to decide the matter in question is age-appropriate.

If your ten-year-old daughter believes she has the freedom to come and go at will, then what will stop her from wandering off when you are together at

References / Notes

the mall or at the beach? It is not just the wandering off that is our concern, but the child's premature confirmed sense of independence from parental guidance. This is another type of freedom that can place your child outside the funnel. Please consider the subtlety here. There is nothing wrong if a child wants to go next door to play, nor if his parents consent to this wish. But parents should ask: Who is ultimately making the final decision? The child or the parent? The child that only informs his parents of his decisions but never ask for permission beforehand, is a good candidate for becoming "wise in his own eyes".

How can you change this? With a simple shift in thinking and the child's speech. Try this: Have your child "ask" for permission rather than "inform" you of his decision. Something simple like: "Mom, may I go over to Matthew's house and play?" rather than, "Mom, I'm going. . ." goes along way in bringing your child back under your influence. Young children need the security that parental leadership brings and seeking permission form their parents provides subtle overtones of security while helping them avoid becoming "wise in their own eyes."[n]

How many of these children do we see in society today? Shopping malls, amusement parks, and airports are full of children with too many freedoms. A child who never has to ask permission functions without restraint. And that is something you would never want to wish on any child, least of all yours.

Verbal freedoms are more than just a child claiming his right to come and go at will. It is also a problem of tone. Listen to the way your child talks to you and to others. Is he characterized by being bossy? How does his tone sound? Is he rude to his siblings? Does he always need to have the last word? Is his speech demanding? "Mommy, now! I want it right now!" Does he routinely tell you no, leaving you to wonder who's really in charge? These are all classic signs of a child with too many verbal freedoms.

If your child lives under the impression that he is a verbal peer with you, your instructions and desire for compliance move from a "need-to-do" list to a "wish list." Mom and Dad, let us remind you that you are the parents. Control the tone that flows from your precious child's little lips.

Fixing this problem requires pulling in the child's verbal boundaries. (Do not worry, you will not be stifling your child's freedom of expression, just modifying the character behind it). Here again is that workable, but simple solution: Insist that the child responds to the calling of his name with, "Yes, Mommy," or "Yes, Daddy."

If you are in the retraining process, and you know that your child is going to verbally battle your every request, then establish in your instructions the parameters of his response. "Timmy, Mommy wants you to pick up your toys now. And Timmy, Mommy wants to hear a "Yes, Mommy."

"But, but, but—"

"No, Timmy. "Yes, Mommy" is the only response you are allowed to give me right now."

"Yes, Mommy."

Other mothers have approached this challenge in the following way. If Timmy answers with, "But, but, but," Mom can say, "Timmy, you do not have

n. If your just beginning to pull in the reigns with your child's freedom, then you must have an equal portion of resolve to stick with your decisions. For example, if your child asks permission to go outside to play, and you say "No," and the child reacts with an emotional meltdown, what will you do? To compromise while insisting on a behavioral change only undermines your attempts to bring change. Properly applied parental resolve seals within the mind of a child the significance of parent's authority.

" Remembering to ask permission to do things when you do not have the freedom to make your own decision is not hard even for little kids. I remember as a kid, there were several times when I got caught doing things without permission and every time, without fail, I would use the 'I forgot' excuse. I didn't actually forget, I just decided not to remember. My parents didn't buy my excuse, and they always gave me consequences and eventually I stopped saying that." - Donovan, age 15

References / Notes

❦

" When my freedoms were taken away because I was not using them correctly, it made me want to step it up and earn them back for two reasons. First, I was embarrassed that I did not handle the freedom in the way that I knew I should. I want me parents to know that I can handle the responsibilities I have been given so that I have the right to have the freedoms I had lost. I wanted them to know they could trust me. Second, I enjoy the freedoms that were taken away, so I wanted to work hard to earn them back!" - Courtney, age 13

o. When evaluating your child's funnel, ask yourself:

• Where does your child have freedom of choice? Another way to look at this is to ask yourself, what does he do that he does not ask permission for?

• What does your child do if you make a choice for him he does not like?

• Is your child whiny, bored, argumentative, negative?

• What does he do with time that is not structured for him?

(Mom's Notes presentation, "Understanding the Funnel")

the freedom to talk back to your mother."

Add some resolve to your request, and the problem is usually fixed fairly quickly. The new habit of speech begins to override the old.

THAT'S ME! WHAT CAN I DO?

If you find yourself somewhere in this chapter, do not despair! Choice addiction is treatable. First, evaluate just how bad the addiction is. From mealtime to reading time to bedtime, are you continually offering choices? Is it a way of life for you and your child? Is the choice problem multiplied by too many verbal and physical freedoms on the part of your child?

Second, get the whole family to work together on limiting any of the three problems mentioned above. You must narrow the boundaries. One way to do this is to take back ownership of those freedoms you have given out prematurely. Instead of letting your four-year-old son decide what he will have for breakfast, you decide. Instead of giving him the freedom to decide when to come and go, you start directing him. In our previous series, *Preparation for the Toddler Years,* we offer specific guidelines and suggestions to help parents structure their child's day. That is a great place to start. If your child is four years of age or older, consider sitting him down and explaining what you are up to. "Jackson, Mom has been letting you make all your decisions. From now on, Mom will start helping you make them. Some days, I will ask you what you want for breakfast. Other days, Mommy will pick for you. The same goes for what you are going to wear, what you are going to watch, and how you are going to play."

The breakfast conversation might sound something like this:

"Jackson, today you are having cereal for breakfast."

"But Mom, I want pancakes!"

"No. Breakfast today is Mom's decision. Jackson, I would like to hear a 'Yes, Mommy' from you."

"Yes, Mommy."

There will be days when the child can choose, especially as he demonstrates contentment with you being in charge. But right now you must take back ownership of this vitally important lost ground. You can give him back the freedom to choose after he has learned to accept your choices without insurrection—or even grumbling or whining. Most days, you or your spouse will decide what is for dinner, what is to be worn, when there will be organized playtime, and when it is time to come inside, and parents do need to work together on this. You want your children to find wisdom in your leadership and to avoid becoming "wise in their own eyes."

But what happens when your child throws a fit because he did not get his sugar-laden Choco-Bombs? How do you handle correction in that moment when you are just starting to reclaim this territory? The answer is do nothing—nothing at all. Consider this moment a chance to take inventory of just how deeply seated the addiction is.º The natural inclination is to fix the problem right in that moment. However, you must do more than fix the moment—you must change the child's perspective (and maybe your own) on your biblical obligation to guide his young life by your authority and influence.

ONCE UPON A TIME IN REAL LIFE

The letter below summarizes just how fast a turnaround you might experience:

Mr. Ezzo,

I wanted to tell you how the "addicted to choice" material has impacted our three-year-old daughter. This information came to us at a most opportune time. Our daughter was beginning to have uncharacteristic temper tantrums. She had two fits in which she was throwing things, hitting, kicking, screaming. Way out of character for our little girl.

When I found your material on choices, I started paying attention at home. I noticed that both my wife and I offered her choices on almost everything. My wife would regularly fix our daughter special meals if she thought our daughter might not like what we were having. Our little girl was free to choose what she was going to wear, what she was going to do, and where she was going to play.

I explained to my wife about your choice addiction idea, and she jumped right on it. We both agreed it was time for a change. We explained to our daughter what we were going to do and then radically restricted her choices.

Something amazing has happened: Our daughter is much happier. She's sleeping better, eating better, and behaving better. It was almost as if she is glad to have the limits. I expected her behavior to improve and the tantrums to stop, but I didn't expect her to enjoy the boundaries we set for her. Now, she reminds us if we give her a choice she feels she shouldn't have!

Father from Sisters, OR

SUMMARY

To avoid re-parenting, which is usually less than satisfactory, you should continually evaluate what you allow your child to do and how many and what kind of freedoms you have granted given his age, maturity, and abilities.[p] Are you giving him inappropriate freedoms? Parent the constant factors and control the variables until the child has the moral capacity to handle the freedom those variables bring. Such parenting facilitates our third equation, which is: Freedoms granted that are equal to a child's level of self-control equal developmental harmony. Harmony! What a beautiful word for a child. The word "harmony" means "putting the parts into a pleasing and orderly whole." That is exactly what parents should strive to do with their children. That comes when you move your child from age-appropriate restraint to age-appropriate freedoms. That freedom comes gradually—from the playpen, to the backyard, to the neighborhood, to the world at large. As he demonstrates age-responsible behavior and sound judgment, he earns another level of freedom. This type of training results in a child who is a joy to everyone and has achieved a sense of affirmation within himself.

p. If you find that your child needs to be brought back into the funnel, take it one step at a time. First, make a list the freedoms areas that you see as a problem. Second, begin to set boundaries. For example, your daughter is talking on the phone instead of doing homework. The boundary here has her asking permission to talk on the phone. Your response will be based on whether her homework is done. So what happens if you find her talking on the phone without asking for permission? She loses the freedom to use her phone, (at least while she is doing her homework), until she learns to take ownership of the task in front of her. (See more helps in the Mom's Notes presentation, "Understanding the Funnel")

References / Notes

❦

"I did not feel strange when my parents required me to ask permission for things I wanted to have or do when I was growing up. It got to be a habit that lasted through my teen years. In fact, it has been much harder to make my own decisions than to let my parents do the thinking for me. The freedom here at college is tremendous, but so are the responsibilities, and likewise the consequences when I make a foolish choice. Even now I ask for permission for things when I am home from college as a courtesy to my parents." – Christopher, age 20

Questions for Review

1. From the side-bar notes, briefly explain how allowing a child to progress into his new and expanding world in an orderly fashion enhances learning.

2. What is implied by the phrase, "Parenting outside the funnel"?

3. How does the way we speak to our children or allow them to speak to us influence patterns of behavior?

4. What does it mean to be "wise in your own eyes"?

5. Explain what "addicted to choice" means.

This Week at Home

This week, evaluate the number of freedoms already granted your child. Write them down and be prepared to share some examples with the class. Also, be prepared to share with the class what happened when you decided to remove some choices in your child's life.

Session Fifteen Outline

and Chapter Fifteen

Discipline Issues (Part Two)

I.   Introduction

II. Whining
     A. Whining is an unacceptable _____ of communication.

     B. Why do children whine?
         1. Children know it is ineffective to challenge the parent
             _____.

         2. Children whine because they've learned it _____.

     C. Understanding age-appropriateness
         1. Dealing with younger children
             Teach your children _____.

         2. Whining in older children

III. Power Struggles
     A. Power struggles result when parents fail to exercise their authority
         _____. That is, they allow themselves to be forced into a "must-win" situation over a seemingly minor conflict.

     B. Allow your child to surrender with _____.

IV. Micro- vs. Macro-Rebellion
     A. Macro-rebellion

     B. Micro-rebellion

V.   Siblings
     A. Sibling conflict

Notes

B. Sibling rivalry

VI. Tattling
   A. Instruct children to attempt to work things out on their own.

   B. Acceptable times
      1. They come for _____ and _____ issues.

      2. They come for _____ .

      3. They come out of legitimate concern.

   C. Unacceptable times
      1. Their coming gives them pleasure.

      2. They come without _____.

VII. Stealing
   A. Stealing is a graded offense.
      Stealing a cookie at home from the cookie jar is different than stealing a cookie from the bakery.
      1. Stealing within the family shames the _____.

      2. Stealing outside the family shames the _____.

   B. How to deal with stealing

VIII. Lying

   A. Why do Children Lie?
      Basic reasons:
      1. To get _____
      2. To gain _____
      3. To get _____
      4. To escape _____
      5. To be _____
      6. To balance out parents unfairness
      7. Parental _____

   B. Summary of what to do:
      1. Work on the opposite _____.

2. Consider the child's _____

3. Consider the _____ for lying.

4. Consider the overall _____ of the child's behavior.

IX. The Three Candy Speed

X. Temper Tantrums/Frustration Tantrums
    A. A temper tantrum needs an _____ to work.

    B. Dealing with temper tantrums
        1. With younger children
        2. With older children

Key Principle: Training children to restrain their unkind speech is one of the most overlooked areas in parenting.

15

Discipline Issues (Part Two)

The preceding chapters served to bring the workings of biblical discipline within the plain view of the reader. We surveyed both the encouraging and corrective elements, breaking down each component to consider its function in the overall scheme of training. If any one truth emerged from those chapters, it should be that biblical discipline is not a random field of subjective options; it is an objective method of correcting and encouraging the heart of a child to do right, to love God, and to serve others.

The purpose of this chapter is to bring into focus the relationship between the principles of discipline and the common behaviors associated with early childhood. Those behaviors include whining, power struggles, temper tantrums, lying, tattling, sibling conflict, hyperactivity, and much more.

We desire to make our position clear from the onset. Although all children tend to engage in such conduct, and will try to do so if they find it useful to advance their goals, these behaviors are not outside the control of parents. Even more significant is the fact that parents will either encourage or discourage these behaviors by what they themselves do or do not do. This process is called reinforcement training and can apply to every issue to follow.[a]

WHINING

Whining is an unacceptable form of communication that becomes annoying to the listener if left unchecked.[b] Besides being obnoxious, it is often a subtle challenge to parental authority. Whining is a learned trait, not a warning of deep-seated, emotional problems. There are two reasons why children attempt whining. First, they whine to protest an instruction or decision given by the parent. Because a young child will not dare to directly challenge his mother or father, he will attempt a half-cry whine. "I dooonn wannn tooo," might be overlooked, while, "No, I won't!" might bring immediate correction. The second reason children whine is the most basic reason of all—it works. Persistent and uncorrected whining can wear down the best of mothers. She may become frustrated enough to give in, but not enough to correct the behavior.

Providing an Alternative

The root of the problem is not the whining, but the lack of communication alternatives. Children between 8 and 12 months of age are cognitively able to communicate but are not yet verbally capable of doing so. To prevent whining and to facilitate his verbal skills, start at 8 months of age to teach your infant

a. Generally, there is a purpose behind a child's actions. To achieve his purpose, the child may use methods that help him and drop those which do not. Any behavior that is supported by parents is called reinforcement training; behavior which is discouraged by them is called non-reinforcement training. Both good and bad behavior are subject to reinforcement training. If parents give in to whining, for example, they reinforce it. If they take immediate steps to correct and prevent the whining, they discourage it. If parents praise a child for self-generated initiative, such as making his bed in the morning without being told, they further encourage the behavior. When parents do not give praise, they discourage the behavior. Parents need to be cognitive of the benefits and liabilities of reinforcement training. Positive behavior should be encouraged; negative behavior must be discouraged.

b. At what age might whining begin? It starts as soon as your child begins to communicate. Though halfhearted at the outset and not done with rebellious motives, if reinforced, whining will become either a bad habit or a manipulative tool. Whining prior to 15 months of age usually reflects a limited vocabulary. For example, if your baby wants more food, he may use a half-cry communication to ask for it. Although this is an expression of whining, it is not a protest or a challenge to authority at this age.

References / Notes

c. Work on one expression at a time, taking the child's hand through the motions while saying the word. Begin with, "Please," adding the name of the requested item to the end. For example, "Please, more cheese," "Please, more meat," or, "Please, more drink." When you sense that your child understands but refuses to say it back, use logical consequences to reinforce the correct response. If he desires more food, do not give him any until he signs. If he desires to get down, keep him in his chair. If you find yourself getting into a power struggle, isolate the child rather than give him the opportunity to challenge you directly.

" I was a whiner and my parent took care of it, although at the time I didn't think it was a big deal. When I was twelve I started to baby-sit. That is when I began to realize just how bad of a habit my parents delivered me from. My parents knew the family I sat for. I remember asking them if I sounded like the five year old I sat for. They said " no." Then my dad said, "You were worse." I hugged them and thank them for correcting the whining habit right out of my life. I cannot believe I sounded like that!" – Jenny, Age 14.

how to communicate through sign language.[c] You can effectively teach the following phrases: "Please," "Thank you," "No thank you," "More food," and, "All done." Your local library has books illustrating basic sign communication. Here are four reasons to teach a young child to sign.

1. You are teaching and reinforcing habits of self-control.

2. It eliminates wrong communication methods.

3. Signing aids discretionary correction in the future. There will be times when you cannot correct your child publicly or verbally. The silence of signing and Mom's facial expression communicate the same intent as verbal correction.

4. You are actually teaching your child a second language during a time in his life when he is most receptive to language formation.

Take your time, be consistent, and above all, be patient with the child.

Whining and the Older Child

Mrs. Jones helped Becky become victorious over her whining by providing clear instructions. Knowing the potential for whining, Mrs. Jones said, "Becky, I want you to listen carefully to Mom's instruction and think before you respond. There is to be no whining." Such admonishment helps Becky focus on her weakness, helping her break the habit. The parent must encourage right responses in the moment.

You can extinguish whining in preschoolers by first clearly establishing the inappropriateness of whining in the child's thinking. Second, if the child asks for anything in a whining tone, turn on a stove timer for three to five minutes. Then, invite the child to ask again at the sound of the bell. Having to wait is the natural consequence that will cause him to focus on how to ask properly the next time.

Third, if the appropriate consequences are not a sufficient deterrent, make the offense an objective violation. Have the child repeat what you are requiring. For example, a mother may respond to whining with the following dialogue: "Nathan, repeat after me, 'Yes, Mom, no whining'." The child responds, "Yes, Mom, no whining." Once a child has heard himself verbally agree to the instruction, he usually will not violate it. The use of isolation would be sufficient consequences if he still chooses not to heed instruction.

TEMPER AND FRUSTRATION TANTRUMS

You cannot expect a child will achieve maturity in emotional behavior any sooner than he will achieve maturity in other areas of development. How he controls and expresses his emotions is far more important than the fact that he merely controls or expresses himself. As we all learn from life lessons, there are right ways to express feelings and wrong ways. Throwing temper tantrums is a wrong way. Temper tantrums often occur because the child in the past has successfully negotiated previous conflicts and found parental resolve not to be all it should. Oftentimes, parents simply do not know what to do and give up, allowing the child to gain strength.

To say that throwing temper tantrums is a normal phase of development that children will eventually outgrow only demonstrates a lack of understanding of childhood propensities. Without correction, the only event that is outgrown is the kicking and screaming. The attitude underlying the tantrum is still there. It will emerge again and again as long as parents treat only the symptoms and not the basic illness. The kicking and screaming in protest will later develop into more serious verbal and physical violations. The world is filled with adults still throwing temper tantrums.

A temper tantrum is a rejection of parental authority in that moment.[d] When a parent responds, the goal should not be to suppress a child's emotions, but to help him gain self-control in moments of disappointment and learn the proper methods of expression. Without such training, the child can easily be brought under the dominance of his emotional impulses. As a result, others can easily take advantage of him.[e]

Reasons for Temper Tantrums

Children throw temper tantrums for two reasons—blackmail and revenge. Little Stevie blackmails his mother into submission with temper outbursts. He has found this to be an effective method of control, especially in public. Mrs. Jones gives in to him, only to reinforce the behavior. If a child senses that his mother's mind may not be changed, revenge may become the motive. Some children find that throwing a temper tantrum is worth all the associated pain, knowing it pushes a parent to the breaking point. For these children, that is sweet revenge.

What should a parent do when challenged in this way? The answer will depend on the child's age. For a child under two-and-a-half years of age, either walk away or isolate the child. With very little talking, pick up the child and deposit him in his bed. Children will not indulge in temper outbursts if no one is paying attention. A tantrum needs an audience to be successful, and isolation removes the child from center stage.

Follow the same procedure for children over two-and-a-half years of age. During a preschooler's tantrum, never spank him, talk to him, or compromise with a bribe in hopes of getting him to stop. Rather, inform him that when he settles down after his temper outbursts, he will receive his spanking. And do it. Without a follow-up consequence, a tantrum has real value to the child. A child must learn that he cannot get his way with tears, stubbornness, or bursts of anger. There are acceptable methods of communication, but a temper tantrum is not one of them.

Frustration Tantrums

Frustration and temper tantrums are not the same activity. With the first, a

d. Children with the Choleric temperament throw fits, as the major sin weakness of that temperament is anger. Parents need to stop the anger at the first sign it is coming. Before they get to the point of throwing a fit, most children show signs of their displeasure. Does your child whine, cross his arms over his chest, tell you he does not want to do it? At the first sign, put him in reflective sit time, telling him to get self-control. You will be surprised how effective at stopping tantrums this is. (Mom's Notes presentation, "Working with Your Child's Besetting Sin," Part 1 - 'The Choleric')

e. Proverbs 25:28 provides a warning about the man or woman who does not have control over himself or herself. "Whoever has no rule over his own spirit is like a city broken down, without walls." The word picture from this verse is clear. The person or child who has no self-control over his own spirit is one whose mind can easily be robbed. Protect your child by training him to learn how to get self-control when he needs it.

child's motor skills and ability to control his environment are not yet matched with his perceptual ability. For example, when Becky tried to place her dolls in a circle, one kept toppling over. She knew in her mind what she wanted to do but could not physically make it happen. Frustration tantrums take place when children know what they want to accomplish but do not know how to accomplish it. Frustration is the root problem and not rebellion, since the basis of the tantrum does not relate to parental instruction.

We naturally desire to help our children when they get emotionally upset. However, do not be too quick to jump in. Make yourself available, but first insist that the child ask for your help. A simple statement such as, "Mom will help you if you want, but you must ask me," puts the burden of cooperative problem-solving on the child. This virtue will be needed later in life. If you sense a growing frustration and there is no hope of resolving it, then playtime is over.

POWER STRUGGLES

A power struggle results when parents fail to exercise their authority wisely. That is, they allow themselves to be forced into a "must-win" situation over a seemingly minor conflict. There will be some early parent/child conflicts in which parental resolve must be victorious, but you should choose well which hill you are willing to die on. Wise parenting is superior to power parenting.

The gas heater was off limits to 18-month-old Ryan. When he touched it, he received a verbal reprimand from Mom and a swat on his hand. Undeterred, he began to bang on it again. Once more he heard the word, "no" and received a second swat. He looked at her, then touched it a third time, and then a fourth. Back and forth they went. Ryan's mom is now in a full-blown power struggle. If she gives up, Ryan learns that persistence pays off and obedience is optional. If she continues swatting him, she moves perilously close to abuse.[f]

This is a common scenario played out by toddlers and young children. There is a way to defuse the potential power struggle and maintain the integrity of your authority. Drawing from our example above, Ryan's mom, after the second swat, should have isolated Ryan to his crib or physically moved him to another room. In either case, she would wisely exercise parental authority and defuse the power struggle.

DISHONESTY

Both authoritarian and permissive parents raise children with a heightened propensity for dishonesty. The parents who raise their child subject to strict discipline, in which spanking is the answer for everything, will find that their child will attempt to escape the inevitable punishment by using a form of dishonesty that brings immunity. Children raised under permissive and democratic methods of parenting are not looking for escapes as much as ways to usurp power and influence those blocking their goals. They calculate their dishonesty and attempt to deceive others in hopes of gaining an advantage for themselves. The three related sister sins of dishonesty are lying, stealing, and cheating.

f. Children should be allowed the freedom to surrender with dignity. Let's return to Ryan and the gas heater to demonstrate this concept. A child will often defy a parent when the parent makes the option of surrender intolerable. That is, a child will persist with wrong behavior if a parent does not give him room to surrender with dignity. When Ryan's mom battled him toe-to-toe, her very presence made surrendering to her authority difficult, if not impossible. If she had walked away from him after her second swat and verbal reprimand, he most likely would have left the gas heater alone. Mom's presence extended the conflict. By leaving, he would have room to surrender with dignity rather than face a continued challenge. If she had to go back a third time, then removing Ryan would have been the best option. Again, this is wisdom parenting, not power parenting.

Lying—The Ultimate Family Sin

Honesty is more than simply not lying; however, one of the most common forms of dishonesty is lying.[g] Everyone lies, both adults and children. Psalm 58:3 says, "The wicked are estranged from the womb; they go astray as soon as they are born, speaking lies." That means man is not a liar because he lies, but he lies because he is a liar. One of the six abominations listed in Proverbs 6:16-19 is a lying tongue. Proverbs 12:22 states, "Lying lips are an abomination to the Lord." Lying is an insidious and grievous sin destroying all certainty.[h] It attacks and destroys the bridge of confidence and trust linking each family member to the others. Weaken one link and you weaken them all.[i]

What to Do When Your Child Lies

What should you do when your child lies? Consider the following factors: the child's age, motive for lying, and characterization of behavior.

CONSIDER THE CHILD'S AGE

When determining the appropriate consequences for lying, a parent should first consider the child's age. The lie of a three-year-old is different from that of a ten-year-old. The younger the child, the more shallow will be his moral, relational, and family experience. The three-year-old child does not understand how his lie impacts his relationship with Mom, Dad, or siblings. An older child, however, is more advanced in his understanding of close relationships. Lying by a preteen or a teen is devastating because it is a barometer measuring what the child thinks of the people around him. Punishment in such cases serves to cause regret but usually not repentance.

CONSIDER THE MOTIVE FOR LYING

Many times parents are the unintentional cause of their child's lie. Listed below are seven basic reasons for lying. They are not presented to defend lying but to examine motivation. Rather than excuse lying, these reasons may help to understand it better. Children may lie for the following reasons:

1. To get attention
2. To gain control over an object or relationship
3. To get revenge
4. To escape responsibility
5. To get accepted
6. To balance out the parents' unfairness
7. Because of parental example

First, parents need to consider these seven possible motivations. If a child is lying to gain revenge, then the job of the parent is to teach him how to let God handle the fairness or unfairness of the situation. If his motivation is to get accepted, examine your parenting practices, looking for subtle ways you or his siblings might be communicating nonacceptance. Go through the list, honestly evaluating the possibility that you may be indirectly causing your child to be

g. *Colossians 3:9-10 tells us, "Do not lie to one another, since you have put off the old man with his deeds, and have put on the new man who is renewed in knowledge according to the image of Him who created him." One reason Paul makes this appeal is because of the impact lies have on the truth of the gospel. For it is very difficult to proclaim God's truth to your sphere of influence, including your children, if you are known as a person who is characterized by lying, deception, or jesting. Psalm 51:6 says, "Behold, You desire truth in the inward parts, and in the hidden part You will make me to know wisdom."*

h. *Telling half-truths, being deceptive, exaggerating, little "white" lies, "I do not remember," "I forgot," and "I do not know" are all forms of lying. Never let lying go unpunished. Have your child sit until he is willing to seek forgiveness for the lie. Chastisement is the most effective correction for lying. (Mom's Notes presentation, "Working with Your Child's Besetting Sin," Part 2 – 'The Sanguine')*

i. *Children with the Sanguine temperament's greatest weakness is lying. They lie because they do not want to get into trouble. When people with this temperament understand their chronic lying destroys other's faith and trust in them, and as a result, they will lose the approval of others, this will help direct them to truthfulness." (Mom's Notes presentation, "Working with Your Child's Besetting Sin," Part 2 – The Sanguine")*

References / Notes

j. A person addicted to the pleasure of gossip is called an abomination by God (Proverbs 6:19). There can be restoration with the one who lies and then seeks forgiveness. Likewise, there can be restitution for the one who steals the possessions of another. But the one who steals another man's good reputation by slanderous gossip can never pay back what he has taken. His life must be spent knowing he can never pay back what he has illegally taken and for this he or she will answer to God. The warning is simple: mind your own business, and do not be quick to involve yourself in the scandals of others. Learn for yourself and teach your children that slanderous gossip is destructive. Guard your tongue.

k. Children quickly learn how to cheat. Unfortunately, they often learn it from their parents. How morally credible can a parent be who says to his child, "Tell them you are only 12 years old, then they will let you in free"? Not very credible. Do you sometimes let your children cheat at games, hoping they will find pleasure in victory? How backward is such thinking! Children never feel good about themselves at the expense of sin.

dishonest. Again, knowing the motive does not justify the lie itself, but it does give you a starting point toward correction of this sinful behavior.

CONSIDER THE CHARACTERIZATION OF BEHAVIOR

There is a difference, of course, between the child who habitually lies and the one who does so in a moment of weakness. The one who is characterized by lying is saying loudly that relationships mean very little. That child is consumed with self-interest and is not capable of rightly relating to others. For him, lying is a pragmatic act, so honesty is not a value worth upholding.

The child who is not characterized by lying should not receive the same punishment as the one who is, but should still receive the same explanation of the importance of honesty, trust, and family loyalty. The consequence a parent should apply must be in light of the rarity of the offense.

Stealing

Stealing is another cancer that attacks the family's immune system. Unlike lying, the sin of stealing is a graded offense. That is, the offenses may be graded according to the seriousness of the theft. Taking a cookie from the jar without permission carries a different weight of punishment than stealing $100 from Dad's wallet. The punishment must equal the crime. More significant is the context of thievery. Two children may steal items of similar value, but for one the sin may be much greater. There is a difference between the child who steals a cookie from a jar and the one who steals a cookie from a bakery. Stealing within the family shames the child; stealing outside the family shames the family.

A theft is not always tangible. We can steal someone's time as well as their wallet. But the most perfidious way to rob another human being is to steal their good reputation.[j] Gossip destroys reputations, which can never be completely restored no matter how hard one tries. Unlike smoke, which fades away quickly, gossip and slander is a long-lasting toxic cloud.

Cheating

Cheating is an act of deceiving or defrauding another. Teachers throughout the years have claimed that, when you cheat, you are only hurting yourself. The biblical description of the effects of cheating is not limited to oneself but includes others. Scripture twice calls cheating an abomination. Proverbs 11:1 says, "Dishonest scales are an abomination to the Lord, but a just weight is his delight." Proverbs 20:10 says, "Diverse weights and diverse measures are both like an abomination to the Lord." The word abomination is not a pretty one. In both a general and a contextual sense, it refers to something that is repulsive, disgusting, wicked, and foul. What God calls an abomination should be avoided. God loathes attempts to take advantage of another by cheating.[k]

SIBLINGS AND CONFLICT

When we consider the various brothers and sisters mentioned in the Bible, we might draw the conclusion that sibling conflict is legitimate. Cain and Abel, Jacob and Esau, and Joseph and his brothers are a few examples of sibling problems. From the earliest days of human history, sin has worked at ruining what could be the most precious of all relationships. In His punishment of Cain, God made it clear that He would not tolerate those who do not consider themselves to be their brother's keeper. So sacred was the role of siblings that Jesus and the Apostles referred to the relationships among believers as brothers and sisters in Christ. "Whoever does not practice righteousness is not of God, nor is he who does not love his brother" (1 John 3:10b).

Sibling conflict is not simply a phase that children go through but a moral and relational weakness in need of strengthening. Although sibling conflict is very frustrating for any parent to observe, maintaining biblical love between siblings is hard work, but it can be done. Here are a few suggestions to help you have a more harmonious family.

Resolving Conflict

1. Teach your children how to resolve their own conflicts.[1]

Our children learned very early that peaceably resolving their own conflicts was far better than having Dad come and resolve them.

No Tattling

2. Make a rule of no tattling.

Children bring reports to their parents about siblings for many reasons; some are legitimate, and others are not. The legitimate reasons include health and safety concerns or the honest desire for parental intervention and justice. With the latter, the child has learned that it is much better to have his parents provide justice than for him to strike back at a sibling.

A sure sign of actual tattling is when a brother or sister snitches for the single purpose or pleasure of getting another sibling in trouble. This is known as malice, the desire to see others suffer or receive pain. In the hierarchy of childhood crimes, this action may be one of the worst offenses.[m] Often, it is done in hopes of gaining both parental approval and assistance—approval for not being the one doing wrong, and assistance in gaining the upper hand on his sibling by bringing the matter to his parents' attention.

Our children knew the difference between coming out with a legitimate concern and coming to get her sister in trouble. Humility instead of a haughty heart permitted one sibling to report on another. How can a parent know if what they are hearing is a legitimate concern or tattling? Look at the child. Evil intent will manifest itself on the child's face and in his attitude. A parent can see a pure heart in the eyes of the child, and a parent can also see evil imaginations. Proverbs 14:25 says, "A true witness delivers souls, but a deceitful witness speaks lies."

Demonstrate Verbal and Physical Kindness

3. Require verbal and physical kindness among the siblings.

References / Notes

" I think the way my parents have trained me has made a great difference in my relationships with my siblings. I know some teens, even Christian ones, who seem to hate their own siblings, never wanting to be around them, and they are always putting them down. My family is not like that; we genuinely love each other, and although we have the occasional clash now and then as everyone does, we are always able to restore the relationships, due to the principles we have been taught."
– Kara, age 14

l. Sibling conflict is different from sibling rivalry. Rivalry takes place when, either in actuality or not, a child perceives that he is not loved. First, he may act out to gain his parents' attention. If that does not work, he will act up against his parents.

m. Do not leave a tattling attitude unchallenged. Unkind speech only fosters sibling conflict. In our home, the tattler received our attention more than the sibling she was tattling on. Tattling in Scripture is closely associated with gossip, tale bearing, and being a busybody (Proverbs 18:8: "The words of a talebearer are as wounds, and they go down into the innermost parts of the belly." Proverbs 26:20: "Where no wood is, there the fire goeth out: so where there is no talebearer, the strife ceaseth." 1 Timothy 5:13: "And with all they learn to be idle, wandering about from house to house; and not only idle, but tattlers also and busybodies, speaking things which they ought not." 1 Peter 4:15: "But let none of you suffer as a murderer, or as a thief, or as an evildoer, or as a busybody in other men's matters.')

References / Notes

n. Teach your children to love sacrificially. Ultimately, your desire should be to bring your child to the point of Christ-likeness, demonstrating God's love in self-generated action. "Greater love has no one than this, that one lay down his life for his friends" (John 15:13). Your children did not choose the family to which they would belong. Do not be satisfied with siblings who just tolerate each other. Instead, aim for the higher standard of sacrificial love. We have found that the way a child treats his siblings is often the way he or she will treat his future spouse and children. Do not curse your future grandchildren by not encouraging sufficient love between brothers and sisters now.

o. Parents can teach their children (8 years old and up) to resolve the conflicts that arise between them by having them sit together in a quiet place. Give them a time limit to get this done, telling them you will check back in 10 minutes. When they say they are done, ask if they have worked through the repentance, forgiveness and restoration process with each other. (Mom's Notes presentation, "Dealing with Sibling Conflict," Part 1)

Teach verbal and physical self-control. Give your children guidance in relation to their treatment of siblings and friends.[n] These include no hitting, pushing, talking back, or the general lack of self-control (Proverbs 15:1, 29:11). Take advantage of family times (such as at the dinner table or driving in the car) to share what each one appreciates about another member of the family.

NO HITTING OR PUSHING

One common-sense rule is for children to keep their hands to themselves. If a sibling gets hit, rather than strike back, he must have the confidence to know that his parents will bring justice. The Scriptures are clear that Christians are not to "return evil with evil" (Romans 12:17). The door of escape is not retaliation, but seeking out the one in charge, whether it be Mom at home or a teacher on the playground. Justice comes from rightly exercised authority.

NO BAD TALK

You have heard it said, "If you do not have something nice to say, do not say anything at all." Your children should never speak poorly to each other.[o] Evil intended remarks such as, "I do not love you," "You're dumb," or threats like, "I'm going to tell," are unacceptable in a Christian home. Keep watch! Training children to restrain their unkind speech is one of the most overlooked areas in parenting (Proverbs 15:4, 16:27, 17:20; Eph. 5:4; James 1:26). Children should not simply learn how to avoid the wrong, but learn how to esteem others.

Esteem Others

Teach your children how to respect each other. The following areas of training are often overlooked:

1. Listening attentively to a brother or a sister

2. Responding with the basic courtesies and greetings such as, "Please," "Thank you," "Good night," "I'm sorry," or, "Will you forgive me?"

3. Interrupting properly, with only one person speaking at a time

4. Sharing property that is reasonable to share

5. Praying for brothers and sisters

6. Being happy when something good happens to a sibling

As you train your children to esteem others, you must teach them the moral reason for doing so! Knowing God's moral reason will ultimately bring them to love siblings in a sacrificial way.

SUMMARY

Some parents see the need to make their children happy as their duty, never recognizing that this treatment may deprive their little ones of the strength that comes from wise restrictions and loving corrections. These parents give minimal guidance, and may even consider guidance to be an intrusion into the child's personality. They bend over backwards to allow the child self-expression regardless of any offensiveness. They avoid correction or calling a child's errors to his attention so as not to give the child an inferiority complex.

Children need help in knowing what is good for them. Loving restrictions and consistent correction are ways of communicating concretely to the child that he or she is loved. Only when children are sure that their parents care about their actions can they feel desirous of following their parents' lead.

Questions for Review

1. What three steps will help to extinguish whining in older children?

   a.

   b.

   c.

2. How do you correct a temper tantrum for:

   a. children who are younger than two-and-a-half?

   b. children who are over two-and-a-half?

3. What is a power struggle? How can you avoid it?

4. Why is lying so devastating to the family, especially in the teen years?

References / Notes

" If my parents did not teach me to have self-control, I would be ill-tempered, loud, and most likely obnoxious. Basically, that's how kids without self-control seem to be to me, so I am guessing I would not be any different." – Kassidy, age 13

" Because my parents taught me self-control, I am better able to focus and concentrate as a baseball pitcher even when an umpire makes a bad call. I can complete my schoolwork every day in a timely manner, and I have been able to make progress in other areas of my life that I would not have been able to otherwise." – Stephen, age 14

5. Why is stealing another person's good reputation so damaging? What should you teach your child about guarding his tongue?

6. How can a parent know whether his child is tattling or only voicing a legitimate concern?

This Week at Home

Be prepared to give an example of how you were able to encourage your children to be happy when something good happened to one of their siblings.

Session Sixteen Outline

and Chapter Sixteen

The Appeal Process

I. Introduction
 A. Scriptural Commands
   1. Colossians 3:20—"Children, obey your parents, for this is well pleasing to the Lord."

   2. Colossians 3:21—"Fathers, do not exasperate your children."

 B. Bridging the Two Commands
   The appeal process allows you as parents to rightly exercise your authority, while saving your children from unnecessary _____.

 C. Television Example

 D. The Biblical Precedent
   1. Daniel 1:8-16

   2. Paul—Acts 25:11, Philemon verse 10

II. How Does the Appeal Process Work?
 A. To activate the appeal process, the _____ must initiate the conversation with the parent by providing _____ information, realizing that, "Yes," "No," and, "Maybe" are all possible answers.

 B. Examples of the appeal process
   1. Scenario One

   2. Scenario Two

III. Guidelines for Making an Appeal
 A. The appeal process is only for children who are old enough to understand the concept and who are characterized by first-time _____.

 B. The appeal must be made to the parent currently giving _____. That is, if Dad is instructing, the child cannot take his appeal to Mom.

C. Parents should only entertain an appeal when the child comes in _____.

D. Appeals can only be made _____. In other words, a child cannot repeat or plead his case.

E. Start by teaching your children to use the exact phrase, "May I _____."

F. The appeal process is a _____, not a way to avoid objectionable tasks or to get out of personal responsibility.

G. If the appeal process is to work effectively, parents must be _____ and flexible. Think about why you say no. Is there a good reason it cannot sometimes be yes?

IV. Teaching Your Children to Make an Appeal
   A. Sit down with your children and work through the principles, examples, and guidelines of this lesson.

   B. Set up a few scenarios that might fit your family situation. Include in each an example of how to correctly and incorrectly make an appeal.

   C. Once your children have mastered the concepts, test them. Allow the natural consequences of wrong choices to reinforce your training.

Key Principle: The 'Appeal Process' helps make obedience attractive.

16

The Appeal Process

References / Notes

" The appeal process helps balance an awkward situation. It prevents me from not knowing what to do in certain situations or from doing something I might regret later on."
– Russell, age 16

Authoritarian and permissive parents have difficulty assimilating the concept of appealing to authority. The first sees authority as absolute, regardless of parental error or misjudgment. The second rejects the role of authority, and therefore has no use for its safeguards. For those standing between these extremes, the appeal process can help bring authority into focus. To appeal to authority is to acknowledge another's rule in your life. To be in a position of leadership and to hear an appeal is to accept our human imperfection. Remember, we are not perfect parents continuously making perfect and informed decisions.[a]

THE NEED FOR AN APPEAL

In Chapter Nine, we described the character of obedience as immediate, complete, and without complaint or challenge. That response is a difficult task to require of a child. Therefore, sensitivity must be present throughout the training process, or we risk emotionally exasperating our children. Discernment dictates that a parent not ask a child to turn off an approved television program only a few minutes before its conclusion. Nor would a discerning parent ask a child to put away a game if it were very near completion. Those are the types of actions that unnecessarily frustrate children and thus violate the admonishment of Colossians 3:21 and Ephesians 6:4.

Yet, even the most discerning parent will, at times, be insensitive to special situations. That is precisely why the appeal process is necessary. The child becomes proactive in providing needed information that will help the parent make an informed decision about his or her previous instruction.

For example, Mrs. Jones did not realize that only five minutes remained before Nathan's video was over when she instructed him to wash up for dinner. As a result, tension existed between instruction and compliance. Should he leave the program and be frustrated but obedient, or should he risk disobeying his mother in order to satisfy his desire to watch the story's conclusion?

Given these circumstances, obedience would leave Nathan in a state of exasperation, violating Colossians 3:21.[b] If he took a chance and ignored her instruction, his disobedience would violate Colossians 3:20. The appeal process bridges the two verses, preventing disobedience, and equally important, preventing exasperation.

THE BENEFITS OF THE APPEAL PROCESS

The appeal process benefits children, parents, families, and society for the

a. The doctrine of authority and appealing to authority can be traced in both the Old and New Testaments. In Daniel 1:8-16, the young prophet Daniel and his three friends, Shadrach, Meshach, and Abednego, were assigned to King Nebuchadnezzar's court, where they were required to eat his food and drink his wine, which was against their beliefs. "Daniel made up his mind that he would not defile himself with the king's choice food or with the wine which he drank, so Daniel sought permission from the commander of the officials that he might not defile himself." (v. 8) Daniel's appeal won him the favor of his captors. In the New Testament, the apostle Paul stated his desire to appeal to Caesar regarding false charges made against him (Acts 25:11). He was given permission to go to Rome and go before Ceasar to make his appeal. While Paul was in Rome, he became acquainted with a runaway slave named Onesimus, who converted to Christianity. Paul later wrote a letter to his friend, Philemon, who has been the slave's master, appealing to him to forgive Onesimus and take him back into his household (Philemon 1:10). These are two examples where Paul chose to appeal to an authority figure.

b. "Children, obey your parents in all things, for this is well pleasing to the Lord. Fathers, do not provoke your children, lest they become discouraged." (Colossians 3:20-21) *c. We draw your attention back to the discussion in Chapter 9. The very nature of obedience will often frustrate children, but that does not mean we do away with the standard of obedience. Some think Colossians 3:20 and 21 contradict themselves. There is a biblical balance between the command to children to obey their parents and the command to parents not to exasperate their children by asking them to do something they are not able to do. The appeal process will help any parent achieve that balance so parents do not unnecessarily exasperate their children.*

❧

" I see the value of the appeal process because it enables me to respectfully explain to my parents something they may not know when they have made a decision."
– Benjamin, age 13

d. Providing new information is not the same thing as providing a personal opinion. Many children offer a commentary, an analysis, or an opinion on parental instruction. However, that is not providing factual information, which forms the basis of making a legitimate appeal.

following reasons:

1. It makes obedience attractive to children, since they know their parents are approachable and willing to revisit a previously given instruction.

2. It protects children from becoming needlessly frustrated.[c]

3. It prepares children to interact correctly with present and future authorities.

4. It prevents parental authority from being arbitrary, legalistic, or authoritarian.

5. It allows parents the right to change their minds without the fear of compromising their authority.

6. It encourages sibling relationships as each child learns to appeal to the others.

7. It reinforces family harmony during the teen years. When children grow confident of their parents' fairness, the harmony derived is further magnified in the teen years.

8. It helps accomplish the needed transition from *hupakouo*, the duty of obedience, to *hupotasso*, submitting to parents out of devotion. (See Chapter 6 and our discussion on obedience and submission.)

9. It facilitates communication in the classroom or in the boardroom. The appeal process should be used among all relationships, including parent/child, husband/wife, employer/employee, and government constituents.

10. It communicates to the world how biblical authority maintains fairness with integrity.

ACTIVATING THE APPEAL PROCESS

To activate the appeal process, a child must initiate the conversation by providing new *information*.[d] The parent's job is to hear and to act on that information, realizing that, "Yes," "No," and, "Maybe," are all possible answers. Parents who wished that they had taught their children the appeal process and who finally did so as a result of conflicts reported the following scenarios.

Example One

Bob and his family found seats together at the ball game, but Ryan, age seven, sat several seats away. Bob instructed him to move closer and heard,

"No, Dad, I want to sit here!" Ryan's answer challenged authority and created conflict. If Bob repeated himself, he would reinforce Ryan's disobedience. If he gave in, he would be compromising his authority. The "no" response forced Bob to take corrective measures. He chose to physically bring him closer. After receiving a verbal admonishment, Ryan explained, "But, Dad, I sat over there because I could not see all the players with that banner hanging in my way." Was that a legitimate reason to sit away from the family? Yes. Was it handled correctly? No. The entire scene would have been avoided if Bob had trained Ryan in the appeal process.[e]

The appeal process would have brought peace to the situation without compromise or frustration. Upon receiving instructions, Ryan would have moved near to his dad and asked, "May I appeal?" That simple question would have set the proper course of events in motion. Having received the new information about the low, hanging banner, Bob could have reconsidered his son's legitimate request. During this particular crisis, the father realized the power of the appeal process. By using it, parents can eliminate many unnecessary conflicts without compromising their authority or violating their relationship with their children.

Example Two

Two baskets of clean clothes were waiting in the basement on laundry day. While driving the children home from school, Jan said, "As soon as you kids change your clothes, I want you to go down to the basement and fold and put away your laundry." Both children did exactly as Mom instructed. Meanwhile, their dad came home and asked, "Why are those trash cans still on the street? I told the kids to put them in the garage as soon as they got home! They disobeyed me!"

This example demonstrates the basic problem of two authorities giving two sets of instructions that require simultaneous responses. To obey one parent forces the child to disobey the other. How could this have been better handled? Had training taken place in the appeal process, the children would have sensed the freedom to say, "Mom, may we appeal to you? Dad instructed us to bring the cans in from the street as soon as we arrived home. Which task do you want us to do first?" Jan, having received the new information, would be free to reexamine and restate her instructions without compromising her authority or her husband's instructions.[f] If she instructed her children to do the laundry first, then she would have been responsible for explaining the situation to Dad when he came home. Without the opportunity to appeal, obedience becomes anxious and confusing, often leading to unfair punishment.

GUIDELINES FOR MAKING AN APPEAL
The appeal process is often misused. To prevent that, consider these seven basic guidelines.

Guideline One
The appeal process is only for children who are old enough to understand its

"Making an appeal is helpful because it gives me a way to give my parents new information without sounding like I am arguing or complaining."
– Lindsay, age 13

e. Some children may try to use the appeal process to argue or negotiate with their parents. If your child tries this, respond to them with this question, "What is the new information you are providing me?" Another response would be, "Your tone prevents me from hearing what you are saying." These responses put the burden of proof back on the child, for unless your child has new information and is speaking with a humble tone, there is no basis for an appeal. (Mom's Notes presentation, "Training Elementary School Age Children")

f. Dad asks his son to do something he wanted done immediately, but his son was busy doing a chore Mom asked him to do earlier that day. Dad insisted their son stop doing Mom's chore and do what he wanted done. When Mom found out, she was angry and the atmosphere in the home was tense the remainder of the day. When Mom wanted Dad to give preference to what she asked their son to do, she could have made an appeal to him. This shows children that the appeal process works with anyone in the family.

g. *Parents error on this principle on both counts. Be careful not to introduce the concept before your child is old enough to understand the principle behind making an appeal. Again, children with older siblings who use the appeal process may just start making appeals one day. If you find your child knows the words but does not understand the principle behind them, (or before he is characterized by first-time obedience) then pull back on the privilege of making an appeal for 6 months to a year. When you think they are ready to use it correctly, reintroduce it to them properly. On the other hand, do not forget to introduce it at some point or you may exasperate your child by not providing this balance in the process of bringing him to obedience.*

h. *We cannot build a biblical dogma on the phrase, "May I appeal?" but families who have used the principles they learned in this class for many years have found that no other words so clearly signal a child's intent. "May I appeal?" is different enough from 'everyday language' that it stops parents in their tracks and they give their full attention to the situation at hand.*

purpose and who are characterized by first-time obedience. Children seven years old and older can quickly grasp the concept.[g]

Guideline Two
The appeal must only be made to the parent currently giving the instructions. That is, if Dad is instructing, the child is not to make an appeal to Mom. That would only undermine the authority of both parents. To demonstrate parental unity, neither parent should receive an appeal from a child who has not rightly dealt with the initiating parent.

Guideline Three
Parents should only entertain an appeal when the child comes in humility. A gentle spirit communicates the child's recognition of his parents' right to rule and overrule. "Why can't I?", "Do I have to?", and "But Mom!" reflect an attitude which is not an appeal but a challenge to authority. If there is no humility, there is no appeal. The appeal must be made face-to-face and must not be shouted from one room to another.

Guideline Four
Appeals can only be made once. In other words, a child cannot repeatedly plead his case. "But Dad, but Dad, but Dad!" and "Please may I, please may I, please may I?" are not permissible. The child must learn to accept "no" gracefully and to do as told. That will happen when the child learns that his parents are trustworthy, and that they will listen to legitimate appeals.

Guideline Five
Start by teaching your children to use the exact phrase, "May I appeal?" Wrapped up in these three words is the child's acknowledgment of your authority. Phrases such as, "Can I say something?", "But, Mom, I can't!", or "Can I ask why?" do not go far enough.[h]

Guideline Six
The appeal process is a privilege, not a way to avoid objectionable tasks or to get out of personal responsibility. Do not ruin a good thing by letting your child appeal every decision you make. It is not to be used as a forum to state likes and dislikes.

Guideline Seven
If the appeal process is to work effectively, parents must be fair and flexible. Think about why you say no. Is there a good reason it cannot sometimes be yes?

HOW TO TEACH THE APPEAL PROCESS
Introduce the appeal process using the following three steps.

1. Sit down with your children and work through the principles, examples, and guidelines of this chapter.

2. Set up a few scenarios that might fit your family situation. Include in each one an example of how to correctly and incorrectly make an appeal.

3. Once your children have mastered the concepts, test them. Allow the natural consequences of wrong choices to reinforce your training. If they come to you with a wrong attitude or if they fail to bring new information, deny their appeal. If they start to appeal everything, take the privilege away for several weeks.

    Remember, the appeal process is a matter of trust. The child trusts the parent to be fair and flexible, and the parent trusts the child to bring new information that legitimizes the appeal process.[i]

SUMMARY

The appeal process is not a cute trick to avoid conflict. Rather, it is a lifelong, character-building trait. The willingness of an individual to submit to authority is directly related to the fairness exhibited by that authority. In general, life is not fair. Yet, parents can be fair without compromising their authority by teaching their children how to approach them with reasonable appeals.

Questions for Review

1. What is the purpose of the appeal process?

2. Use an example to show how parental instruction can exasperate a child.

3. Explain the spiritual overtones of the appeal process.

4. What two things must happen for a child to activate the appeal process?

References / Notes

" Respecting my parents means I genuinely submit to them. This involves many things they have worked with me on over the years, like looking for ways to serve them and others, saying "Yes Mom" and "Yes Dad", using the interrupt rule, graciously accepting it when they deny my appeals, and completing what they have asked me to do." – Laura, age 16

i. You may have to train your children to use the appeal process. When they get into trouble with you and this situation would have been a good opportunity to use the appeal, tell them, "This would have been a good time to use the appeal. But since you chose not to, now I am going to have to give you a consequence."

5. What should be done when the child approaches one parent with the hope of being released from instructions given by the other parent?

6. What needs to be done in order for the appeal process to work effectively?

This Week at Home

1. Be prepared to share with the class how you taught the appeal process and what the responses of your children were.

2. As an adult, find an opportunity to use the appeal process yourself. Be prepared to share the results with the class.

Session Seventeen Outline
and Chapter Seventeen

Building a Healthy Family

I. Introduction

II. Understanding the Power of God's Grace
    The three ways in which God communicates grace to mankind

    A. _____ Grace

    B. _____ Grace

    C. _____ Grace

III. Building Family Identity
     A. Family identity defined:

     Identity is a socializing process by which a person identifies himself
     with a group he is familiar with, attracted to, or feels empathy with. We
     derive from our identity associations our sense of belonging, and we
     give back to these associations various degrees of _____.

     What type of family identity do you have?

     When your children become old enough to select their own friends,
     will you have given them any reason to select you? Do your children
     consider you to be a part of their inner circle of their most loyal and
     desirable relationships? Be reminded that being their friend is the even-
     tual relational goal of parenting.

     B. The Interdependent Family

     C. The Independent Family

     D. Family Identity and Peer Pressure

     Peer pressure on a child is only as strong as family _____ is weak.

E.   Family identity is good but not enough. Parents need a _____.

F.   Who is raising your child?

Here is a little test you can take to help determine what type of family you are, and who has the greatest influence on your child.

1.   Excluding yourself and your spouse, list all the people who spend at least one hour with your child during the course of a week.

2.   Next to their names, place the total hours per week they spend with your child.

3.   Count the number of people you have listed who have standards and values which differ from your own.

4.   Now count the number of hours they spend with your child weekly.

In relationship to your child and his influences, what type of family are you?

IV.   Understanding the Relational Goal of Parenting
    A.   The text:
    "No longer do I call you servants (disciples), for the servant does not know what his master is doing; but I have called you friends, for all things that I have heard of my Father, I have made known to you" (John 15:15).

    B.   The four phases of parenting
        1.   Phase one: _____ (Birth to 5 years)

        2.   Phase two: _____ (Age 6 to 12)

        3.   Phase three: _____ (Age 13 to 17)

        4.   Phase four: _____ (Age 18 through life)

V.   Approving That Which is Excellent
    A.   Philippians 1:10
        1.   Approve means to test the way of _____.

        2.   Excellence means to go over and _____.

B. Three types of moral initiative

　　1. Good represents the _____ minimum.

　　2. Better represents your _____.

　　3. Best represents _____.

Key Principle: Approve that which is excellent.

17

Building a Healthy Family

" When I was young, my parents were my protectors, guides, and my authority. Now, as a teen, we are gradually becoming close friends. My parents are my closest confidants and that is the way I think it should be." – Aubrey, age 17

What are the marks of healthy families? Our ministry to parents has afforded us a greater-than-average opportunity to observe and study the characteristics of healthy and not-so-healthy families. We have followed a number of their children from highchair graduation to high school graduation. And while not every healthy family will exhibit identical characteristics, it is our experience that they all demonstrate interdependence.

The friendship with your adult children is a parenting dividend you probably will not give much thought to while changing diapers or reading Bible stories. But as children turn into teens, it's important to ask these questions: when my children become old enough to select their own friends, will they have any reason to choose us or their sisters and brothers to be in the circle of trust? Do my children consider our family part of their inner circle of most loyal friends? After two decades of developing, the *Growing Kids God's Way* community is filled with these beautiful outcomes.

Other questions also give insight to the relationship bonds being created within your home. What will your family identity be in another three, five, or ten years? Are you cultivating a team spirit in your home? Have you instilled a God-honoring value system into your children's lives? Who else is raising your children? Family structures promote or hinder healthy parent-child relationships, as well as sibling-sibling relationships.[a] Even in the most natural and closest of human relationships, that of a parent and child, there is no guarantee of future rapport. Though both parties contribute to the strong or poor outcomes in the relationship, for the most part, parents remain in the "driver's seat." They can control or greatly influence the outcome due to the choices they make. One such choice deals with family structure. Are you an interdependent or an independent family? The first is more desirable; the second is dangerous. Let's look at each in turn.

a. Would you like to promote healthy sibling-sibling relationships in your family? The book, 'Making Brothers and Sisters Best Friends,' by Sarah, Stephen and Grace Mally is an excellent resource to help with this. The book is a great project for families to work through together. It is fun, insightful, and thought-provoking for kids and parents alike.

INTERDEPENDENT VS. INDEPENDENT FAMILY STRUCTURE

Please take note of the prefix "inter" in the word interdependent. Like threads in a tapestry or two-by-fours in the frame of a house, each individual part supports the others in order to create a whole. The relationship of each thread or board to the others is mutual. In the same way, each member of the interdependent family is mutually dependent upon each other.

This can be further illustrated by a group of people holding hands while in a circle and facing inward. This arrangement is the best possible one for sending and receiving family values. These values are communicated and demon-

References / Notes

❦

"Our family has always been a haven to come back to when we are under pressure. Being on the same team makes it easier to stand up to challenges with strength." – Emily, age 19

b. *The price a family pays for functioning "independently" is broken relationships, lack of communication, lack of support, differing moral value systems in the teen years, and a desire on the part of all family members to be with others outside the family versus those inside the family. They may live in the same house, but they are not functioning as a unit. (Mom's Notes presentation, "Building a Healthy Family Identity")*

c. *There will always be better jobs, higher positions, more convenient gyms and greater opportunities for self-growth and enrichment. These are all good, and it is hard to say "no" to them. But when parents no longer have time to fulfill their role as the primary moral influence over their children, the resulting vacuum will be filled with the voices of public institutions and their children's peers. The result can't help but be an increase in alienation, indifference, and independence on the part of the children.*

❦

"Being close to my family greatly helps me when I am being pressured by peers to do something that is against my conscience and the standards of my family. I can talk to my parents about it openly, and they gladly share their wisdom with me, which helps so much during struggles like this." – Kara, age 14

strated by Mom and Dad. They're sent to the children, shared with each other, and sent back again to Mom and Dad. Due to steady parental influence, the standards of moral conduct for each family member are established primarily within the home.

Interdependency should not be confused with the popular counseling term co-dependency. When problems arise in interdependent relationships, the issue is confronted, and each individual seeks to restore the whole. When problems arise in co-dependent relationships, fear and insecurity produce behavior that covers up the issue and functions around it.

Interdependent relationships provide satisfaction, protection, and security in the early years, and they serve as a barrier against intrusive values, especially in the teen years. The interdependent family cultivates a sense of belonging, which leads to allegiance to one another and allegiance to the core values of the family. Children grow with a "we-ism" attitude regarding their family, rather than the selfish "me-ism" attitude that leads to lonely independence.

In contrast, an independent family structure means to be free from influence, guidance, or the control of another. It also means to be unaffiliated, alienated, or not committed to one another—in short, to be standing alone. These words are fairly descriptive of the independent family.[b]

Again, we can use a circle analogy to demonstrate this structure. Like the interdependent family, the independent family also is holding hands while standing in a circle. But that is where the similarity ends. Instead of all members looking in toward one another, each member looks out, away from the center.

The independent family looks unified from a distance, but it is far from being what a family should be. Everyone is caught up in his own little world, doing his own independent thing. As a result, children turn to their peers more by default than by choice.

On paper, most people would choose the interdependent family structure. Everyone wants to belong, be supportive, and be supported. But for the structure to work in real life, it means sacrifice; it means being there for one another. As parental heads of the home, it means the process begins with us.[c] Parents simply cannot expect family harmony when other people are socializing your kids with their values. The stronger the outside influences in the early years, the greater the potential division in the teen years.

CONSEQUENCES OF DESIGN

Examining these two family structures in action leads to some interesting conclusions. Children who receive comfort and approval from the intimate and dependable relationships found in the interdependent family tend to look to those same or similar relationships as they move through adolescence.

Within the comfortable confines of the interdependent family, it is parents, not peers, who usually have the greater influence. The very nature of progressive development reveals that teens choose their community identity, that is, their peer friends, only after their family identity is first established and either accepted or rejected. If the family is accepted as the primary source of values and comfort, then the teen not only identifies with but makes friends from among those possessing similar values. This creates positive peer pressure. When there is harmony between the core beliefs of parents and teens, both seek similar values in other families and friends.

In contrast, a child who is weaned on outside influences and is dependent on peers for the satisfaction of basic social needs is more likely to grow up being sensitive to group pressures and disapproval. The tendency is to move in the direction of peers and become indifferent toward non-peer influences such as his parents. That is why ultimately *peer pressure on a child is only as strong as family identity is weak.* Work early on building a strong family identity.[d]

Parents can have the same influence that peers have. They can experience the same loyalty given to a peer group. But to reach that level of association, parents must think long-term and ask themselves: where will our family identity be in another five or ten years? Have we cultivated a team spirit? Have we given our children the basics that will cause them to desire to belong to our family? Have we instilled a God-honoring value system into their lives? How many other people are currently raising our children?

BUILDING FAMILY IDENTITY TAKES TIME

Today, life seems to be speeding by faster than ever before. At times, it seems that the pace of everything has been accelerated, including the rate at which our children grow. Within a few years, your young child will be on the brink of preadolescence and your preadolescent will be on the brink of adulthood. When that happens, will time be on your side? When your child is ready to leave the nest, will he or she have fond memories of family interactions that anchor that child back to you? Here are some practical suggestions to help cultivate a healthy family identity.

Read After Dinner

Reading together is becoming a lost family art, yet it is one of the most pleasant activities that can be shared between parents and children of all ages.[e] After dinner each night, before the dishes were cleared from the table, Anne Marie led our family in a story time. It was one of our greatest pastimes. George Mueller, D. L. Moody, Hudson Taylor...one chapter a night allowed us to walk with the great men and women of the Christian faith. Reading together after dinner did more than add to our minds; it was during times like these that we really gave our children what they needed—a sense of family identity built upon the memories of our togetherness. If you are starting over, reading after a meal is one good place to begin.

Allow Your Kids to Plan a Family Night

Some people think having leisure-time activities with your children is a luxury. It is not a luxury; it's an absolute necessity. Family night helps keep your work and play in perspective.[f] We planned a family night once a week. It was a time when we separated ourselves from work and school and came together for family fun. Family night afforded us an informal setting for relaxing with family members who didn't care how our hair looked or what we were wearing.

d. Is there any hope for parents who find themselves in conflict with a teen? Of course. Parents can make a difference because God makes a difference. In our book, Reaching the Heart of Your Teen, we speak to the process of restoring the years the "swarming locust has eaten" (Joel 2:25). We wrote this book, not only to help parents build strong parent-teen relationships, but to help other parents rebuild faltering ones. Be encouraged; there is hope.

e. Hero Tales, by Dave and Neta Jackson (Bethany House) are wonderful books to read to your children after dinner. The four books in this series share stories about missionaries that will inspire all who read to do their very best for God. The Trailblazer Series, also by Dave and Neta Jackson (Bethany House) put an 8-12 year old in the life of a missionary and share that missionary's story from the perspective of that child. These books would also be good to read as a family, or to have your children in 3rd – 6th grade read alone. When reading as a family, Dad can ask a question or two to promote a time of family discussion, such as, "What do you think you would have done if you had been in that situation?"

f. Many families we talk with don't have family nights consistently because they don't know what to do. Assign each of your children a week during a month to plan "Family Night." Everyone cheerfully does what that family member comes up with. We know of a family whose 12-year-old son colored "Precious Moments" pictures with a smile on his face during a Family Night his 6-year-old sister planned. Two great books are available to help you get started. They are 'Simply Fun for Families' by Gwen Ellis and 'Homespun Memories from the Heart' by Karen Ehman, Kelly Hovermale and Trish Smith.

g. What are the derived benefits from family night? Your children are not just taking ownership of a family night every other week; they are actually taking ownership of your family. It is their investment into the fun portion of other family members' lives. It adds another good reason for them to stick around. Plan family nights. This ensures that your children don't end up with your leftover time.

⟨ornament⟩

"My sisters and I look forward to family night. We're busy with school and church activities turning the week, but family night is special -- it is a time of regrouping, when laughter is plentiful and love and affection is shared by all. I know these are special times that will become treasured memories of my growing up years." - Lindsay, age 13

⟨ornament⟩

"My parents have been very careful to teach us to appreciate any moment our family can share together, strategically arranging and guarding the opportunities we might have to enjoy as a whole. These moments were not necessarily as complicated as a planned vacation or a specific family night, but were as simple as serving at funeral dinners, teaching a two-year-old Sunday School class, or going to a dollar movie. As much as I enjoy the memories made in leisure times, nothing compares to the privilege of serving others as a team." - Mollie, age 18

We eventually added a little twist to our weekly family fun night. Long before our children reached their teen years, they took ownership for every other family night. They did a little budget and planned the evening. We played board and card games, had indoor picnics, or feasted on pizza and fondue and watched a favorite video classic.[g]

Let Them Participate in Building Family Memories

Not only can you encourage your teen to plan a family night, you can take the next step and encourage him or her to help you plan the next family vacation. Whether it be a short weekend camping trip with your church Sunday school or a week-long event away from home, planning and participating adds a positive memory-building dimension for your teen. The more healthy the memories, the closer you grow as an interdependent family.

Building memories with your children means more than taking them places and doing fun things with them; it requires that they become participants in all aspects of the activity. This truth was realized by friends of ours many years ago. For years they left the February cold of northern New England to spend two weeks in warm Florida. Each year, our friends returned home discouraged by their children's constant complaints and lack of appreciation for all that the parents felt they had done.

Then one year, someone suggested they let their kids help plan the next family trip. That included letting them help decide the travel route, make some of the scheduling decisions, and select some of the special events they would attend along the way. It made all the difference in the world. What made the difference? The children became participants in the vacation instead of spectators. And the overall benefit? The work that went into planning and scheduling, the anticipation of seeing those plans realized, and the sense of ownership all factored into building lasting memories for each member of that family.

Take Walks Together

If your response to this is, "Yeah, right—three hundred years ago," give it a chance. It may surprise you that this simple suggestion might get accepted. We found that taking walks with our children—one at a time—brought about conversations we otherwise would not have had. There is something about a twenty-minute walk that causes people to reflect, open up, and share their hearts. Those moments of reflection often led to very personal and private conversations with our children. Walking gave them access to us and gave us access to them. They exposed their inner thoughts, fears, doubts, and hopes. Sometimes they just needed to talk, which meant those walks were good times for Anne Marie and me just to listen. We knew our listening served a purpose; it provided a sounding board to help our children sort things out.

Dining, reading, planning, playing, and walking together—this is just a partial list of the activities we have enjoyed together as a family. Make your own list. See if you can come up with ten options. What are some of the favorite activities of your individual family members? Pick out one or two that you can try doing together this week and do them!

THE POWER OF COMMUNITY

As family educators and as parents, we believe strongly in family identity. But even family identity is not sufficient to carry you through the preteen years. You need something more—something bigger than your family. You need the power of community. The word community can mean many things to many people. We use it to refer to a society of families, tied together, sharing common interests, values, and a significant commitment to an ideal, for the mutual benefit of the individual and the collective membership. In other words, to quote the Three Musketeers, "All for one and one for all!"[h]

Connecting with a Moral Community

Since members of your community are going to teach your children (directly or indirectly), it is vital that you surround yourself with people who share your morals and your values. In a moral community, you will find people who, like you, are striving to live out the precepts of respect and honor and instill in their children a God-centered awareness and consideration of others. These are the kind of people who can provide a support group for you, Mom and Dad.

Another reason you need a like-minded, moral community is that it is within your community (whatever that community may be) that your child will find other kids with whom to spend time. You want those to be healthy, moral kids—kids whose moms and dads are working to instill biblical values in their hearts, just as you are with your child.

In the years ahead, broader interests and attachment to friends will become more meaningful to your son or daughter. In the truest sense, he or she is becoming morally and relationally emancipated and self-reliant. That is why the moral community in which you and your child belong will either be a friend or foe to your family values.[i] Being immersed in a moral community is absolutely necessary if you hope to have your values reinforced. When your child's peers come out of a like-minded community, he or she will be reassured of the importance of family values. Furthermore, confidence in you, Mom and Dad, is strengthened. Once your child finds friends in your moral community, those friends become a source of positive peer pressure and healthy groupthink.

This truth is illustrated by the story of a young girl we know whose orthodontist decided that she needed to wear headgear. Though he strongly recommended that she wear the headgear twenty-four hours a day, he said to her with the greatest sensitivity, "I realize, though, that you probably can't wear it at school because the kids might laugh at you."

"Oh, no," the girl told him. "Not at my school. The kids won't laugh at me there." This child felt secure in her community. She knew she would not be ridiculed. This gave her the strength she needed to help her do what she knew was best—wear the headgear at all times.

How would your child respond in this situation? Would the children in his or her circle of friends say, "Do what's right. Wear the headgear"? Or would they say, "Don't listen to your mom and dad. You look like a jerk"? It is time to take a look at who is in your family's community.

At this point, we must make one important clarification. By stating that you

References / Notes

h. *Why is it important to have a community? Because a community does something that nothing else can; it establishes within the group a sense of "we-ness" that encourages members to work toward a common good.*

i. *The greater the disparity between the values of your family and your family community (from which you and your child will both draw your peers), the greater will be the source of conflict within the home. The opposite of this is also true; shared values between community and home result in positive peer pressure on your child.*

❦

"Some of my favorite family activities include taking bike rides, playing games, and taking walks to the waterfront near where we live – just spending quality time together."
– Nathan, age 13

References / Notes

j. The Mom's Notes presentation, "Understanding Peer Pressure," Parts 1 and 2 talks about the "Circles of Friendship." The Circles of Friendship share how children and teens can balance relationships with morally like-minded friends, people they are in contact with on a regular basis (both Christian and non-believers), and those they can have a silent testimony to. It is a helpful tool for parents to share with their children to help them understand how we as Christians can be "in the world and protected from the evil one" (John 17:15).

k. Many years ago we lived in northern New England where winters were long and cold. Like most homeowners, we made sure that our house, including our floors, ceilings, and outside walls, was well-insulated from the elements. We insulated our home with a two-fold purpose in mind. First, it was to keep the cold outside, and second, it was to keep the warm inside. However, we still had to go outside into the cold weather when we needed to leave the house. By the same token, a moral community insulates your children against the elements of the world. Through association with like-minded peers, our children see family standards reinforced by others who share the same values. The strength they draw from moral peers is the very thing that makes it possible for Mom and Dad to let them participate in ballet or a community soccer league: the support of a moral community.

must surround your family with people who share your morals and values, we are not saying that you should isolate your children from the world. Nothing could be further from the truth.[j] To isolate yourself into a moral community is as unbiblical as it is to say that you don't need a moral community to help you raise your children. Parents should not isolate their children from nonbelievers. But rather manage the moments by insulating their children from corrupting influences.[k]

THE RELATIONAL GOAL OF YOUR PARENTING

Many parents spend their entire parenting career attempting to be friends with their children. They suspend the requirement of obedience in the early years in hopes of cashing in on the child's friendship in the latter years. From a parenting perspective, what sounds more noble or more captivating than a family made up of friends? Certainly that is an admirable idea, even appealing to a generation that may have wondered about the absence of friendship with their own parents. But is it right?

Building a friendship with your child must be the relational goal, not the starting point of your parenting. As stewards of God's special gifts, He calls us to a discipling relationship with our children, bringing them from innocence and foolishness to maturity and wisdom (Proverbs 4:1-7). That is the model our Lord gave His disciples. "No longer do I call you servants (disciples), for the servant does not know what his master is doing, but I have called you friends, for all things that I have heard of my Father, I have made known to you" (John 15:15).

What a pointed illustration of the passing on of wisdom from one to another! In His final hours, Jesus summarized His relationship with the men with whom He had been most intimate, His disciples. From the early days of gathering His men right up to the Last Supper, our Lord continually passed on His wisdom to His disciples. Throughout the process, He was not afraid to remind them that the student is not greater than the teacher. As their shepherd, He brought conformity to their thinking by creating a like-mindedness and direction for life. In John 15, the Lord brought the discipling of His men to completion and entered into a new relationship with them which He called friendship.

Christian parenting follows the same pattern of discipleship. From the beginning, we should be passing on the wisdom of the Father to those entrusted to our care. The wisdom of God, or the lack thereof, establishes the superiority and inferiority of men. Our role as parent automatically grants us the position of teacher; our children are our students.

There will be plenty of time for friendship later, and when parents disciple their children wisely, plenty of reason for it. But friendship with our children is not the starting point of our parenting; it is the goal. Only when we have brought our children to a common like-mindedness of who we are as a family will we be in a position to enjoy our children and give them a reason to enjoy us. Before the friendship phase arrives, parents pass through three building-block periods with their children. The success of each phase is dependent on the success of the preceding phase.

Phase One: Discipline

This phase covers the period from birth to five years of age. Your primary goal as a parent is to establish your right to lead their little lives. The leadership you speak of is not oppressive but authoritative. It is a phase of tighter boundaries, not unlimited freedoms. These boundaries will give way to freedoms as the child demonstrates responsible behavior. Your task is to get control of the child so you can effectively train him. If you cannot control your child, you cannot train him to his full potential, nor will anyone else be able to do so.

Phase Two: Training

The training phase of parenting takes place from ages 6 to 12. To use a sports analogy, a trainer works with an athlete each day in different settings, going through drills and exercises. He can stop the player at any time and make immediate corrections, explaining the reasons and showing him what to do and how to do it. During training, our children are not yet in the real game of life; they are only in practice sessions.

Phase Three: Coaching

The third phase, from ages 13 to 17, is the coaching phase. Now our children are in the game of life for themselves. We can send plays in from the sidelines and huddle during the time-outs, but we can no longer stop the game for extended periods of time and show them how it is to be played. They now call the plays themselves and move forward. How well you coach your children determines how they run through the plays of life. What kind of trainer you are determines how they respond to your coaching. The type of disciplinarian you are determines your ability to train your children. How well you have established your right to rule determines what type of disciplinarian you are.

Phase Four: Friendship

The relational goal of our parenting is friendship with our children.[l] Although the parent-child relationship does not cease, both parent and child enter into a new season of life. Just as it was with the Lord and His disciples, it should also be with you and your children—a discipleship relationship culminating in friendship. The process begins with tight boundaries, which give way to responsible behavior, leading to freedom.

THE FINAL CHARGE: APPROVING THAT WHICH IS EXCELLENT

The apostle Paul told the Philippian church to "approve that which is excellent" (Philippians 1:10a).[m] How can you teach your child to approve that which is excellent? How do you get children to "go beyond what is required" with the values that are in his or her heart? How can you move your son or daughter beyond just external compliance to the letter of the law? It all begins with Mom and Dad. Here is an example of such.

Not too many years ago, we went to Arizona to visit some church representatives working in our ministry. When we got out of the car, we noticed eight-year-old Timarie standing on the sidewalk waiting for our arrival and

l. Four-year-old Katelynn was digging in her little garden. By her side was a bucket of bright bougainvillea leaves. "What are you doing with those leaves, Katelynn?" Grandpa asked. "I'm planting the pretty leaves to grow more pretty leaves." Grandpa explained that the beautiful leaves that give the vine its glory come from seeds and not the pretty bright petals she was putting in the ground. Katelynn thought petals now would mean petals later. Many parents work from that same misconception, thinking that friendship now will mean friendship later. They see the pretty petals of friendship and want to start there. Unfortunately, it doesn't happen that way. The process starts by planting a seed. Then you let the seed grow into a sprout. You nurture the sprout until it grows branches. You allow the branches to bring forth their beauty in their time. In parenting, you start by being a loving and guiding mom and dad who are guardians of your child's soul. At the end of the growth comes the harvest of friendship. The process takes time. Don't rush the fruit.

m. The word approve means, literally, to test the way of excellence or to know what is genuine. The word for excellence, the Greek "diaphero," means to do over and above and to go beyond what is required. This does not mean that we are striving for perfection; perfectionists do not enjoy the real world because they are critical of themselves and often the shortcomings of others. However, we should be striving for moral excellence, not mediocrity, when it comes to "doing all to the glory of God" (1 Corinthians 10:31).

" When I look at the lives and relationships of many of my peers with their parents, I can see a sample of what my relationship with my parents would be if they didn't stick to the principles taught in Growing Kids God's Way. The more I look around the more I appreciate Mom and Dad and all that they taught, and the standards they held me to when I see where I would be without them." - Titus, age 16

n. When training your child in a specific virtue and you see it demonstrated, ask him, "Good, better or best, which of those did you just show?" If his response is "Good," ask, "What could you do for it to be "Better"?" If his response is "Better," ask "What could you do for it to be "Best"?" Children will strive for "Best" when they are lovingly and consistently encouraged in that direction. (Mom's Notes presentation, "All of a Sudden")

o. Proverbs 20:11 tells us, "Even a child is known by his deeds, whether what he does is pure and right." A child's moral disposition will show itself. Just as the new bud leads to a blossom and the blossom to fruit, what is in your child's heart will blossom some day.

subsequent visit with her parents. We made eye contact and said, "Hello. Are you one of the Smith children?"

"Yes," she responded. Then she walked toward us with adult-like confidence and put out her hand to shake ours. As she graciously looked into our eyes, she said with all sincerity, "Hello, Mr. and Mrs. Ezzo. It is very nice to meet you. Did you have a nice trip over to Tucson?"

Were we impressed? Yes, very much so. Timarie's interest in us was clearly genuine. A few minutes later, we met her siblings who, in their own way, demonstrated the same moral sensitivity. Later in our visit, we asked the parents what they did to bring their children to this level of moral sincerity. They told us they had taught their children three levels of moral responses—good, better, and best.

Doing "good," they explained to their kids, represents who you are as a person. It also represents the minimum courtesy required in a moral situation. If someone said, "Hello," Timarie and her siblings knew that the appropriate response was to acknowledge the greeter by saying, "Hello," in return. If the person extended a compliment, such as, "Those are pretty ribbons in your hair, Timarie," the minimum courtesy would be to say, "Thank you."

Doing "better," the parents went on to say, represents our family—who we are and what we stand for. Better takes all of us beyond the moral minimum to take the next step in extending a courtesy. For example, Timarie's parents encouraged and showed their children how to reach out and shake hands with any adult to whom they were introduced. They stressed that greeting a person with the eyes is just as important as shaking hands. They also taught that if a child or adult is sitting when a visitor walks into the room, that person is to stand and acknowledge the newcomer's presence. Such a gesture is based on 1 Corinthians 13:5, "Love is not rude."

Doing what is "best," this couple taught their kids, represents God. This involves going over and above what is required. Rather than simply saying "Hi" in response to the extension of a hand, the children become the initiators of kindness. Not only did Timarie say, "Hello," and walk toward us with her hand extended, she also initiated conversation. "Did you have a nice trip over to Tucson?" Those few words went a long way. "Good" is acceptable and "better' is preferable, but "best," seeking to please God, is most desirable.[n]

When young Timarie extended her hand and asked about our welfare, she was extending a courtesy. This was not anything her parents required of her. It was not an obedience issue; it was part of the training and teaching process which she had been involved in throughout her childhood.[o] Timarie's moral disposition showed itself through right principles, because right principles were placed there by her parents. It will always be the right time to encourage your children to go beyond good and better. Encourage your children to strive for best. We trust what you have learned in *Growing Kids God's Way* over these many weeks will help facilitate that goal.

Questions for Review

1. Describe the difference between independent and interdependent family structures.

   a. Independent family:

   b. Interdependent family:

2. What do interdependent relationships serve as a barrier against in the teen years? Explain.

3. Why is it vital that you surround yourself with people who share your morals and your values?

4. According to the authors, what is the relational goal of your parenting?

5. In parenting, what do good, better, and best each represent?

Epilogue

Throughout the last seventeen chapters, we have endeavored to communicate biblical principles of moral conduct that can strengthen your family. We want you to enjoy your children. More than that, we want others to enjoy and to be blessed by your children. The principles of *Growing Kids God's Way* aim first and foremost to help parents glorify God through their families. Yet, the principles are not just for your family's comfort and joy; they are an investment in the preservation of the nation.

America at one time embraced the benefits of a common moral consensus and values derived from the Character of God guided that conscience. That does not mean we were a "Christian" nation, but it does mean our founding fathers choose to guide the nation with virtues and values that were inherently Christian and derived from the God of the Bible. It was upon these truths that the US Constitution is based. And yet, the constitution loses it's protective value, if the moral foundations upon which it was enacted are no longer the defining expression of right and wrong, good and evil. That is why the moral destiny of our society will always be in the hands of the present parenting generation. By that, we do not mean to imply that God is not in control, but rather that His sowing/reaping principles are at work (Matthew 7:17-20; Galatians 6:7).

What children become in the future will largely be a reflection of what their parents believe today, for the family continues to be the values-generating institution of our society. There is little hope for our collective future without a God oriented sense of otherness, fairness, compassion, honesty, and justice. Our society cannot survive without biblical ethics, and biblical ethics cannot survive without a strong Christian witness maintained within each generation.

That is where parents come in, and why proper parenting is so important. The saving grace of Christ must be realized by what we say and do within our own moral neighborhoods and communities. Yet, we do not live "right" to save our culture; we live "right" to obey God. Obedience to God is what brings blessings to the nation. This may be why the apostle Paul told Christians to "be careful to maintain good works." Why? Because such a lifestyle is "good and profitable to all men" (Titus 3:8). Yes, our obedience to God profits all, even those who choose to live apart from God.

We speak then with a tremendous sense of urgency. Take ownership of your children's moral destiny. By doing so you carry forward the sacred trust as guardians and protectors of the values that gives meaning and protection to *life* itself. We trust that *Growing Kids God's Way* has encouraged you along the way. May God bless your efforts in pursuing the life that He gives more abundantly.

Gary & Anne Marie

Quotes and More

In the modern American society, it is a commonly held belief that parents and their teenagers will do battle. Pain, misery, and sorrow are accepted as a normal expression of family life, and anything less is now viewed outside the norm and deemed unheahlty. The fundamental problem with such descriptions of the present parent-teen experience is just that—they are simply descriptions. Statistics, surveys, and other clinical studies assume the validity of the power of observation. The process works this way: statistics tell us what is common; what is common then becomes what is normal; normal is deemed inevitable; and finally, what is seen as inevitable is labeled healthy. In fact, according to some psychologists, the lack of teenage rebellion is a signal that something is terribly wrong with a child. Yet such logic is flawed. "Common" and "normal" are not interchangeable terms.

While we are well aware that most contemporary schools of parenting believe in the inevitability of the "storm and stress" years, we do not! From the beginning to the present, our message about the adolescent years has always been very positive, upbeat, exciting, and filled with plenty of encouragement. We wanted parents to look forward to the fun-filled years of adolescence and we worked hard to give every reason to hope for and experience strong, positive, healthy, and lasting relationships.

The quotes that made this edition were only a sampling of what we actually received in a two-day period. We regret that we could not include every response and statement received by the community of *Growing Kids* teens. Yet, there was a common thread among all the responses—building strong relationships within the family. Many comments were made about friends who had poor relationships with their parents and siblings. This made the *GKGW* teens very thankful for the strength of their family. What did their family have that the others didn't? Four themes stood out: 1) the moral foundations laid down by parents; 2) a strong family identity; 3) Mom and Dad's commitment to glorifying God through their parenting; and 4) a Mom and Dad that knew how to lead at the appropriate time by the strength of their relational influence. For your encouragement here are a few more testimonies. God bless you as you taste the blessings of His grace on your family.

"As a young adult, I have learned two principle things about my parents. They aren't perfect, and they are two of the most honorable and heroic people in the world. I count it an honor to have them as my best friends and guides." - *Emily, age 19*

"I am thankful for the teaching my parents found in the *Growing Kids God's Way* material. The godly wisdom in *GKGW* is rich and practical. It was not always easy to grow up in a home that held different standards than most of the other families I knew. I will admit it was often confusing. Yet, I enjoyed being with my family. My parents could make something extraordinary out of the ordinary, whether it concerned celebrating a birthday or a time when we, on our own initiative, did something special for someone who needed it. When I first arrived at the Christian college I attend, I was surprised how few girls in the dorm knew how to be responsible in the way they governed their lives. It hindered them greatly. How thankful I am that my parents always kept the "big picture" in mind while they were raising us. I look forward to using the biblical principles in *Growing Kids God's Way* when I have a family of my own." - *Briana, age 21*

"The process of restoration not only repairs the relationship, it also clears my conscience. Without having been taught the importance of this principle, I would only know guilt and frustration rather than freedom in forgiveness." - *Laura, age 16*

"I believe *GKGW* is a huge reason that my relationship with my parents now is more of a friendship, even at 18. So many of my friends are struggling with their parents, mostly because their parents do not treat them like adults. I actually end up counseling many of my friends because they get so frustrated and I think the reason they come to me is because my parents have learned that relationship is so important and my friends want that." - *Shannon, age 18*

"Reaping the benefits of my parents biblical training has been the biggest blessing of my life. It has shown me that I have three best friends (my brothers) living with me everyday that I will cherish the rest of my life. Many days, sitting on my bed was not pleasant, but those moments of training are what molded my life and transitioned me from obedience to my parents to a contented, submissive relationship to Christ. That right there is the most important thing a parent can give their child." - *Amanda, age 19*

"I know that without the principles my parents learned from the *GKGW*, our family would be completely different. I know this because I can see the families that did not apply the Growing Kids principles. First of all, without these principles our family would be completely different; it would not be the love-filled haven of security that it is to me now. Second, my life would revolve completely around myself and my peers; I would not want to have anything to do with my family or my parents. I honestly do not want to even think about, much less say what I would be like without these principles." - *Kristen, age 17*

"Looking at my friends and the relationships that they have with their parents, I am grateful that my parents have gone through *GKGW* because relationships are a main priority that we have had in our family. I know I can share my thoughts with my parents and that they can help me, I can trust them and they trust me." - *Ashley, age 13*

"One of the reasons I'm thankful that my parents took *Growing Kids God's Way* is because now that I'm an adult, our relationship is more important to them than rules. There is an expectation of mutual respect that I do not always see in my friends and their parents. I've often kidded my parents about what I would have become without *GKGW* and the biblical parenting it teaches. I'm sure it would not have been good." - *Shane, age 19*

"My relationship with my parents is based on trust and respect. It took a while to build a strong relationship between us. Now, as I look back, I can see that our relationship has really grown in the last few years. I look to my parents with respect. They are still in authority over me, but as they help me grow in the Lord and as a sister and daughter, I am thankful for the relationship I have with them." - *Courtney, age 13*

"If I were asked, 'What kind of relationship do you think you would have with your parents if they didn't raise you with the principles they learned in *Growing Kids God's Way*? My answer would be, 'Not a very good one.'" - *Timothy, age 13*

"I would probably would have the same unstable, distant relationship with my parents that a lot of parents and teenagers have if it wasn't for *GKGW*. I can not even imagine our family without it!" - *Rebecca, age 14*

Appendix One

The Parent & God Factor

How were you parented? From time to time, reflecting on the past can shed light on the present. For many, childhood can seem distant and unrelated to present circumstances. After all, many years have gone by since you were subject to the rule of your own parents. Yet, one does not easily escape the habit-forming attitudes of childhood.

We have all heard, and you may have said yourself, "When I become a parent, I won't do that to my children." Or, if you sensed deficiencies in your upbringing, you might have said something like, "When I become a parent, I'm going to do. . . with my kids." How have personal pledges such as these worked their way into your parenting? Unfortunately, many adults parent in response to their own unresolved childhood fears, conflicts, and disappointments. They do this by projecting their own fears and disillusionment with life onto their kids. They create strategies that fit comfortably with their pain threshold. The pain and pleasure of childhood can powerfully, yet silently, shape our inventory of needs when it comes to raising our children.

For example, if the growing-up years were pleasant, there is a strong tendency to employ training techniques similar to those by which you were raised. If your childhood and teen years were stressful, the tendency is to swing to the opposite extreme of your parents' parenting methods when rearing your own children. For example, parents brought up under unfair, restrictive, or even abusive methods often unknowingly move toward permissive parenting, allowing their children to become self-centered. These parents in many ways become more concerned about their children's feelings than about their actions. They elevate psychological health above moral health, and any standard of right and wrong is subject to how their children feel, not what they do.

In contrast, when parents find that their unhappy childhood resulted from a permissive upbringing, they often become very strict, especially if they feel the lack of guidance was a great handicap to them. For example, those who lived morally relaxed lives in their youth will often overcompensate with their own children by becoming overly protective and sheltering. These parents find their security in control.

In both cases, there is a driving force to change the status quo. So what happens? Permissive/child-centered parents fear inhibiting the child, so they go to the extreme of creating an environment of unrestrained freedom. This results in an under-controlled child. Authoritarian parents fear spoiling their child, so they see their salvation in the power of rules and limitations. Their methods usually produce an over-controlled child.

The problem is further complicated when personalities and parenting styles within the home clash. If one parent is easygoing and flexible, and the other parent is structured and predictable, unhealthy conflict tends to prevail in the home. A balanced style of parenting, where the two styles of parenting meet somewhere in the middle, is nowhere to be found. Rather than becoming closer in their approach to parenting, these parents usually drift further apart. This happens because each one considers it his or her duty, in the name of love, to compensate for the other's weaknesses. Instead of complementing each other by drawing from each other's strengths, they find themselves at war, using each other's weaknesses to shoot bullets at each other. The result? Divided leadership produces disloyal troops, and everyone, including the children, lead with the battle cry of, "Divide and Conquer!"

Parenting Extremes

It is interesting to listen to parenting perspectives. The permissive parent looks at the authoritarian parent and says, "I do not want to be like that mother or father. They're too strict!" The authoritarian parent looks at the permissive household and says, "I do not want my children acting like that. They're out of control!" Unfortunately, parents do tend to move to these extremes. The permissive parent who controls too little and the authoritarian parent who controls too much both deprive their children of basic skills necessary for healthy adolescence. Let's take a closer look at each parenting style.

Authoritarian Parenting

Authoritarian parenting was the norm for the first sixty years of this century and was most closely associated with the Judeo/Christian ethics. Because it was predominantly concerned with restraining evil, authoritarianism paid little attention to elevating good. That means there was a greater emphasis placed on what children should not do than on what they should do. Parenting by restraint resulted in the attitude that the ends justify the means, or one can do anything to bring about conformity to societal rules. During the reign of authoritarianism, social engineering was the task of parents, neighbors, churches, and teachers, but not of the State. Although children typically conformed and did virtuous acts, they did so out of the fear of reproof, not because of the love of goodness. The child heard, "You will do it or else." The "or else" became the motivation for right behavior, not a resident principle of the heart.

Permissive Parenting

Since the late 1960s, permissive theories have dominated the American culture. Permissive parenting is not concerned with suppressing evil or elevating good. At the core of this theory is the concern over creating the right environment for the child, not behavioral results.

Parenting arouses many different emotions. The emotions of love, joy, peace, contentment, and confidence are easily matched by the emotions of frustration, disappointment, and discouragement, and on some days, despair. Parenting to achieve all the right emotions is not the genesis of child training. Yet such a belief is the common denominator of permissive parents. For them, child-rearing is reduced to avoiding all negative emotions and pursuing all positive ones. Thus, right and wrong training are measured by how parents think their child feels rather than by the end product—their child's behavior. Feelings belonging to both parent and child become the basis of nurturing and their ethics. If the child feels happy, the parent is satisfied. If the child feels sad, then the parent works to create an environment that will eliminate his sadness.

We believe that both permissive and authoritarian parenting styles are wrong and are detrimental to the welfare of a child. That is why this manual endeavors to guide parents according to the basic rules of biblical ethics.

ONLY BY THE GRACE OF GOD

The duty of Christian parents to instruct their children in the knowledge of God cannot be achieved apart from His grace. We know this in our own family. Next to our computer screen is an Easter picture of our grandchildren. Ashley, then seven years old, has her arms stretched out across the shoulders of her siblings and cousins.

At times, I look at that picture and think and reflect on my own grandparents. It was nearly a century ago when, as children, each of them found the way of salvation in Jesus Christ. From those spiritual roots, our family's Christian heritage began. As adults, my grandparents passed on the message to their children who in turn passed it on to their own kids. We then taught our own children about Jesus Christ, and they in turn are now actively passing on their faith to our grandchildren. By God's grace, Christianity has followed our bloodline for five generations.

As a parent, you want many things for your child, but the most important issue must be your child's salvation. You may wonder what you can do to influence your child's decision. "Isn't salvation a personal issue?" you ask. "I certainly do not have the power to make it happen." This is true. As the Bible says, salvation occurs "by grace alone, through faith alone" (Ephesians 2:8-9). Yet many parents wrongly conclude that dependency upon grace means they should relinquish all responsibility or "let go and let God." The belief follows this logic: Why should parents bother to develop the moral character and conduct of their children if grace and salvation, the supreme goals, are not the direct result of moral training? As the Bible states, "Therefore no one will be declared righteous in His (God's) sight by observing the law…" (Romans 3:20).

The simplest answer to that question is that God requires the training of children. Proverbs 22:6 calls parents to "Train a child in the way he should go, and when he is old he will not depart from it." Proverbs 23:13a says, "Do not withhold correction from a child." The New Testament command is found in Ephesians 6:4. It reads, "And you fathers do not provoke your children to wrath, but bring them up in the training and admonition of the Lord."

In his essays on the duties of a parent, the nineteenth-century English cleric John C. Ryle warned parents to beware of the delusion that parents can do nothing for their children—that they must leave them alone, wait for grace, and sit still. Pastor Ryle understood the importance of early training and passionately exhorted parents to participate in the communication of God's grace by opening the child's mind to and directing his ways in God's moral law. In this way, children are brought to a knowledge of God.

Of the various means by which God communicates His grace, three deserve our attention here. First, there is a common grace given to all mankind. Its benefits are experienced by the whole human race without discrimination. For instance, God brings refreshing rain on the righteous and the unrighteous alike.

Second, there is sanctifying grace. God's grace flows to families through the sanctifying grace of believing spouses and parents. That is, when Mom and Dad have come to a saving knowledge of Jesus Christ, children receive the overflow of God's grace as it is poured out on their parents. The blessing is multiplied by each generation. God's favor is extended through our obedience. If we want to claim for our children the blessings in God's Word, we must believe and be faithfully obedient to God's revelation. Without faith, we have no right to any blessings of promise. Without obedience, we cannot expect the favor of God nor the communication of His grace on our children or on our efforts. Grace is communicated to each household when parents stay vertically aligned with the Lord. As we are blessed, so will our children be blessed. This is the power of sanctifying grace.

Yet we know our children cannot live off of our blessings, but must obtain their own. This is done through the third means by which God communicates His grace—regenerational grace. This truth is basic to our entire presentation. No morality or conformity to the moral law can be acceptable to God, except that which is exercised in total dependence on Jesus Christ from a heart secured by Him.

God delights in right behavior that arises from a right heart. Apart from receiving a new heart from the regenerating work of the Holy Spirit, no child has direct and personal access to God's grace.

Does this negate the divine call for parents to "Train up a child in the way of the Lord"? Most certainly not. It only serves to emphasize even more the parents' need to cooperate with the grace of God. A biblical view of grace doesn't call for parents to labor less. Rather, it calls them to labor fervently, all the while acknowledging their utter dependency upon God.

Seek diligently the salvation of your child that he or she might enter into the fullness of God's power and influence, and out of a love response to God, serve Him wholeheartedly. In parenting, grace and labor are not enemies but divinely appointed comrades in the work of the Lord. You cannot parent by your own strength and still achieve a godly outcome. Remember, let God through His grace do His work, while you, through obedience, do yours.

Appendix Two

Let Them Play

A little voice down the hall engages in a one-way conversation. "Now girls, look at Mommy's face and pay attention. We're going to the store and the two of you need to obey Mommy with a happy heart," says three-year-old Ashley to her favorite dolls. Seldom do we stop and think about the importance of imaginative play. Yet in the life of children, it is a natural thing. In fact, having varied forms of play is one of the strongest indicators of healthy emotional growth and a significant component of a child's orderly development. Play is not simply a time when a child amuses himself. With all the pressure these days to educate young children early (even starting in utero), parents can take heart. One of the most active forms of learning is play.

In *Preparation for the Toddler Years* we introduced our readers to the learning mechanism of curiosity and the role it plays in a toddler's learning ability. There we defined curiosity as a natural stimulus, a child's birthright—a survival mechanism. It is the key that unlocks the treasures of knowledge and opens a world of discovery for young children. Curiosity serves the child as a necessary precursor to the advanced skills of logic and reason.

While curiosity draws a child to an object, a second force holds him there. That force is attention. Attention is what holds a child in the moment of exploration, whether it is ten seconds or ten minutes. Attention is the power of attraction. Attraction is the result of sensory nerves working together, holding a child's interest to an object. It could be the color of a magazine, a shiny new pen, the odd-shaped lamp, or the musical ring of your cell phone. Color, shine, shape, and sound—all are in need of investigation. Curiosity, attention, and attraction all lead to investigation, which brings to the young child the excitement of discovery and learning.

Remember when your toddler was sitting on the rug eagerly engaged in playing with a toy? As a toddler he was not limited by rules and regulations, starting or ending points of formal play. He played with the object as long as he wished, until he became interested in something new. He often manipulated his toy with his hands, pushing and pulling, pounding and banging, even attempting to test and taste the surface with small bites. The developing brain was working, processing, reinforcing, and gaining usable sensations. This is all part of a toddler's learning mechanism. In the process of investigative play, your toddler derived as much enjoyment from the stimulation of his senses and motor capacities as he did from the toy itself.

But as your child approaches three years of age, an even more powerful force comes into being. This force, your child's imagination, will cause you to marvel at its limitless possibilities. This natural endowment is a function of play as much as it is a function of higher learning. Whether this is accomplished through imaginative friends or educational toys, it is part of a child's world.

PLAY AND IMAGINATION

Behold the wonders of your child's imagination! Evan rushes to park his bike on the front walk, grabs the coiled rope hanging off the back, and dashes for the front door. "Fire! Hurry! Spray the flames!" he shouts breathlessly, aiming the rope's end at the porch. Then circling back to the garage for assistance, he reaches for a make-believe axe to chop open an invisible door. One slightly amused black Labrador lifting her head for a second, curiously looks on. She's seen similar antics a million times before.

At three years of age, make-believe and other imaginative activities begin to occupy an important place in the child's mental world. Imagination will do what curiosity cannot. It will carry a child beyond the boundaries of time and space. It can take him to places he has never been. He can move mountains with his imagination and test his own feelings without fear of reprisal. Through the imaginative process, a child gives life to inanimate objects, while assuming a controlling role as chief operator of his own play.

In *On Becoming Toddlerwise* we shared the story of two-year-old R. J. and the Tommy Train he received for his birthday. At this age, R. J. showed only curious interest in the Tommy Train box cars and engine. He touched the tracks, spun the wheels, and even tried to stack the cars. But he did not understand how to play with a train.

At three years of age, the train set came out again and curiosity gave way to R. J.'s developing imagination. Now a more dominant cognitive process began to rule R. J.'s thinking. Now he plays the role of engineer. His mind constructs mountainous terrains out of pillows, wobbly bridges from a shoe box, and special tunnels through the legs of a chair. Train sounds begin to accompany each circle of the track as the train became real in R. J.'s mind. Big changes took place in one year. The same will happen with your child.

There is more! Your child's imagination is facilitated by another significant facet of a child's life, and that is play. Sometimes your child's imagination can interfere with your reality. Perhaps you casually remove the stuffed brown monkey from the kitchen counter only to learn you've inadvertently cut short the show he is performing for an audience of one. Now someone besides the monkey is decidedly unhappy. Other times, and this is the good stuff, your child's imagination enhances your reality. In other words, Mom should take advantage of the child's imagination to achieve some healthy goals. Like when the lumps of steamed broccoli become foot soldiers preparing to march off to war against the formidable flu germ enemy causing his cold. Get clever, make his imagination work for you.

Play, whether a child does it by himself, in a small group, or with Mom at the park, is one of the most underestimated and often misunderstood components of a child's healthy, developing cognitive world. Play creates learning opportunities and experiences that uniquely connect a child to his world, which otherwise could not be obtained. Through play, a child is first introduced to problem solving techniques, development of moral and social skills, improved motor coordination, logic, reasoning, and strategy. Plus, play has educational value and provides therapeutic benefits. Play complements and reinforces gender identification and encourages appropriate risk-taking.

Overall, play is the single most important means by which a child connects with his world and the people around him. Think of play as the hub on a wagon wheel. Moving from the center outward, spokes connect to the outer rim of life and learning. Play generates multiple activities that go into shaping the child, reinforcing values and stimulating learning. Please take note of this in our wagon wheel diagram on the next page. Everything about play accents a child's understanding of his world. From right and wrong to parental expectations, play reveals in a public way how a child thinks, reasons, and applies concepts learned the day before. Through his imaginative play, he mimics actions, traits, and social expectations by becoming another person and in this way he gains the experience of self-confidence necessary for proper socialization. By denying a child opportunity to play, a parent is in grave danger of collapsing the bridge connecting a child's discovery, knowledge, and experience to learning.

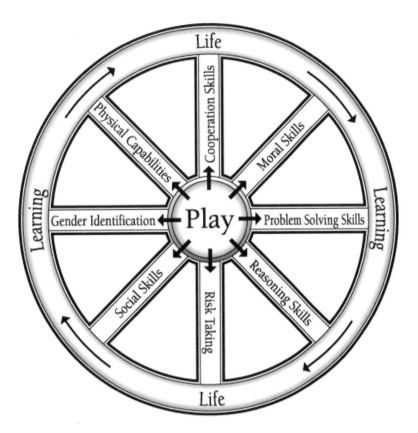

THE BENEFITS OF PLAY

Play is your child's tutor. It goes far beyond simply encouraging learning activities. Through attraction, it becomes a means by which a child stretches himself beyond his present circumstances. He takes chances. When you think about it, play often contains an element of risk. There is some risk involved when a child ventures out on his first steps without the aid of Mom or Dad. There is risk involved when a child shares a new toy with a visiting friend or for the first time, reaches out to pet the neighbor's puppy. There is risk involved when a child stands on a stage reciting a single line in the Thanksgiving play. He takes risks whenever the group's activities call for running, jumping, and bumping. There is risk associated with being picked on a team or not picked at all. In this sense, play motivates a child to step beyond the present to a new level of experience.

Play also has important educational value. During playtime a child picks up, manipulates, and studies toys of all types. He learns shapes, colors, sizes, and textures and how parts of object fit the whole of the object. His mobility allows the development of life through the games he plays and the contact he makes with others. In time a child learns to formulate plans, develop strategies, and exercise his assessment skills in problem-solving because of play.

Developing socialization skills is one of the corollary affects of education. Through play, children learn that their personal gratification often depends on the cooperation of other children. Play teaches children about partnership, teamwork, and fair play. It is through play that a child's primitive understanding about "rules" is reinforced, because most games have rules. Interestingly, while the home environment may be more forgiving or patient with the bending of the game rules, it is quickly apparent to your child that his playmates are far less tolerant of a rule being violated. He quickly learns that he must "follow the rules" or be at the mercy of his peer group.

Play is also therapeutic both physically and emotionally. Physical play releases the pent-up energy stored during times of sitting still. That is why recess time at the school yard is so noisy and fun-filled. The children are released to play with others. Physical play is a pressure valve allowing for the release of energy. In the preschool years, play must have some outside activity that has a physical dimension attached. Swinging, chasing after the dog, marching in Dumbo's imaginary parade, hide-and-seek, or any activity that can get their little hearts pumping, growing legs moving, and developing minds stimulated provides therapeutic benefits.

Imaginative, emotional play is freeing to your child. Such play allows him to test his desires, fears, and hopes without the risk and hardships of judgments and boundaries associated with reality. He is able to think outside the boundaries of logic, reason, and reality. He is able to manage and direct ideas that only he understands and he does it in fragmented ways. He can take a big box and a blanket, make it become first Davy Crockett's fort, then a service station for his trucks, followed by a broadcast booth like the one he saw yesterday on television at the Macy's Thanksgiving Day parade. In any event, the child is in control of something he can control and should control. Children need to be able to control some things. Parents too often err in allowing these "things" to be Mom and Dad instead of the events of imaginative play.

A child's imagination leads to other forms of play. Children mimic. Have you notice that? In our opening example, three-year-old Ashley recounted what she knew about going to the store with Mom and let her imagination direct her play toward her dolls. Obviously, she had an impression from her life that she transferred into her make-believe world. Thus both imitation and imagination work hand in hand.

The value of such play is worth noting. It not only stimulates a child's thinking, but also reflects what he is learning and how he is learning it. The next time you overhear your child's one-way conversation, listen carefully to the tone of voice used. For better or for worse, you might hear your own. Another aspect of play is the element of repetition. Much more is taking place in a child's's play than what appears on the surface. Repetition gives the child the chance to consolidate skills needed to solve board games and puzzles, to stack blocks or connect Hot Wheels racing tracks. Even though your child appears to be doing the same thing over and over again, his activities are leading somewhere. For example, a four-year-old may have mastered elementary motor skills necessary for running and dodging a ball. Repetitious play advances him to the next level of skill called 'anticipation', where movements are predicated not as a response to the person throwing the ball, but to the anticipated throw itself. Here again, strategy, thinking, and reasoning skills merge to bring the reward of success. Success and accomplishment reinforce the cycles of learning.

Anticipation is not limited to the realm of physical movement, but extends also to imaginative activity. To have expectations based on the belief of what will happen tomorrow, a child must be able to imagine. Imagining what will happen next, good or bad, is part of the thinking exercise of our humanity. Parents give little consideration to the fact that if a child is in any way deprived of imaginative emotional play, either through discouragement or the lack of freedom at self-play, he will equally be deprived of what it is to know hope. For hope itself is not only a measure of the imagination transcending time and space, but of our very humanity. It all comes back to the importance of play.

Play also contains the element of construction. Man by nature is a builder. The Jewish Old Testament gives an account of a man named Nimrod, called "the builder of cities" (Genesis 10:6–12). In fact, he built eight mighty cities by which he established his kingdom. One component of play common among children worldwide is the construction component. Children are builders and their efforts reflect the knowledge of our day. With their amazing imaginations, they construct buildings, boats, spaceships, mountains, overpasses, and tunnels. They use blocks, sticks, paper, and grass. They erect tall buildings out of discarded oatmeal boxes and bridges out of spare Lincoln Logs. Complete with sound effects, little boys move massive amounts of soil with their powerful diesel trucks, which may be nothing more than a thick piece of tree bark. Little girls also use construction in their play, but tend to make finer and more delicate objects such as doll clothes and paper dolls. They set up beautiful tea parties and arrange their neat little house with a few empty cardboard boxes, a folding chair, and a spare blanket. They love Grandma's old dresses and play endless hours as beautiful princesses or fancily dressed ladies right out of old Victorian neighborhoods.

It is through the medium of play that a child first develops his sense of fairness and cooperation. It is in play that moral strengths and weaknesses show up. How your child moves the board game pieces, scores his game, follows the rules, and shares with others reflects his developing moral identity. The child that sulks because he didn't get his own way or bullies, manipulates, or quits a game because he is not winning reveals much about a child's underdeveloped sense of fairness, sharing, cooperation, and justice. Play not only reveals moral strengths and weakness, but in the right or wrong environments, it can encourage both.

Such moral attitudes, healthy and not-so-healthy, develop early and are continually reinforced by moral lessons taught throughout the day. Lessons in right and wrong and consideration for others drive a child's social experience. Children do not like bullies and quitters, but they enjoy children who know how to play by the rules and are willing to share. Your child's moral sense creates either a positive, rewarding, and affirming response from other children or rejection. Most socialized play will always have a moral component. How well prepared is your child?

PLAY HAS LIMITS

Does play have limits? Yes, several. Play has developmental, emotional, intellectual, and moral limits.

Play Has Developmental Limits

The technical word among clinicians for developmental limitations is 'maturation.' Before certain types of play can be attempted, a child must demonstrate a level of maturity that includes the readiness of the mind and necessary motor skills to participate. If a child lacks basic eye-hand coordination, he is not ready for T-ball any more than he is ready for an international Ping-Pong competition. But there is more to consider. Significant yet often elusive complements of physical readiness are the mental activities associated with play. These include a child's level of interest, his willingness to take chances, his self-confidence in play, his ability to overcome fearful anticipation of play, and the ability to handle defeat or victory that comes from play.

Also, the personal satisfaction derived from being able to do something well is an important influence on a child's development of "self." This was not a concern for your two-year-old, but it will be a concern for your four-year-old. If a child is rushed into any type of physical play that leaves him continually on the short end of victory because of his lack of readiness skills, he tends to back away from other good avenues of play that can lead him to competency in other areas of his life. When a child begins to shun games that test his skills because of a pattern of failure, he tends to form defensive strategies that carry into other areas of endeavor including school, friendships, and his own sense of self-worth. A child who holds dearly to the belief that "I cannot" because of repeated failures often translates this belief later in life to "I will not even try because I will fail." Be careful not to push your child prematurely into organized play activities prior to his readiness.

Play has emotional limits

"My four-year-old falls apart if he does not win!" This statement usually signals that a child is playing a game beyond his emotional readiness. Do not push your children into games or types of play for which they are not emotionally ready. Some games are too emotionally challenging for children. Your four-year-old should not be playing the marble-dice board game, 'Aggravation' (by Milton-Bradley/Hasbro). The repetitive range of emotions experienced from excitement and anticipation of victory to a sudden loss of all your marbles (literally and figuratively) and imminent defeat are far too many emotional ups and downs for a young child to handle. We are not saying that your child should avoid games that challenge his emotions and test his limits. We are saying it is wise to avoid games that are developmentally beyond his emotional limitations. If your child is routinely falling apart emotionally, the games he is playing are beyond his age-readiness. This often happens when children are playing games with their older siblings that are designed for that sibling's age. Going to bed with tears and a sense of defeat does not make for sweet dreams for your little darling.

Play has intellectual limits

Because of differences in cognitive skill levels and childhood interests, children need to participate in types of play that fit their intellectual needs and abilities and can challenge their thinking without crushing their spirit. Pushing a child into a game before he is intellectually ready does not serve the child well. No matter how insistent your four-year-old might be, or how well he can "wheel and deal" with you, do not entertain the idea that he is ready for a game of "Monopoly" (Parker Brothers, 1935). He is simply not ready for the type of competition, the skill level, or the logic of buying and selling Pennsylvania Avenue property. Nor is he able to comprehend underlying meanings or sustain his own interest through the length of time is takes to finish the game. This will only lead to unnecessary four-year-old frustration tantrums.

Play has moral limits

Children from the earliest days of memory face the impact of moral decisions and obligations made on their behalf and by themselves. From the time they were able to first understand language, they were reminded what is good, bad, approved, or naughty. The idea of what they are obligated to do or not do, how to behave or not behave, is fairly imbedded in daily thought and expected conduct. Therefore, any type of play that undermines or is antagonistic to your family's moral values should be avoided. Any type of play that weakens your child's developing conscience undermines the fullness of his public character. Any type of play that interferes with basic respect for parents, property, and other people must be discouraged.

When you compromise the moral aspect of play, all sorts of bad things can happen to your child's mental world, from poor self-esteem to poor play habits. In time, this leads to weakened friendships and shunning from other kids. On and on the downward spiral goes when lines of moral play including fairness, sharing, and following the rules are crossed. The best prevention that parents can provide when it comes to play is stressing to their children that it must be "play by the rules" or "do not play at all."

Play has gender limits

Every grandma knows that if you put a toy car, ball, stick, doll, blanket, and dishes in a room, little boys immediately gravitate toward the car, ball, and stick while little girls drift to the doll, blanket, and dishes. It really does not matter where a child is from, whether it be a complex society likes ours or a simple tribal setting in the rain forest, little boys have a trail of masculine adjectives that distinctly separate them from little girls. Social conditioning? There might be some, but not sufficient enough to alter male and female predispositions embedded in nature's endowment of gender. The fact is, male and female brains are wired differently. Yes, little boys love trucks and little girls love dolls.

We bring this up as encouragement and as a warning. When it comes to play, parents should not attempt to gender-neutralize their little boys or girls, but rather appreciate the differences and work with each propensity. A delightful example of this was demonstrated by Dr. George Lazarus, an associate clinical professor of pediatrics at New York City's Columbia University College of Physicians and Surgeons. He recounted a mother sensitive to gender-neutrality who gave her daughter several toy trucks only to find her daughter later tucking them into bed.

Understanding gender difference helps parents make proper evaluations about their child's progress both in play and life. It helps avoid speculative evaluations. For example, when a mother says, "But his sister was talking at his age," she is making a comparison in language development. But research confirms that girls tend to have a verbal advantage over boys early on. They speak sooner and more comprehensively by three years of age than their male counterparts who arrive at the same level of competency around age four-and-a-half years.

Yet, boys have other strengths including aptitudes for math skills and completing calculations in their heads sooner then girls. Even the construction of their building blocks demonstrates gender predispositions, or lack of, toward engineering tendencies. Boys are also wired for action. That might be one reason they are always on the go, while their sisters are content to sit and play with their dolls or be entertained in a single location. This is why play is so very different for each.

Finally, notice how little boys play together compared to how little girls play. Girls are more relational and will work together to accomplish a common goal. Boys however, are far more likely to try and do things "on their own." Of course, any wife understands this truth. Just think through the times you may have offered directions to your husband only to hear, "I know where I'm going," as he is starts again to make a wrong turn.

SUMMARY

It is almost startling to realize just how important play is to a child's emotional, moral, and social development. Play is not simply an activity that a child wants to absorb himself in; it is a necessary framework for understanding his world. As we have seen previously, play involves many facets and connects children to life in many ways.

But this too can be taken to an extreme with the old adage, "if a little is good, more must be better." Play is not an isolated experience in a child's life, but only one significant component surrounded by other aspects of learning. Not all education comes in the form of play. A child will learn from playing with a toy, but more importantly, he must develop specific skills that he can only gain at the hands of Mom and Dad. Sitting, focusing, and concentrating skills are not play, but they are necessary aspects for life. Following instructions and being kind, fair, and honest will be used in play, but are not necessarily learned there. The learning process of these skills starts with Mom and Dad's acute awareness that a three-year-old heart is in need of training to think about the feelings of others first.

Questions and Answers About Mr. and Mrs.

This appendix is related to Chapter 7 and our discussion of Mr. and Mrs. There are a number of common questions raised as a result of that lesson. The following addresses the ten most commonly asked questions.

QUESTION ONE:
What do you do when someone does not want to be addressed by their last name?

Explain that you have chosen to have your children use these terms as a vehicle to communicate the biblical principle of respecting elders. Most adults will agree with your goals and comply with your desires to provide this tool for your children. In some cases, an adult may insist that your children not address them by their last name. Consider the context, the preciousness of others, and your child's moral maturity and determine if deferring to the adult's preference in this situation would be appropriate. Your children can also address people in positions of authority by their titles rather than their name. "Coach", "teacher", and "pastor" are examples of this. There is always a way to put a principle into action!

QUESTION TWO:
What should our children call their babysitter?

When our children babysat, children called them Miss Amy and Miss Jenny. That title reinforced the position of authority in the child's mind, while acknowledging that the babysitter was not yet an adult.

QUESTION THREE:
What about the grandparent type of relationships children have with older members of the church?

Whether your child is in a babysitting relationship or acquainted with a close family friend through church, the title "Grandma" or any other term of endearment would be appropriate. The same is true with very close friends of the family. There is nothing wrong with children calling a very close nonbiological friend "Aunt" or "Uncle," but it should only be with a few of them—not the entire church!

QUESTION FOUR:
How should young adults address older adults?

That answer really depends on both your personal preference and that of the person being addressed. As we move into adulthood (21 years of age), our peer group relationships may expand to 30 or 40 years. A 21-year-old may be in a peer relationship with a person who is 55. In this situation, addressing him by his first name would be appropriate.

QUESTION FIVE:
Can my child feel as close to our friends if he calls them Mr. and Mrs.?

Yes, absolutely!

QUESTION SIX:
What should a child call a stepparent?

We can recommend some basic guidelines, but no hard-and-fast rules. If you are in a stepparent relationship with children under three or four years of age, you may be able to get away with the stepparent being called Mom or Dad. Over this age, the biological parent should be called Mom or Dad, and the stepparent should be addressed by their first name or by another term of endearment.

The reason for the first name in the latter situation is because you cannot force upon a child a maternal or paternal relationship that is not naturally there. From the child's perspective, you may be a husband to his mother, but that does not make you his father. You may be a wife to his dad, but that does not make you his mother.

Mr. and Mrs. or Sir and Ma'am are too formal for this type of relationship. On the other hand, Mom or Dad may not be appropriate or fair to the child who already has a history or memories of his natural parent.

QUESTION SEVEN:
What about the child who uses Mr. and Mrs. but does not have a respectful attitude, as compared to the child that does have a respectful attitude and still calls an adult by his first name? Is not the second child more respectful than the first?

Absolutely! The attitude and heart of your child is most important. The biblical principle of respect for elders is the goal you are pursuing. However, it is important to remember that with children actions precede beliefs. Training your child to use titles of respect provides a practical tool for a child to reflect an attitude that is consistent with the biblical standard of respect. Titles are helpful vehicles, but do not elevate the vehicle to the same level of the principle that is behind it.

QUESTION EIGHT:
How do we start introducing the titles Mr. and Mrs. with friends who are used to being called by their first names?

Start with those who are supportive and understand what you are attempting to accomplish—possibly the members of your *Growing Kids God's Way* class. For those who are unfamiliar with what you are learning, let them know what you are doing as a family without becoming a fanatic or arguing over the issue. (See question one for help with those who do not seem to be supportive of this change.) As new friends enter your life, begin your relationship with Mr. and Mrs.

QUESTION NINE:

Will my child become confused during the transition period when I start introducing my friends as Mr. and Mrs.?

No. Children do not have a problem adapting—only adults do. You can help your child, though, by letting him know that when he cannot remember someone's last name, he can address the person as Sir or Ma'am, whichever is appropriate.

QUESTION TEN:

Should I concern myself with how other children address me?

Yes and no. Your primary concern is training your own children. You are not responsible for someone else's child. If a child calls you by your first name, you can say to them, "I would prefer to be called Mrs. Smith." You can also take advantage of natural opportunities to introduce yourself as Mr. or Mrs. For example, when you phone a friend's home and the children answer, say to them, "Hi, Ryan, this is Mr. Brown calling. Is your dad home?" If a child is visiting, ask for his help. "Ryan, will you please take this dish outside and give it to Mrs. Smith?"

SUMMARY

It is worth restating that the use of the titles Mr. and Mrs. is not a biblical principle but a vehicle to deliver the principle. A child should acknowledge that time has not made him equal to adults in life's experience, wisdom, and knowledge. It is a valid way to fulfill the command of Leviticus 19:32.

Growing Kids Topic Pool

Sometimes you just need something extra. Even Mary Poppins with all her charm relied upon a spoonful of sugar to "help the medicine go down." And while we cannot promise you toys that march by themselves to their box, we do have a few nifty tools and ideas to share that can help your little one march to the beat of your drum. Bearing in mind that every child is unique, often requiring an added measure of effort in specific areas, we offer the following topic pool of ideas, suggestions, and explanations. We have consolidated a number of common topics of interest into one location to better serve your query. This final appendix is both practical and highly relevant to parents of our day. For convenience sake, we arranged the topic pool in alphabetical order. You will want to become familiar with the list. Parents will typically come back to this resource many times over, sometimes in just one day. Also, please remember there are many more parenting resources available on the minsitry website at: www.GrowingFamiliesUSA.com.

ENCOURAGEMENT TOOLS
Parents all over the world have found the following three activities to be a great way to motivate children to do chores, care for others, pick up their toys in a timely manner, and be responsible.

Cheerful Chore Cards

Let's face it, getting kids to do their chores can be tiresome. Mom is constantly prodding and endlessly checks for progress; the children are stalling, whining, and bickering. It almost makes a parent want to just give up and give in. Family chores play a significant role in building loyalty, unity, and responsibility into your child. Therefore, parents must find a way to work through the agony of getting a child to do his chores. Connie Hadidian, author of *Creative Family Times*, offers a creative approach to accomplishing family chores for preschool-age children.

You'll need colored three-by-five-inch index cards, an index card box, three-by-five-inch dividers, and a black marker. Divide your chore card box into four sections. Pick one color to use for each child's personal tasks (i.e., blue for Matthew's personal tasks, red for Rachel's). Personal chores include making the bed, brushing teeth, picking up the child's room, etc. Choose another color to represent chores that your children are capable of doing. The book *What Every Child Should Know Along the Way* helps parents decide what chores their children are capable of doing at a given age. Paste or draw a picture on all the cards to represent the task or chore you want your child to be responsible for. Finally, pick a color of cards to be used as special "See Mom for a treat" cards.

Here is how it works. Each morning, Matthew's chore cards are placed out for him on the kitchen table or the counter. This will consist of his personal task cards and his chore cards. Mom sets the kitchen timer for an appropriate amount of time. Matthew works through his cards, flipping each facedown when the task is completed until all chores are done. They must all be done before the timer goes off.

The last card in Matthew's stack reads, "See Mom if you think you are done." This card is helpful for two reasons. First, it lets you know if the chores are done before the timer goes off, and second, you can check to see if the job is done to your satisfaction. Every once in a while, Mom throws in the special card, "See Mom for a treat." When your child discovers this, after his squeals of delight die down, express your appreciation for how well he is doing. The special treat might be going out for an ice cream cone, a dollar bill, or some other small treat.

Here are some advantages to this method:

- It takes only a few minutes each morning to gather the children's chore cards for the day, or you can put them out the night before.
- It teaches children responsibility and self-discipline.
- The system is flexible. You can add or delete chores as needed and as your child grows older.

Here are a few more samples of chores age-appropriate to children:

- Dress themselves
- Make bed
- Wipe up their own minor spills
- Help set and clear table (do not expect perfection)
- Put dirty clothes in hamper
- Pick up socks and shoes
- Empty small wastebaskets
- Dust baseboards and bottom of kitchen chairs

While none of the above will be accomplished exactly the way you would like, these activities are getting the child into the habit of tidiness. Keep it simple, stay with it, and please remember the following helpful guidelines:

- Do not expect him to do the task alone the first time. Work alongside him until he understands what to do and how to do it himself.
- Do less and less for your child as he becomes more and more responsible.
- Praise your children for great attitudes and jobs well done!

Finally, regarding motivation, remember that simply getting outward performance is not the goal of your parenting. The goal is to help create a servant's heart in your children. Chores are one way to teach the virtue of otherness (putting the needs of others before yourself). Your children need to feel that they are important contributing members of your family. Having them do chores is one way to accomplish this, and yes, it can start as early as age three.

Charting Positive Action

By using the principles in Chapters Nine and Eleven, we believe you will begin to see progress in the correction arena. However, sometimes we all need something a little extra. The Positive Action Chart is a nifty tool that can move a child from the not-doing-wrong stage into the spontaneously-doing-right stage. This calls for the creation of a colorful chart. Make a special trip to the craft store with your little one to purchase the needed material. Let your child help create the chart, as this will further enhance his ownership of it. Select poster board and markers and a variety of fun-filled stickers. Before creating the chart, consider specific traits you would like to see developed in the heart of your child. Love, joy, peace, patience, kindness, goodness, faithfulness, gentleness, and self-control are good starting points. These form a portrait of a tender heart that looks to the needs of others before his own.

On the left-hand column of your chart, list the attributes we mentioned above. Write the days of the week across the top. Now post this chart in a prominent place in your home. The kitchen is a good place, or your child's bedroom—if you do not mind him dragging every visitor into his room to check out the cool poster the two of you created. Here's how it works. Each time your child demonstrates one of the positive attributes on the chart, you point it out. You explain exactly what happened and how it relates to the desirable trait. He gets to put a sticker on the chart. When you start actively looking for, say, kindness, you may find it where you least expect it. This can be surprising to moms who have been focused on restraining the negative behavior of their children. Watch how your child's face lights up as you begin to notice the good, inspiring actions he does every day. This will encourage him to keep up the good work!

For areas of development where your child needs extra help, offer bigger stickers when that trait is demonstrated. For every ten stickers that are accumulated on the chart, a reward is given. This may be a trip to the ice cream parlor, or purchasing a new book. When fifty stickers have been accumulated, create a wonderful memory for your child to savor, such as a trip to the zoo. The encouragement he receives from seeing his own virtues mount up is worth more to him than any scoop of mint chip or visit with a chimpanzee. However, it is nice to be rewarded for the good things he does! Being recognized for a job well done is a major shot in the arm in his journey toward the kind of character any parent could be proud of.

Marbles for a Cause

GFI leaders Tom and Evangeline Reed offer this great idea. There are days when Mom feels like a referee, sorting out battles between siblings. Much of this strife is caused by tattling. "Mommy! Justin hit me!" is a frequent refrain heard in homes where more than one child resides. We have another helpful tool parents can use to promote harmony in the home.

Get a large plastic jar and a bag of marbles. Whenever anyone catches another family member doing something good, he gets to put a marble in the jar on behalf of that person. When the jar is full, the family chooses something fun to do together. When another family member puts a marble in the jar because a child did something good, this alone is enough immediate recognition to inspire similar behavior in the future. Do not think of this as a type of bribe. The difference between a bribe and a reward is this: A bribe is offered upfront. Beth gets a piece of candy before she picks up her toys. That's a bribe. A reward is given after the desired behavior occurs. Beth gets a piece of candy after she picks up her toys because she did so without being reminded. That's a reward.

To avoid dependency on rewards, some ground rules must be established. First, no one gets to put a marble in the jar because he did something good. Someone else has to notice another's goodness. Second, there may be no complaining if a child's "good deed" goes unnoticed. Sometimes life will be unfair. But that is when you teach your children that we all should be willing to do good things, not for the praise of another man but simply because it is the right thing to do.

Before you start, you must actually consider what the desirable traits look like in order to not overlook too many. For example, following through on a task is faithfulness. Not crying when a treasured candy is dropped and crushed in a carnival stampede is surely self-control. Playing nicely together for a prolonged period of time brings much-treasured peace. And sharing a new birthday present with another anxious onlooker demonstrates love. Take a few minutes during dinner for family members to share the good things other family members have done. When Mom and Dad agree that the thing mentioned is worthy of a marble, then the child gets to put it in the jar.

Teaching the "Three Candy Speed"

Your little guy's dentist appointment is in just a few minutes. You completely forgot about it last month, so you want to be on time. All you've got to do is have your son pick up his markers and put away his paper. You instruct him to do so. He gives you a nice "Yes Mommy" and begins to clean up. But for some reason you feel like you've entered the "Twilight Zone." Right before your eyes, your son, who normally has all the energy in the world, suddenly goes limp on you. He moves slower than the 1950's movie, *The Blob*. "Sammy, you have to pick up your crayons right now." One marker is picked up. Pause. Another marker. Yawn. "Come on, Sammy. Now! I mean it. We have to get going." One more marker. Pause. Another marker. Scratch. "Sammy, move faster! Sammy, we're going to be late because of you. Come on, Sammy, move faster!" For Mom, this whole episode has transformed into a slow-motion dream. Each of the boy's limbs seem attached to an invisible stretchy web, pulling against him as he reaches for the marker's purple cap.

What's happening here? Clearly, he sees your rush to get out of the house. You prompt him, reminding him to hurry so you do not steal the dentist's time by being late. You find yourself rambling on with insignificant, energy-draining adult reasoning until you are ready to scream. Instead, you clean the coffeepot, stick some glasses in the dishwasher, nervously glancing over your shoulder at the clock, then at your son to check his progress. You know he can move faster. But how do you get him to pick up the pace without sounding like a slave master?

The problem is that your child doesn't know what "fast" looks like. It is an abstract concept. Three Candy Speed is a way to show him what accelerated movement is. Surely if your child's favorite candy waited at the end of his task, you'd see lightning-fast movement on his part. You might be thinking that we are encouraging you to bribe your child. Not at all. Keep reading!

Try this sometime when you're not rushed. Begin with a slight mess that your child needs to pick up. Put three small pieces of candy on the counter, and call your child over. Tell him that you are going to set the timer and that he should begin cleaning up when you do so. Inform him that if the toys are picked up and neatly put away, these three pieces of candy will be his reward. At this point, his energy is on full alert and he takes his mark. Go! The child moves faster than you've ever seen, thus beating the timer. This is his Three Candy Speed. You just established in concrete form a benchmark of time that becomes a future reference point for you both.

While Sammy is consuming the candy (and before the sugar rush kicks in), sit him down and explain to him that the speed he just moved at is called Three Candy Speed. You need to tell him that he will not be getting candy every time you ask him to do something. In fact, this is the only time he will get candy for moving fast. Tell him you just wanted him to feel himself going fast so that later, when you need him to move quickly, you can just tell him to go at Three Candy Speed, and he'll know what that feels like. The next time you need to get moving lickety-split, all you have to do is tell him to pick up his toys at Three Candy Speed.

FEARS OF CHILDHOOD

How old were you when you first saw the ghoulish monkeys dispatched by the wicked witch of the west to pick up Dorothy and her dog, Toto? Do you remember the scene of winged monkeys spreading the gentle Scarecrow "here, there, and everywhere"? These scenes from the movie, *The Wizard of Oz*, when observed by this writer, were some of the most frightening scenes that a twelve-inch black-and-

white screen could project to the pounding heart of an eight-year-old boy.

Fear! It is part of the overall human experience and not simply a childhood phenomenon. Some childhood fears might appear irrational, even silly, to parents because they do not arise from any real external danger, but they are very real to your child and should be respected as such. Although the cause of fears may not always be discovered, we know there are general categories of fear that children experience. Knowing the origin of fears may not always eliminate them, but it may lead parents to better management and reduction of fearful stimuli. Consider these sources:

• Natural Fears—In spite of the fact that fears vary from child to child, there is evidence that certain fears are characteristically found at specific ages. These are referred to as "typical fears." Many fears are learned from direct association of experiences with fearful stimuli. The most frequently displayed fears for children come from animals such as dogs, snakes, and rats. These are followed by the fear of strange people, being left alone, and dark or high places.

• Fear of the Unfamiliar—Among the primary fears of young children is the fear of the strange and unfamiliar (strange from the point of view that something stands apart from the child's previous experience). It could be a person, event, situation, or activity. This type of fear takes place because young children do not have cognitive tools to adequately measure the legitimacy of their fear and thus lack the ability to understand the cause and effect associated with fearful situations. For example, a child with an ice-cream cone may not understand that it was the food that attracted the neighbor's puppy and not a wolflike desire to devour the child. Yet the fear, although misplaced, is still very real in the mind of the child.

• Developing Imagination—We have already discussed the developmental benefits of a child's imagination in Appendix Two, *Let Them Play*. Imagination can also create fearful expectations, especially when the imagination develops faster than the child's reasoning abilities. Imaginary fears include ghosts, skeletons, bogeymen, or any combination of the above.

• False Beliefs—Some fear is the result of bad experiences, such as the fear of the dentist or the hospital or a visit to the doctor's office. The frightening experience becomes an expected reality and thus apprehensiveness occurs. Your child will even react with fear to a new situation that in and of itself, normally would not arouse fear. Other fears are passed on to children by the false beliefs of their parents, siblings, and friends.

• Parental Anxiety—Parents sometimes unwittingly arouse fears in their children and introduce attitudes of apprehension by their own overprotective anxiety. Constant warnings of restraint such as "Be careful, you are going to fall down," "Do not pet the dog or he will bite," "Do not climb in the tree or you will fall and break your leg," or "Do not go by the road you might get hit by a car" might keep a child in an atmosphere of fear and continuous dread. Note the operative word above is constant. Of course there will be times in which you might say all of the above. This is not the same as constant warnings of danger that place a child in a perpetual state of anxiety about his own welfare.

Helping Children Manage and Overcome Fear

Some fears need to be managed, while other fears can be overcome with time and education. Here are some facts and suggestions to consider while working with your child's fears.

• Fear itself is not a cure for fear—Forcing a fearful child to "face his fears" is not the best way to help him overcome them, nor is ridiculing a child for being afraid or commanding him to ignore his fears. This approach goes against the very thing the child needs—that being the full confidence that his burden of fear is being shared with Mom and Dad or big brother or sister. Ridiculing and name-calling are antagonistic forces to companionship and trusting relationships.

• Education—Methods that promote self-confidence are the best ways to help children overcome their fears, and this can be done in part through education. Children are less likely to be fearful if they have some understanding of the object of fear. When the child learns that the puppy's actions are playful not threatening, and that the snake is behind the glass and cannot get out, or that thunder has an explanation, he will better be able to manage potential fear with the assurance brought by such knowledge. Educating a child about his natural fears is one of the best ways to reduce fear that parents can use with their child.

• Getting acquainted—Giving your child opportunity to get acquainted with the fearful object or situation is another form of education. This may take time since the child's confidence in the knowledge of what is safe must grow stronger than the fearful experience of the past. Gradually introducing your child to the object of dread through role-playing, actual encounter with the object, or parental example helps alleviate his fears. When your child sees that Mom is not afraid to play with the puppy, he will join in the fun and in time overcome his fear. In contrast, if Mom overreacts to the excited puppy by hopping on a chair, the child will not be far behind her.

• Removing fearful stimuli—Remove all inappropriate fearful stimuli from your child's life. *The Wizard of Oz* is not a movie for preschool-age child to watch. Even the movie *Dumbo* can create apprehension. Poor little Dumbo, separated from his Mom and forced to work the circus scene as an oddity, is way beyond the context of your child's sense of security. Take note of what your child is watching on television, including cartoons. Given the state of the world, even the nightly news can be fear-provoking to children (and adults).

• Substitution, not just suppression—Universal in application, this particular suggestion should not be limited to the single category of fear, but applied to any circumstance that employs moral and virtuous opposites. For example, the Ezzos were once approached by a father asking how to deal with his son's obsessive jealousy. That question leads to a broader one—how do you deal not only with jealousy, but all attitudes of the heart and emotions, including fear? Children of all ages are better served by substitution than by suppression. The father mentioned above was frustrated by his efforts to suppress his son's jealousy. No matter how hard he tried to keep the lid on it, jealousy continued to leak out.

The problem here and for many parents is not simply the presence of a vice or a weakness, but the absence of a virtue and strength. Suppression of wrong behavior is often achieved by encouraging the opposite virtue. If you want to suppress jealousy, give equal time to elevating the opposite virtue, which in this case is contentment. If you have a child struggling with envy, teach charity. For anger, teach self-control. For revenge, teach forgiveness. Substitution will make all the difference in the world. This same principle applies to childhood fears. Often the problem is not the presence of fear but rather the absence of courage. Parents, by the language they use, tend to focus primarily on the fear (the negative) and not on courage (the positive). Instead of saying, "Do not be afraid," parents should consider saying instead, "Be brave" or "Be courageous." This type of encouragement is not meant to satisfy a moment of fear, but to establish a pattern of belief for a lifetime.

• Prevention—Most of the suggestions above that can help overcome fears can also be employed to prevent many fears. Giving a child a heads-up about the neighbor's dog or how loud the fireworks will sound makes good sense. When dealing with young children, some form of pre-activity warning is better than the shock of discovery.

The fears associated with early childhood are significantly different than those of older children and adults. For that reason, parents must demonstrate a liberal amount of patience, empathy and understanding . They should never view their child's fears as "silly", attempt to delegitimize them, or insist their child "toughen up" or "just get over it." Rather, they should become a calming and reassuring voice. After all, the last thing you want to create is a condition in which your child fears telling you about his fears.

MANNERS AT MEALTIME

Back in the colonial days when horse, buggy and Southern plantations were a way of life, visitors to sprawling country estates would often travel days on dusty and muddied roads before arriving at their destination. As a result, they tended to extend their visits for weeks at a time, enjoying the company and hospitality of their host. However, just as it happens today, the guests would sometimes overstay their welcome. . . but unlike today, the ethics of civility ruled all public discourse. No master or mistress of the home would ever be so "forward" to ask their guest to leave, however they did have a unique way of communicating that exact message.

At one of the meals, the host would serve a cold shoulder of mutton or ham, which usually had a higher fat content and thus was a less desirable cut of meat. When the guests received this "cold shoulder" they knew their welcome had come to an end, and a few days later they would be on their way back home. While some social customs surrounding meals have changed over the years, gracious and yes, "civil" mealtime behavior is never out of fashion. Children acquire good manners in two ways: through education and instruction, and by parental example. The latter, of course, is as important as the first. If Dad asks Mom to "Please pass the potatoes" and then replies to Mom with "Thank you," such courtesies are easily accepted by a child as integral parts of his speech and patterns of behavior. The context of mealtime is one of the best for teaching courtesies that have lasting social value. They are "other-regarding" rather than "self-regarding" and hence become a useful tutor in preparing a child for otherness virtues that are necessary to get along with others. In short, good manners become an integral part of a child"s character, and thus a well-mannered child is a gift returned to society.

Good manners will always accompany good morals. Children with good manners shine brightly wherever they go. While sitting with your children in a restaurant, you just might hear the voice of a stranger comment, "What well-mannered children you have. They're so polite." Such compliments are the result of correct training in social graces, particularly in mealtime etiquette, and they are well worth the effort.

Etiquette refers to one's behavior in the presence of others and should manifest itself in a demonstration of courtesy, politeness, and respect. Your goal is to train your child in such a way that he practices these courtesies both at home and away. Listed below are some basic recommendations of politeness and respect as they relate to mealtime behavior. Here are some general courtesies to work on with your kids.

Positive mealtime manners include:

- Complimenting the cook
- Chewing quietly, keeping your mouth closed
- Saying "Please" and "Thank you"
- Not leaning on the table
- Not reaching across the table
- Not stuffing your mouth
- Not talking with your mouth full

Recommendations for Various Mealtime Settings
There are five mealtime settings families will experience. They include:

- Dinner at home with no guests
- Dinner at home with guests
- Buffet-style dinner with guests
- Dinner away from home as guests
- Dinner at a restaurant

Keep in mind, most of these settings require practice at home for a period of time before your child tries his manners on others. Look for conflict-free opportunities and comfortable avenues for introducing these different environments. Invite close friends over specifically for this purpose. Ask a relative if he or she might have you over for lunch, especially if you have an outing on the horizon in which you wish your children to shine. Practice! And remember, your example does make a difference. Do not get so focused on your child's behavior that you forget to praise the meal that is in front of you or the table setting, placemats, or centerpiece. Anything that seems appealing will resonate in your child's mind and provide fuel for future compliments he may make.

The following etiquette suggestions can assist in training your children in gracious mealtime behavior. The following are our recommendations:

Dinner at Home with No Guests
- No one begins to eat until all are seated. This is a very tangible way to show appreciation to the cook and server.
- Children should eat what they are served.
- Children may not play with their food.
- General requests such as "I want more potatoes" should be changed to "Mom, may I have some more potatoes, please?"
- Whatever a little finger touches he must eat. If your child touches a piece of chicken while exploring the plate, he gets the first piece he touched. In this way he shows respect to those he shares the meal with and also learns the social importance of a serving fork and spoon.
- No one starts to eat dessert until the server sits down and joins the family. Everyone eats together. This is similar to the first point above and communicates both appreciation and respect for the server.
- No one leaves the table until everyone has completed their meal. Children especially need to ask their parents to be excused from the table.

Dinner at Home with Guests

In addition to the above, the following two recommendations will help emphasize the importance of showing hospitality and respect for those outside the family who are joining you for a meal in your home.

• Teach your children to honor your guests by offering food to them first. This is a form of hospitality and a sign of welcoming your friends to your table.

• Again, children should not leave the table unless first excused by parents. They should then acknowledge the adult guests with, "Excuse me, Mr. and Mrs. Smith." This is a picture of courteousness.

Buffet-Style Dinner with Guests

Here are few suggestions for entertaining in a buffet style when at home:

• Whenever practical and possible, invite the oldest guests to go through the line first. This is a wonderful gesture of respect for age.

• After the adult guests serve themselves, the children are assisted by the hostess or parents.

• The host and/or hostess should be available at the buffet table for serving and directing. Their presence and supervision will help keep things orderly.

Dinner Away from Home as Guests

There are two additional recommendations that will help your children recognize and respond appropriately to the hosts when in someone else's home for a meal.

• Children should not to begin serving their plates or eating until the host or hostess directs them to do so. This shows respect for the host/hostess.

• Children should not leave the table or wander around unless they ask the host or hostess to be excused (after asking Mom or Dad for permission first).

Dinner at a Restaurant

Taking your children to eat in public settings is not a problem when sufficient training has taken place at home. Added to the recommendations above, these two guidelines fit the restaurant scene.

• Keep dining out simple and limit it to good fast-food restaurants until your child is able to demonstrate social courtesies and politeness in more formalized settings. After all, you are sharing the restaurant with others who are in hopes of enjoying a meal.

• Do not let your children be disruptive or rude. And please remember this—while your child's actions may be cute to you, other diners may not agree with you.

PARENTING YOUR CHILD'S EMOTIONS

"My two-and-a-half-year-old son doesn't like it when I correct his four-year-old brother. He becomes sad because his brother is being taken away for correction and he will lose his playmate. What should I do?" the mother asked. "I'm thinking it might be better if I didn't correct my four-year-old if it makes my two-year-old sad."

Every child enters life with the propensities for both pleasant and unpleasant emotions. Most parents realize this truth and consequently attempt to find ways to make childhood a happy time for their offspring. Parents recognize that a happy child is a pleasure to be with, is easier to teach, and exhibits longer sustained periods of self-control and self-entertainment. But is happiness really the ultimate goal of parenting?

One of the greatest mistakes a parent can make, however, is attempting to parent a child's emotions and not the child. Please note this distinction. We are not saying a child's emotions are not important, but rather attempting to parent the single category of emotions is not the same thing as attempting to parent the whole child. Every child will experience both pleasant and unpleasant emotions. Hopefully, your child will know much more of the first than the second.

The experience of positive emotions, like joy, happiness, affection, esteem and the sense of discovery leads to feelings of security and confidence. This in turn helps the child face and properly react to the negative emotions of worry, jealousy, envy, fear, disappointment, anxiety, and frustration. But parenting to create all the right emotions and avoid all the negative emotions is both unwise and unhealthy. Such an approach holds the parents hostage. Everything is guess work.

When you attempt to create all the right feelings, you abandon other significant values necessary to raise a well-adjusted child. In our opening example, the mom was willing to put aside her four-year-old's wrong behavior to satisfy the happiness of her two-year-old. She was willing to suspend a life-needed lesson in virtuous self-control, a tool of life, for a momentary state of happiness.

If happiness is the highest value to offer children, then other "good" values such as honesty, compassion, self-control, self-entertainment, obedience, submission, and patience are all subservient. If there is a context that pits virtues with the emotion of happiness, then happiness must dominate. But the developmental fallouts with this approach are numerous. The child that is pampered or shielded from unpleasant experiences is ill-prepared to meet the disappointments, frustration, and other unpleasant experiences that life brings. Parenting a single emotion or a range of common emotions is a poor substitute for parenting the whole child—his heart, his head and body, and emotions.

Our evaluation of this situation above brought us back to the principles of parenting the whole child: body, soul, heart, and mind. It is from these four capacities that we are to love the Lord. (c.f. Mark 12:29-30) This mom placed greater value on the younger son's emotions than on her older son's character faults in need of correction. She was willing to allow her older son to bully his sibling for no other reason than she feared her younger son would not be happy for a moment.

We're pleased to say that we were dealing with a very open and teachable mom who created for herself a clever reminder. She hung on her refrigerator door a small chalkboard. On it she wrote, "Parent the whole child, not the single category of emotions." That friendly reminder stayed there until the principle was second nature to her. As a result, today she has a four year-old who shares his things, and a happy two-and-a-half-year-old.

THE SLEEP FACTOR AND CHILDREN'S ABILITY TO LEARN

Last night was a rough one. The dog was barking, and the electricity went out, causing phones to beep and bedside clocks to flash when some time later power was restored. Throughout the ordeal, you stayed horizontal. You do not specifically recall being really awake, although you are aware the outage occurred. The end result is a dead giveaway—this morning you are cranky, edgy, and wondering if an eighteen-wheeler drove across your bed looking for the highway. Simply put, you got a lousy night's sleep and every raw nerve ending on your body stands ready to proclaim it.

Now transfer this sleep quality to your child. When it comes to children, parents tend to think only in terms of two categories; their child is asleep or he is awake. There is actually a gradation of sleep and wake times. Sleep ranges from a completely relaxed state, to active sleep, to groggy wake time, to complete wakefulness. Optimal wakefulness is directly tied to optimal sleep, and optimal development is directly tied to optimal wakefulness.

We cannot overemphasize that point. Children who suffer from the lack of healthy naps and nighttime sleep also experience a type of passive chronic fatigue, effecting maximum alertness. Who would want to live continuously in this condition? While a child may not suspect an off-course tractor trailer, nor even pinpoint the source of his agitation, the effect of too little sleep is equally devastating. It creates an alertness deficit, which further increases the child's inattentiveness while decreasing his focusing and concentrating skills. This child is easily distracted and often physically hyperactive. He is also more demanding, lacking the ability to interact within a learning environment for sustained periods of time. In contrast, children who have established healthy sleep habits are optimally awake and optimally alert to interact with their environment. Having observed a generation of these children now, we see some common threads among the school-age population. In classroom settings, I have consistently found these children to be more self-assured, happier, less demanding, more sociable, inspired, and motivated. They have longer attention spans and become faster learners because they are more adaptable. Mediocrity among this population is rare, while excellence is common.

In our earlier series, *Preparation for Parenting,* we spoke about a child's ability to learn. We noted that while parents cannot alter a child's intelligence quotient, they can maximize or limit it. One way this is done, both positively and negatively, is through sleep. The impact healthy and not-so-healthy sleep has on educational outcomes was first noted in a 1925 study conducted by Dr. Lewis M. Terman. Amazingly, his insights and conclusions related to factors influencing I.Q. continue to stand unchallenged to this day. His study looked at 2,700 children with superior intelligence and found one common link—all of them had experienced healthy nighttime sleep. Good sleep habits are not a child's choice, but a parental decision and are so often impacted by the presence or absence of routine.

QUIETING THE WIGGLES

We introduced this concept in the DVD portion of our presentation and wish to offer it here as well. We know that some of our readership have one. You know, a mover and a shaker, a high energy, perpetual motion, chase-his-own-tail kid. How many times have you tried to slow your little missile down with words such as these: "Calm down," "Settle down," "Sit still," "Stop moving," "Stop kicking," "Put your hands down," or "Sit on your hands"? Has it ever worked for longer than a millisecond?

Have you ever thought about what "settle down" or "slow down" looks like to a three-year-old child? These are abstract concepts, metaphors. A three-year-old doesn't have a clue what you mean. Louise called her friend Jessie in a moment of desperation. "Jessie, I'm getting a little apprehensive about our breakfast meeting with the Ezzos this Saturday. My two little ones do not do well sitting for long periods of time. Help!" "Louise," Jessie said, "there is a nifty little thing that helps children gain self-control in moments when you most want it and they most need it. Are you ready?" "Yes!" came Louise's response. Jessie continued, "When you begin to see those early signs that your kids are going to lose it physically or verbally, instruct them to fold their hands and work on getting some self-control. That is all you need to do."

Louise began the training immediately. She and her family did meet the Ezzos that Saturday for breakfast. Toward the end of the meal, a little wandering leg propped itself up on sister's chair. That would normally be enough of a catalyst to energize the two-and-a-half-year-old and four-year-old into all-out playtime right there in the restaurant—but Mom had another plan. Instead of the classic begs, bribes, and threats, she simply said, "Girls, we're not quite ready to go yet. I want you to fold your hands and get some self-control."

Would you believe that in less than a minute those two little girls sat still, with their hands folded in their laps, subduing their impulsive behavior? And this without a war of words with Mom! Mom then pulled out some crayons and let them color on the paper napkins. Teaching your child that self-control begins with the folding of her hands is a wonderfully concrete way for her to understand calmness. Her eyes focus on those peaceful hands lying still in her lap, and soon physical and verbal self-control is achieved.

We have all heard the slogan that starts out, "An ounce of prevention. . ." Parents should always try to help a child gain self-control before he or she crosses the bridge of trouble, not afterward. The folding of the hands exercise does exactly that. It is a wonderful tool that can be used at grocery checkout counters, school functions, sporting events, dentist's offices, or during that longer-than-usual sermon.

When a young child folds his hands to get self-control, it handles all the excessive body energy that makes self-control so difficult. After all, if you want your child to settle down, his energy has to go somewhere. Now, instead of it going into squabbling, cartwheeling, or whispering, it can go into the hands.

Another amazing thing about hand-folding is how quickly it brings about self-control. Usually only thirty to ninety seconds needs to elapse before Mom can say, "Okay, kids, you can let go of your hands." Your child only needs to fold her hands long enough to gain self-control in that moment. Once that is accomplished, Mom can redirect the child's energy to productive activities (like coloring on paper napkins).

It is important to teach this technique to your children when things are calm. If you are already in conflict, your children are not going to be especially attentive pupils. You may have your child practice this at the table while you finish up last-minute mealtime preparations. Make it a fun game in the beginning. Demonstrate how to achieve self-control during a peaceful time so that when things begin to get out of hand, you've got the cure in place.

This simple technique will become second nature to your child and will work wonders in creating the peace your family deserves.

VACATION/TRAVELING WITH YOUNG CHILDREN

"My husband and I will be traveling for the next couple of weeks with our young son. How do we maintain his routine, especially when we move through other time zones?" This is one of the most common questions received in our office. There are two considerations to focus on when traveling with toddlers and young children: For your infant and/or toddler, begin 1) training your child to sleep other places than in his crib or bed, and 2) adjusting your child's routine to each new time zone.

In preparation for travel, begin a few weeks in advance putting your child down for his naps or nighttime sleep in other places. This will of course depend on the age of your child. Infants can sleep in a playpen. For a couple of nights, put the playpen in the living room, family room or your bedroom. Drape the outside of the playpen on two sides with towels or extra child blankets, then take those blankets or towels along on your trip or borrow some towels when you arrive at your destination. The blankets or towels serve to enclose the child's sleep environment and reduce potential distractions. If your child pulls the towels into the playpen, then stop using them. You want to avoid a situation that could endanger his health or safety. Toddlers can be trained in the same way but use a small mattress that becomes his or her special bed. Be creative with the sheets. Use something fun that he or she would not normally get to sleep on in their own bed.

If your trip is to an adjacent time zone, time adjustments will be fairly automatic. However, when flying through three or four time zones, make the adjustments to your child's routine once you arrive. The type of adjustment depends on whether you are traveling east to west or west to east. With the first, you have an extended day; with the second, you have an early night. If you have an extended day, add another feeding and possibly a catnap. If you go east, split the bedtime difference in half between the old and new time zones. For example, your child's 7:00 p.m. West Coast bedtime is equivalent to 10:00 p.m. East Coast time. Splitting the difference between the two time zones would make your child's first East Coast bedtime 8:30 p.m. Over the next couple of days, work his bedtime back to 7:00 p.m., making as many adjustments as needed to his daytime routine.

We suggest you limit sweet drinks and snacks while traveling. A long trip is a particularly bad time to add extra sugar to your child's diet, and extra snacks can suppress hunger to the point where it can affect behavior. Disrupting your child's routine can affect his sleep/wake cycles, something neither you or your child want to have happen while traveling.

Carla Link provides some practical insights to vacationing with children. She starts with a wisdom warning: There are three things that in combination lead to an out-of-control child. They are; too much sugar and soft drink, too little sleep, and too many freedoms. Avoid these three. Wise parents will plan the best way to manage their children while on vacation. The following are some of her suggestions. Again, please make adjustments for the ages of your children.

1. Looking at the entire vacation, determine how to get naps in for your younger children and rest times for your older preschooler. If it is not possible on a particular day for your child to have a nap, then try to see that he gets to bed earlier than his normal bedtime on that particular night. Over-tired children are difficult to deal with and can easily make vacation a memorable trip for all the wrong reasons! Try to plan your activities so that your child gets to bed at his normal time every other day.

2. If you are staying with relatives and want to go out at night, ask them if they know of teens who will child-sit for you.

3. Try to avoid a steady diet of fast-food. Prepare sandwiches in advance—keep these and fresh fruit and juice in a cooler. If you are going to frequently use hotels, consider purchasing a cooler that serves as a refrigerator (available at truck stops) and can be plugged into a cigarette lighter in a vehicle and with a converter into a wall socket in a hotel room. Your child will behave much better if you avoid giving him pop to drink and fast food and pizza as a steady diet.

4. Do take a Pack-and-Play (playpen) along if your child has not yet transitioned into a bed.

5. If you are driving on a long-trip with your child, figure out how many hours you will be in the car each day. Plan activities for your child using the same schedule you use at home, working in 15 minute to 1/2 hour segments. Rotating toys will keep him occupied for longer periods of time. Many vehicles have some sort of television. Do use videos, but keep in mind the attention span of a child, keep them to 30 minutes and rotate them with other activities.

6. Do stop often for potty breaks at rest stops and let your child run on the grass/picnic area. Give him an inflatable ball to chase around.

7. If you are flying, make sure you take advantage of any opportunity to pre-board. Determine the amount of time you will be traveling, including time sitting between flights, if applicable. Again, using the routine you have at home, rotate activities for your child. If you have a long wait between flights, take your child for a walk so he can burn off some energy before he is expected to sit on the plane again.

8. Check with your airline regarding food options. This seems to change frequently with most

airlines. And remember, airlines now are starting to sell their lunches rather than provide them for free, so pack food for your child and yourself. And do not forget to take his favorite stuffed animal and blanket on the plane.

9. Whenever traveling, whether by car, train, or plane—do take a stroller. If you are limited by weight restrictions, consider purchasing an inexpensive "umbrella" type stroller for the trip. There will be times your child will be too heavy for you to carry. He can't be expected when sight-seeing to "keep up" with those with longer legs. Do realize when you are vacationing in the summer that long periods of time in the sun and heat will wear your child down and make him crankier than usual. If you are vacationing on the beach consider getting a large beach umbrella and have him sit under it for periods of time during the day. This can be used for blanket time. Enjoy your vacation.

Notes and Resources

Barnes, Bob, *What Makes a Man Feel Loved?* (Eugene, OR: Harvest House Publishers, 2006)

Barnes, Emilie, *What Makes a Woman Feel Loved?* (Eugene, OR: Harvest House Publishers, 2007)

Blackaby, Henry and Richard, *Experiencing God Day-By-Day* (Nashville, TN: Broadman and Holmes, 1998)

Chapman, Gary, *The Five Love Languages* (Chicago, IL: Moody Press, 1995)

Decker, Barbara, *Proverbs for Parenting* (Boise, ID: Lynn's Bookshelf, 1987 & 1991)

DeMoss, Nancy Leigh, *Choosing Forgiveness* (Chicago, IL: Moody Press, 2006)

Durbin, Kara, *Parenting with Scripture* (Chicago, IL: Moody Publishers, 2001)

Eggerich, Dr. Emerson, *Love and Respect* (Nashville, TN: Integrity Publishers, 2004)

Ehman, Karen, Kelly Hovermale, and Trish Smith, *Homespun Memories from the Heart* (Grand Rapids, MI: Fleming H. Revell, 2005)

Elliot, Elisabeth, *The Shaping of a Christian Family* (Grand Rapids, MI: Fleming H. Revell, 1992)

Ezzo, Gary and Robert Bucknam, *On Becoming Toddlerwise* (Mt. Pleasant, SC: Parent-Wise Solutions, 2003)

Forster, Pamela, *For Instruction in Righteousness* (Gaston, OR: Doorposts, 1993)

George, Elizabeth, *A Woman After God's Own Heart; Life Management for Busy Women* (Eugene, OR: Harvest House Publishers)

Harley, Willard F., *His Needs, Her Needs* (Grand Rapids, MI: Baker Books, 2001)

Harper, Anne and David, *Light Their Fire for God* (Chicago, IL: Moody Press, 2001)

Hendricks, Howard, *Heaven Help the Home Today* (Colorado Springs, CO: Cook Communications, 1993)

LaHaye, Tim, *The Spirit-Controlled Temperaments* (La Mesa, CA: Tyndale House Publishers, 1992)

Link, Carla and Joey, *The Mom's Notes* (Selected Topics) (Burlington, IA: J & C Ministries, 1997-2004)

Mally, Sarah, Stephen, *Grace, Making Brothers and Sisters Best Friends* (Cedar Rapids, IA: Tomorrow's Forefathers, 2001)

Martin, Gail, *What Every Child Should Know Along the Way* (Mt. Pleasant, SC: Parent-Wise Solutions, 1998)

Moore, Diane, *Parenting the Heart of Your Child* (Minneapolis, MN: Bethany House Publishers, 2005)

Planet, Paul, *Let's Hug* (Bayside, NY: Once Upon a Planet, 1981)

Trent, John and Cindy, Gary and Norma Smalley, *The Treasure Tree* (Nashville, TN: Thomas Nelson, Inc., 1992)

Wilson, Dennis and Dawn, *Christian Parenting in the Information Age* (Nampa, ID: TriCord Publishers, 1996)

Wright, Dr. H. Norman, *Be a Great Parent* (Colorado Springs, CO: Cook Communications, 2006)

Yates, John and Susan, *Character Matters* (Grand Rapids, MI: Baker Books, 1992)

Yates, Susan Alexander, *And Then I Had Kids* (Grand Rapids, MI: Baker Books, 1998)

Index